TEST BANK

J. Richard Christman
U.S. Coast Guard Academy
New London, CT

Kenneth Brownstein
University of Maine — Orono

to accompany

FUNDAMENTALS OF
PHYSICS

FOURTH EDITION
INCLUDING EXTENDED CHAPTERS

David Halliday
University of Pittsburgh

Robert Resnick
Rensselaer Polytechnic Institute

Jearl Walker
Cleveland State University

John Wiley & Sons, Inc.
New York   Chichester   Brisbane   Toronto   Singapore

ISBN 0-471-58879-2

Printed in the United States of America

10 9 8 7 6 5 4 3 2 1

TO THE INSTRUCTOR

Roughly 2200 multiple choice problems have been culled from the many thousands accumulated over the years and are presented in this collection. They come from numerous sources, chiefly our own examinations and files and examinations sent to us by others. As far as we are aware, all are meant to be freely used. Most have been altered somewhat, either to meet the circumstances of our own courses or to improve them over repeated uses. Several hundred have been created expressly for this test bank to achieve uniformity of coverage. Users will, no doubt, be led to invent their own problems as natural follow-ups or as variants on those in this set.

Problems are organized according to the chapters of *Fundamentals of Physics*, Fourth edition, and numbering is restarted with each chapter. Each problem is self-contained, with an appropriate figure if needed. Instructors can retype any desired problem or can photocopy selected pages, then cut and paste an examination. Answers to all problems are included.

The problems are also available from Wiley on computer disks for IBM PC and compatibles and for Macintosh computers. The set of disks contains a program which will allow you to select and preview problems on a monitor screen, then print an exam and answer key. Tests can also be stored on disk for retrieval later and may be edited using a word processor.

Acknowledgements. The contributions of the following people at Wiley is greatly appreciated: Cliff Mills, Physics Editor; Catherine Donovan, Administrative Assistant; and Joan Kalkut, Supplements Editor. Their help speeded the project and smoothed the publication process. It was a joy to work with these people.

J. Richard Christman
Kenneth R. Brownstein

CONTENTS

1. The standard of time is based on:

A) the daily rotation of the earth
B) the frequency of light emitted by Kr-86
C) the yearly revolution of the earth about the sun
D) a precision pendulum clock
*E) none of these

2. A nanosecond is:

A) 10^9 s   *B) 10^{-9} s   C) 10^{-10} s   D) 10^{-10} s   E) 10^{-12} s

3. The standard of length is based on:

A) the distance from the north pole to the equator along a meridian
   passing through Paris
B) wavelength of light emitted by Hg-198
C) wavelength of light emitted by Kr-86
D) a precision meter stick in Paris
*E) the speed of light

4. In 1866, the U. S. Congress defined the U. S. yard as exactly
   3600/3937 international meter. This was done primarily because:

A) length can be measured more accurately in meters than in yards
B) the meter is more stable than the yard
*C) this definition relates the common U. S. length units to a more
   widely used system
D) there are more wavelengths in a yard than in a meter
E) the members of this Congress were exceptionally intelligent

5. Which of the following is closest to your height?

A) 0.02 m   B) 0.2 m   *C) 2 m   D) 200 m   E) 2000 m

6. There is no SI base unit for "area" because:

A) an area has no thickness; hence no physical standard can be built
B) we live in a three (not a two) dimensional world
C) it is impossible to express ft^2 in terms of m
*D) area can be expressed in terms of m^2
E) area is not an important physical quantity

7. The SI base unit for mass is:

 A) gram
 B) pound
 *C) kilogram

 D) ounce
 E) kilopound

8. A gram is:

 A) 10^{-6} kg   *B) 10^{-3} kg   C) 1 kg   D) 10^3 kg   E) 10^6 kg

9. Which of the following is closest to your mass?

 A) 0.06 kg   B) 0.6 kg   C) 6 kg   *D) 60 kg   E) 600 kg

10. $5.0 \times 10^4 \times 3.0 \times 10^6 =$

 A) 1.5×10^9 B) 1.5×10^{10} *C) 1.5×10^{11} D) 1.5×10^{12} E) 1.5×10^{13}

11. $5.0 \times 10^4 \times 3.0 \times 10^{-6} =$

 A) 1.5×10^{-3} *B) 1.5×10^{-1} C) 1.5×10^1 D) 1.5×10^3 E) 1.5×10^5

12. $5.0 \times 10^5 + 3.0 \times 10^6 =$

 A) 8.0×10^5 B) 8.0×10^6 C) 5.3×10^5 D) 3.5×10^5 *E) 3.5×10^6

13. $7.0 \times 10^6 / 2.0 \times 10^{-6} =$

 A) 3.5×10^{-12} B) 3.5×10^{-6} C) 3.5   D) 3.5×10^6 *E) 3.5×10^{12}

14. The number of significant figures in 0.00150 is:

 A) 2   *B) 3   C) 4   D) 5   E) 6

15. The number of significant figures in 15.0 is:

 A) 1   B) 2   *C) 3   D) 4   E) 5

16. $3.2 \times 2.7 =$

 A) 9   B) 8   *C) 8.6   D) 8.64   E) 8.640

17. 1 mi is equivalent to 1609 m so 55 mph is:

 A) 15 m/s   *B) 25 m/s   C) 66 m/s   D) 88 m/s   E) 1500 m/s

2

18. A sphere with a radius of 1.7 cm has a volume of:

*A) 2.1×10^{-5} m^3
 B) 9.1×10^{-4} m^3
 C) 3.6×10^{-3} m^3

D) 0.11 m^3
E) 21 m^3

19. A sphere with a radius of 1.7 cm has a surface area of:

 A) 2.1×10^{-5} m^2
 B) 9.1×10^{-4} m^2
*C) 3.6×10^{-3} m^2

D) 0.11 m^2
E) 36 m^2

20. A right circular cylinder with a radius of 2.3 cm and a height of 1.4 m has a volume of:

 A) 0.20 m^3
 B) 0.14 m^3
 C) 9.3×10^{-3} m^3

*D) 2.3×10^{-3} m^3
 E) 7.4×10^{-4} m^3

21. A right circular cylinder with a radius of 2.3 cm and a height of 1.4 cm has a total surface area of:

 A) 1.7×10^{-3} m^2
 B) 3.2×10^{-3} m^2
 C) 2.0×10^{-3} m^3

*D) 5.3×10^{-3} m^2
 E) 7.4×10^{-3} m^2

22. A cubic box with an edge of exactly 1 cm has a volume of:

 A) 10^{-9} m^3 *B) 10^{-6} m^3 C) 10^{-3} m^3 D) 10^3 m^3 E) 10^6 m^3

23. A square with an edge of exactly 1 cm has an area of:

 A) 10^{-6} m^2 *B) 10^{-4} m^2 C) 10^2 m^2 D) 10^4 m^2 E) 10^6 m^2

24. 1 m is equivalent to 3.281 ft. A cube with an edge of 1.5 ft has a volume of:

 A) 1.2×10^2 m^3
*B) 9.6×10^{-2} m^3
 C) 10.5 m^3

D) 9.5×10^{-2} m^3
E) 0.21 m^3

25. During a short interval of time the velocity v in m/s of an automobile is given by $v = at^2 + bt^3$, where the time t is in seconds. The units of a and b are respectively:

 A) $m \cdot s^2$; $m \cdot s^4$
 B) s^3/m; s^4/m
 C) m/s^2; m/s^3

*D) m/s^3; m/s^4
 E) m/s^4; m/s^5

26. Suppose A = BC, where A has the dimensions L/M and C has the dimensions L/T. Then B has dimension:

*A) T/M   B) L^2/TM   C) TM/L^2 D) L^2T/M E) M/L^2T

27. Suppose $A = B^n C^m$, where A has dimensions LT, B has dimensions L^2T^{-1}, and C has dimensions LT^2. Then the exponents n and m have the values:

A) 2/3; 1/3   *D) 1/5; 3/5
B) 2; 3   E) 1/2; 1/2
C) 4/5; -1/5

1. The average speed of a moving object during a given interval of time is always:

A) its speed at any point
*B) the distance covered during the time interval divided by the time interval
C) one-half its speed at the end of the interval
D) its acceleration multiplied by the time interval
E) one-half its acceleration multiplied by the time interval.

2. Two automobiles are 120 miles apart and traveling toward each other. One automobile is moving at 35 mph and the other is moving at 45 mph. In how many hours will they meet?

A) 2.5   B) 2.0   C) 1.75   *D) 1.5   E) 1.25

3. A car travels 30 miles at an average speed of 60 mph and then travels 30 miles at an average speed of 30 mph. The average speed of the car for this 60 mile trip is:

A) 35 mph   *B) 40 mph   C) 45 mph   D) 50 mph   E) 53 mph

4. A car starts from Hither, goes 50 km in a straight line to Yon, immediately turns around and returns to Hither. The time for this round trip is 2 hours. The magnitude of the average velocity of the car for this round trip is:

*A) 0
B) 50 km/hr
C) 100 km/hr
D) 200 km/hr
E) cannot be calculated without knowing the acceleration

5. A car starts from Hither, goes 50 km in a straight line to Yon, immediately turns around and returns to Hither. The time for this round trip is 2 hours. The average speed of the car for this round trip is:

A) 0 km/h
*B) 50 km/h
C) 100 km/h
D) 200 km/h
E) cannot be calculated without knowing the acceleration

6. The coordinate of a particle in meters is given by
   $x(t) = 12 - 3.0t^2$, where the time t is in seconds. The particle is
   momentarily at rest at t =

   *A) 2.0 s   B) 3.0 s   C) 4.0 s   D) 5.0 s

7. A drag racing car starts from rest at t = 0 and moves along a
   straight line with velocity given by $v = bt^2$, where b is a constant.
   The expression for the distance traveled by this car from its
   position at t = 0 is:

   A) bt^3 *B) $bt^3/3$ C) $4bt^2$ D) $3bt^2$ E) $bt^3/2$

8. A ball rolls up a slope. At the end of three seconds its velocity is
   20 cm/s; at the end of eight seconds its velocity is 0 cm/s. What is
   the average acceleration (in cm/s^2) from the third to the eighth
   second?

   A) 2.5   *B) 4.0   C) 5.0   D) 6.0   E) 6.67

9. Of the following situations, which one is impossible?

   A) a body having velocity east and acceleration east
   B) a body having velocity east and acceleration west
   C) a body having zero velocity and non-zero acceleration
   D) a body having constant acceleration and variable velocity
   *E) a body having constant velocity and variable acceleration

10. The position y of a particle moving along the y axis depends on the
    time t according to the equation $y = at - bt^2$. The dimensions of the
    quantities a and b are respectively:

   A) L^2/T, L^3/T^2 D) L^3/T, T^2/L
   B) L/T^2, L^2/T E) none of these
   *C) L/T, L/T^2

11. A particle moves along the x axis according to the equation $x = 6t^2$
    where x is in meters and t is in seconds. Therefore:

   A) the acceleration of the particle is 6 m/s^2
   B) t cannot be negative
   C) the particle follows a parabolic path
   D) each second the velocity of the particle changes by 9.8 m/s
   *E) none of the above

12. Over a short interval the coordinate of an automobile in meters is
    given by $x(t) = 27t - 4.0t^3$, where time t is in seconds. At the end
    of 1.0 s the acceleration of the auto is:

   A) 27 m/s^2 B) 4.0 m/s^2 C) -4.0 m/s^2 D) -12 m/s^2 *E) -24 m/s^2

13. Over a short interval, starting at time t = 0, the coordinate of an automobile in meters is given by $x(t) = 27t - 4.0t^3$, where t is in seconds. The magnitudes of the initial (at t = 0) velocity and acceleration of the auto respectively are:

A) 0; 12 m/s^2 D) 27 m/s; 12 m/s^2
B) 0; 24 m/s^2 E) 27 m/s; 24 m/s^2
*C) 27 m/s; 0

14. At time t = 0 a car has a velocity of 16 m/s. It slows down with an acceleration given by -0.50t, in m/s^2 for t in s. It stops at t =

A) 64 s   B) 32 s   C) 16 s   *D) 8.0 s   E) 4.0 s

15. At time t = 0 a car has a velocity of 16 m/s. It slows down with an acceleration given by -0.50t, in m/s^2 for t in s. At the end of 4.0 s it has traveled:

A) 0   B) 12 m   C) 14 m   D) 25 m   *E) 59 m

16. At time t = 0 a car has a velocity of 16 m/s. It slows down with an acceleration given by -0.50t, in m/s^2 for t in s. By the time it stops it has traveled:

A) 15 m   B) 31 m   C) 62 m   *D) 85 m   E) 100 m

17. Starting at time t = 0, an object moves along a straight line with velocity in m/s given by $v(t) = 98 - 2t^2$, where t is in seconds. When it momentarily stops its acceleration is:

A) 0   B) -4.0 m/s^2 C) -9.8 m/s^2 *D) -28 m/s^2 E) 49 m/s^2

18. Starting at time t = 0, an object moves along a straight line. Its coordinate in meters is given by $x(t) = 75t - 1.0t^3$, where t is in seconds. When it momentarily stops its acceleration is:

A) 0   D) -9.8 m/s^2
B) -73 m/s^2 E) 9.2x10^3 m/s^2
*C) -30 m/s^2

19. A car, initially at rest, travels 20 m in 4 s along a straight line with constant acceleration. The acceleration of the car (in m/s^2) is:

A) 0.4   B) 1.3   *C) 2.5   D) 4.9   E) 9.8

7

20. A racing car traveling with constant acceleration increases its speed from 10 m/s to 30 m/s over a distance of 80 m? How long does this take?

   A) 2.0 s
   *B) 4.0 s
   C) 5.0 s
   D) 8.0 s
   E) cannot be calculated since the time is not given

21. A car starts from rest and goes down a slope with a constant acceleration of 5 m/s^2. After 5 seconds the car reaches the bottom of the hill. Its speed at the bottom of the hill, in meters per second, is:

   A) 1   B) 12.5   *C) 25   D) 50   E) 160

22. A car moving with an initial velocity of 100 m/s north has a constant acceleration of 10 m/s^2 south. After 6 seconds its velocity will be:

   A) 60 m/s north   *D) 40 m/s north
   B) 60 m/s south   E) 40 m/s south
   C) 160 m/s north

23. An object with an initial velocity of 12 m/s west experiences a constant acceleration of 4 m/s^2 west for 3 seconds. During this time the object travels a distance of:

   A) 12 m   B) 24 m   C) 36 m   *D) 54 m   E) 144 m

24. How far does a car travel in 6 s if its initial velocity is 2 m/s and its acceleration is 2 m/s^2 in the forward direction?

   A) 12 m   B) 14 m   C) 24 m   D) 36 m   *E) 48 m

25. At a stop light, a truck traveling at 40 ft/s passes a car as it starts from rest. The truck travels at constant velocity and the car accelerates at 5 ft/s^2. How many seconds will it take for the car to catch up to the truck?

   A) 8   D) 160
   *B) 16   E) none of these
   C) 24

8

26. A baseball is thrown vertically into the air. The acceleration of the ball at its highest point is:

*A) 9.8 m/s^2 down
 B) 9.8 m/s^2 up
 C) changing suddenly from 9.8 m/s^2 up to 9.8 m/s^2 down
 D) zero
 E) cannot be calculated without knowing the initial velocity

27. Which one of the following statements is correct for an object released from rest?

*A) the average velocity during the first second of time is 4.9 m/s
 B) during each second the object falls 9.8 m
 C) the acceleration changes by 9.8 m/s every second
 D) the object falls 9.8 m during the first second of time
 E) the acceleration of the object is proportional to its weight

28. A freely falling body has a constant acceleration of 9.8 m/s^2. This means that:

 A) the body falls 9.8 m during each second
 B) the body falls 9.8 m during the first second
*C) the speed of the body increases by 9.8 m/s during each second
 D) the acceleration of the body increases by 9.8 m/s^2 during each second
 E) the acceleration of the body decreases by 9.8 m/s^2 during each second

29. An object is thrown vertically upward. While it is rising:

 A) its velocity and acceleration are both upward
*B) its velocity is upward and its acceleration is downward
 C) its velocity and acceleration are both downward
 D) its velocity is downward and its acceleration is upward
 E) its velocity and acceleration are both decreasing

30. An object is thrown straight up from ground level with a speed of 50 m/s. If g = 10 m/s^2 its distance above ground level 1.0 second later is:

 A) 40 m   *B) 45 m   C) 50 m   D) 55 m   E) 60 m

31. An object is thrown straight up from ground level with a speed of 50 m/s. If g = 10 m/s^2 its distance above ground level 6.0 s later is:

 A) 0.00 m   D) 480 m
 B) 270 m   *E) none of these
 C) 330 m

32. At a location where g = 9.80 m/s^2, an object is thrown vertically down with an initial speed of 1.00 m/s. After 5.00 s the object will have traveled:

  A) 125 m   *B) 127.5 m   C) 245 m   D) 250 m   E) 255 m

33. An object is thrown vertically upward at 35 m/s. Taking g = 10 m/s^2, the velocity of the object 5 seconds later is:

  A) 7.0 m/s up   D) 85 m/s down
*B) 15 m/s down   E) 85 m/s up
  C) 15 m/s up

34. A feather, initially at rest, is released in a vacuum 12 m above the surface of the earth. Which of the following statements is correct?

  A) the maximum velocity of the feather is 9.8 m/s
  B) the acceleration of the feather decreases until terminal velocity is reached
*C) the acceleration of the feather remains constant during the fall
  D) the acceleration of the feather increases during the fall
  E) the acceleration of the feather is zero

35. An object is released from rest and falls a distance H during the first second of time. How far will it fall during the next second of time?

  A) H   B) 2H   *C) 3H   D) 4H   E) H^2

36. A heavy ball falls freely, starting from rest. Between the third and fourth second of time it travels a distance of:

  A) 16 ft.   B) 32 ft.   C) 96 ft   *D) 112 ft.   E) 256 ft.

37. A heavy ball falls freely, starting from rest. Between the third and fourth second of time it travels a distance of:

  A) 4.9 m   B) 9.8 m   C) 29.4 m   *D) 34.3 m   E) 39.8 m

38. As a rocket is accelerating vertically upward at 9.8 m/s^2 near the earth's surface, it releases a projectile. Immediately after release the acceleration (in m/s^2) of the projectile is:

*A) 9.8 down   D) 19.6 up
  B) 0   E) none of the above
  C) 9.8 up

39. A stone is released from a balloon which is descending at a constant speed of 10 m/s. Neglecting air resistance, after 20 s the speed of the stone is:

A) 2160 m/s   B) 1760 m/s   *C) 206 m/s   D) 196 m/s   E) 186 m/s

40. An object dropped from a stationary balloon hits the ground in 12.0 s. If its acceleration is 9.80 m/s^2, the height of the balloon is:

A) 29.4 m   B) 58.8 m   C) 118 m   D) 353 m   *E) 706 m

41. Neglecting the effect of air resistance a stone dropped off a 175-m high building lands on the ground in:

A) 3 s   B) 4 s   *C) 6 s   D) 18 s   E) 36 s

42. A stone is thrown vertically upward with an initial speed of 19.5 m/s. It will rise to a maximum height of:

A) 4.9 m
B) 9.8 m
*C) 19.6 m

D) 39.2 m
E) none of these

43. A baseball is hit straight up and is caught by the catcher 2.0 s later. The maximum height of the ball during this interval is:

*A) 4.9 m   B) 7.4 m   C) 9.8 m   D) 12.6 m   E) 19.6 m

44. An object is thrown straight down with an initial speed of 8 ft/s from a window which is 24 ft above the ground. The time it takes the object to reach the ground is:

A)
$\sqrt{3}/2$ s
*B) 1 s
C) 3/2 s

D)
$\sqrt{3}/4$ s
E) none of these

45. A stone is released from rest from the edge of a building 576 ft above the ground. Neglecting air resistance, the speed of the stone, just before striking the ground, is:

A) 96 ft/s
*B) 192 ft/s
C) 128 ft/s

D) 256 ft/s
E) 9216 ft/s

46. An object is thrown vertically upward with a certain initial velocity in a world where the acceleration due to gravity is 19.6 m/s^2. The height to which it rises is ____ that to which the object would rise if thrown upward with the same initial velocity on the earth. Neglect friction.

*A) half
 B)
    $\sqrt{2}$ times
 C) twice
 D) four times
 E) cannot be calculated from the given data

47. A projectile is shot vertically upward with a given initial velocity. It reaches a maximum height of 100 m. If, on a second shot, the initial velocity is doubled then the projectile will reach a maximum height of:

A) 70.7 m   B) 141.4 m   C) 200 m   D) 241 m   *E) 400 m

48. One object is thrown vertically upward with an initial velocity of 100 m/s and another object with an initial velocity of 10 m/s. The maximum height reached by the first object will be _____ that of the other.

 A) 10 times   D) 10,000 times
*B) 100 times   E) none of these
 C) 1000 times

49. The area under a velocity-time graph represents:

 A) acceleration   D) change in velocity
 B) change in acceleration   *E) displacement
 C) speed

50. Displacement can be obtained from:

 A) slope of an acceleration-time graph
 B) slope of a velocity-time graph
 C) area under an acceleration-time graph
*D) area under a velocity-time graph
 E) slope of an acceleration-time graph

51. An object has a constant acceleration of 3 m/s^2. The displacement versus time graph for this object has a slope:

*A) that increases with time   D) of 3 m/s
 B) that is constant   E) of 3 m/s^2
 C) that decreases with time

12

52. The coordinate-time graph of an object is a straight line with a
    positive slope. The object has:

    A) constant displacement
    B) steadily increasing acceleration
    C) steadily decreasing acceleration
    *D) constant velocity
    E) steadily increasing velocity

53. Which of the following five graphs represents the motion of an
    object moving with a constant speed?

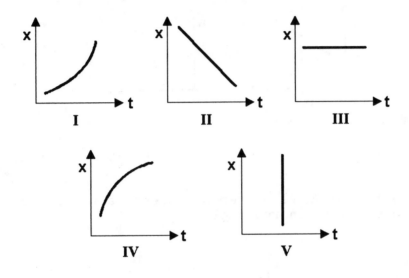

A) I.   *B) II.   C) III.   D) IV.   E) V.

13

54. Which of the five following graphs is correct for an object moving in a straight line at a constant velocity of 20 m/s?

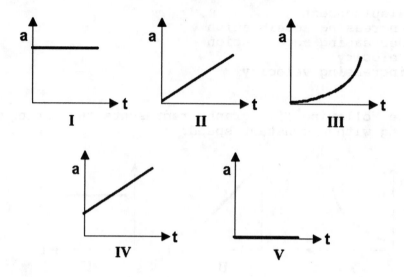

A) I.   B) II.   C) III.   D) IV.   *E) V.

55. Which of the following five graphs represents the motion of an object whose speed is increasing?

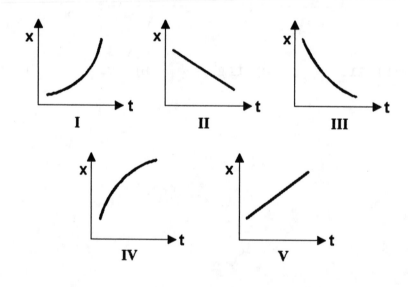

*A) I.   B) II.   C) III.   D) IV.   E) V.

56. A car accelerates from rest on a straight road. A short time later, the car decelerates to a stop and then returns to its original position in a similar manner. Which of the five following graphs best describes the motion?

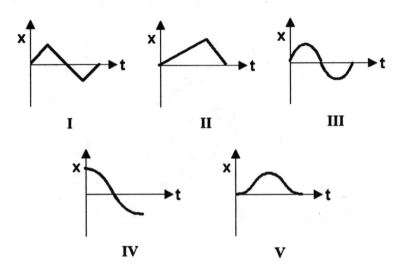

I   II   III

IV   V

A) I.   B) II.   C) III.   D) IV.   *E) V.

57. The acceleration of an object, starting from rest, is shown in the graph below. Other than at t = 0, when is the velocity of the object equal to zero?

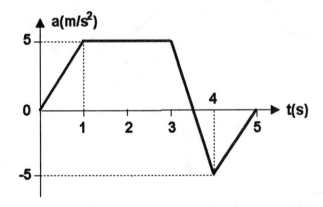

A) during the interval from 1.0 s to 3.0 s
B) 3.5 s
C) 4.0 s
D) 5.0 s
*E) at no other time on this graph

15

58. An elevator is moving upward with constant acceleration. The dashed curve shows the position y of the ceiling of the elevator as a function of the time t. At the instant indicated by the dot, a bolt breaks loose and drops from the ceiling. Which curve best represents the position of the bolt as a function of time?

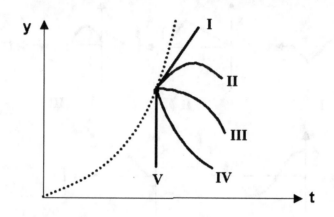

A) I. *B) II. C) III. D) IV. E) V.

59. The diagram shows a velocity-time graph for a car moving in a straight line. At point Q the car must be:

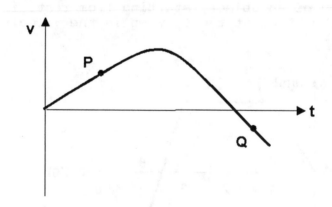

A) moving with zero acceleration
B) traveling downhill
C) traveling below ground-level
D) reducing speed
*E) traveling in the reverse direction to that at point P

60. The diagram shows a velocity-time graph for a car moving in a straight line. At point P the car must be:

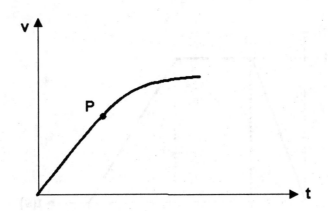

   A) moving with zero acceleration
   B) climbing the hill
 *C) accelerating
   D) stationary
   E) moving at about 45° with respect to the x axis

61. The graph represents the straight line motion of a car. How far does the car travel between t = 2 seconds and t = 5 seconds?

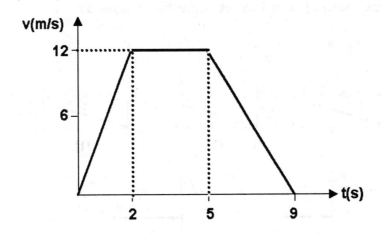

A) 4 m   B) 12 m   C) 24 m   *D) 36 m   E) 60 m

62. The diagram represents the straight line motion of a car. Which of the following statements is true?

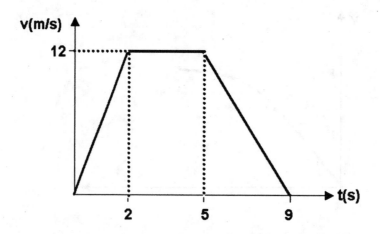

   A) the car accelerates, stops, and reverses
 *B) the car accelerates at 6 m/s^2 for the first 2 s
   C) the car is moving for a total time of 12 s
   D) the car decelerates at 12 m/s^2 for the last 4 s
   E) the car returns to its starting point when t = 9 s

63. Consider the following five graphs (note the axes carefully). Which of these represent(s) motion at constant speed?

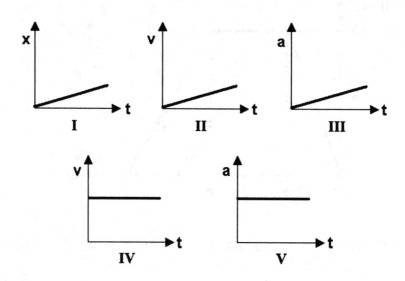

   A) IV only   D) I and II only
   B) IV and V only   *E) I and IV only
   C) I, II, and III only

18

64. An object is dropped from rest. Which of the five following graphs correctly represents its motion?

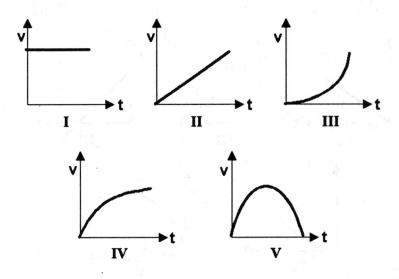

A) I.   *B) II.   C) III.   D) IV.   E) V.

65. A stone is dropped from a cliff. The graph (note axes) which best represents its motion while it falls is:

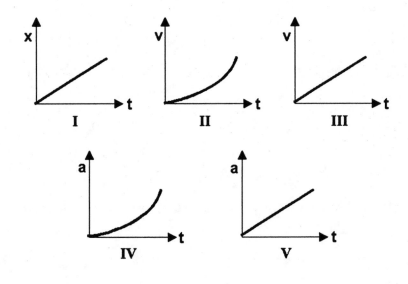

A) I.   B) II.   *C) III.   D) IV.   E) V.

66. An object is thrown vertically into the air. Which of the following five graphs represents the velocity (v) of the object as a function of the time (t)?

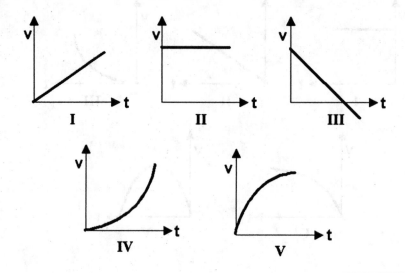

A) I.   B) II.   *C) III.   D) IV.   E) V.

1. We say that the displacement of a particle is a vector quantity. Our best justification for this assertion is:

A) displacement can be specified by a magnitude and a direction
*B) operating with displacements according to the rules for manipulating vectors leads to results in agreement with experiments
C) a displacement is obviously not a scalar
D) displacement can be specified by three numbers
E) displacement is associated with motion

2. A vector of magnitude 3 CANNOT be added to a vector of magnitude 4 so that the magnitude of the resultant is:

*A) zero B) 1 C) 3 D) 5 E) 7

3. A vector of magnitude 20 is added to a vector of magnitude 25. The magnitude of this sum can be:

A) zero B) 3 *C) 12 D) 47 E) 50

4. A vector **S** of magnitude 6 and another vector **T** have a resultant of magnitude 12. The vector **T**:

*A) must have a magnitude of at least 6 but no more than 18
B) may have a magnitude of 20
C) cannot have a magnitude greater than 12
D) must be perpendicular to **S**
E) must be perpendicular to the resultant vector

5. The vector -**A** is:

A) longer than **A**
B) shorter than **A**
C) in the same direction as **A**

*D) in the direction opposite to **A**
E) perpendicular to **A**

6. The vector $\vec{V}_3$ in the diagram is equal to:

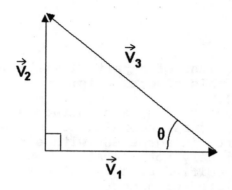

A) $\mathbf{V}_1 - \mathbf{V}_2$
B) $\mathbf{V}_1 + \mathbf{V}_2$
*C) $\mathbf{V}_2 - \mathbf{V}_1$

D) $\mathbf{V}_1 \cos\theta$
E) $\mathbf{V}_1/(\cos\theta)$

7. If $|\mathbf{A} + \mathbf{B}|^2 = A^2 + B^2$ and neither $\mathbf{A}$ nor $\mathbf{B}$ vanish, then:

A) $\mathbf{A}$ and $\mathbf{B}$ must be parallel and in the same direction
B) $\mathbf{A}$ and $\mathbf{B}$ must be parallel and in opposite directions
C) either $\mathbf{A}$ or $\mathbf{B}$ must be zero
D) the angle between $\mathbf{A}$ and $\mathbf{B}$ must be 60°
*E) none of the above is true

8. If $|\mathbf{A} + \mathbf{B}| = A + B$ and neither $\mathbf{A}$ nor $\mathbf{B}$ vanish, then:

*A) $\mathbf{A}$ and $\mathbf{B}$ are parallel and in the same direction
B) $\mathbf{A}$ and $\mathbf{B}$ are parallel and in opposite directions
C) the angle between $\mathbf{A}$ and $\mathbf{B}$ is 45°
D) the angle between $\mathbf{A}$ and $\mathbf{B}$ is 60°
E) $\mathbf{A}$ is perpendicular to $\mathbf{B}$

9. If $|\mathbf{A} - \mathbf{B}| = A + B$ and neither $\mathbf{A}$ nor $\mathbf{B}$ vanish, then:

A) $\mathbf{A}$ and $\mathbf{B}$ are parallel and in the same direction
*B) $\mathbf{A}$ and $\mathbf{B}$ are parallel and in opposite directions
C) the angle between $\mathbf{A}$ and $\mathbf{B}$ is 45°
D) the angle between $\mathbf{A}$ and $\mathbf{B}$ is 60°
E) $\mathbf{A}$ is perpendicular to $\mathbf{B}$

10. Four vectors (**A, B, C, D**) all have the same magnitude. The angle θ between adjacent vectors is 45° as shown. The correct vector equation is:

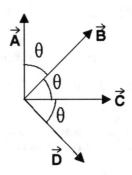

A) **A − B − C + D** = 0

*B)
   B + D − √2C = 0

C) **A + B = B + D**

D) **A + B + C + D** = 0

E)
   (**A + C**)/√2 = **−B**

11. Vectors **A** and **B** lie in the x-y plane. We can deduce that **A = B** if:

A)
   $A_x^2 + A_y^2 = B_x^2 + B_y^2$

B) $A_x + A_y = B_x + B_y$

*C) $A_x = B_x$ and $A_y = B_y$

D) $A_y/A_x = B_y/B_x$

E) $A_x = A_y$ and $B_x = B_y$

12. A vector has a magnitude of 12. When its tail is at the origin it lies between the positive x axis and negative y axis and makes an angle of 30° with the x axis. Its y component is:

A)
   $6\sqrt{3}$

*B)
   $-6\sqrt{3}$

C) 6

D) −6

E) 12

13. If the x component of a vector **A**, in the x,y plane, is half as large as the magnitude of the vector, its y component is:

A) A/2

B) 2A

C) 3A/4

*D)
   $\sqrt{3}A/2$

E)
   $\sqrt{5}A/2$

14. If **A** = 6î − 8ĵ then 4**A** has magnitude:

A) 10

B) 20

C) 30

*D) 40

E) 50

23

15. A vector has a component of 10 in the +x direction, a component of 10 in the +y direction, and a component of 5 in the -z direction. The magnitude of this vector is:

A) zero   *B) 15   C) 20   D) 25   E) 225

16. Let $\mathbf{V} = 2.00\hat{\imath} + 6.00\hat{\jmath} - 3.00\hat{k}$ The magnitude of $\mathbf{V}$ is:

A) 5.00   B) 5.57   *C) 7.00   D) 7.42   E) 8.54

17. A vector in the x,y plane has a magnitude of 25 and an x component of 12. The angle it makes with the positive x axis is:

A) 26°   B) 29°   *C) 61°   D) 64°   E) 241°

18. The angle between $\mathbf{A} = 25\hat{\imath} + 45\hat{\jmath}$ and the positive x axis is:

A) 29°   *B) 61°   C) 151°   D) 209°   E) 241°

19. The angle between $\mathbf{A} = -25\hat{\imath} + 45\hat{\jmath}$ and the positive x axis is:

A) 29°   B) 61°   *C) 119°   D) 151°   E) 209°

20. Let $\mathbf{A} = 2\hat{\imath} + 6\hat{\jmath} - 3\hat{k}$ and $\mathbf{B} = 4\hat{\imath} + 2\hat{\jmath} + \hat{k}$. The vector sum $\mathbf{S} = \mathbf{A} + \mathbf{B}$ equals:

*A) $6\hat{\imath} + 8\hat{\jmath} - 2\hat{k}$ D) $8\hat{\imath} + 12\hat{\jmath} - 3\hat{k}$
B) $-2\hat{\imath} + 4\hat{\jmath} - 4\hat{k}$ E) none of these
C) $2\hat{\imath} - 4\hat{\jmath} + 4\hat{k}$

21. Let $\mathbf{A} = 2\hat{\imath} + 6\hat{\jmath} - 3\hat{k}$ and $\mathbf{B} = 4\hat{\imath} + 2\hat{\jmath} + \hat{k}$. The vector difference $\mathbf{D} = \mathbf{A} - \mathbf{B}$ is:

A) $6\hat{\imath} + 8\hat{\jmath} - 2\hat{k}$ D) $8\hat{\imath} + 12\hat{\jmath} - 3\hat{k}$
*B) $-2\hat{\imath} + 4\hat{\jmath} - 4\hat{k}$ E) none of these
C) $2\hat{\imath} - 4\hat{\jmath} + 4\hat{k}$

22. If $\mathbf{A} = 2\hat{\imath} - 3\hat{\jmath}$ and $\mathbf{B} = \hat{\imath} - 2\hat{\jmath}$, then $\mathbf{A} - 2\mathbf{B} =$

*A) $\hat{\jmath}$ B) $-\hat{\jmath}$ C) $4\hat{\imath} -7\hat{\jmath}$ D) $4\hat{\imath} + \hat{\jmath}$ E) $-4\hat{\imath} + 7\hat{\jmath}$

23. If **A** has magnitude 12 and **B** has magnitude 8, the x component of **A** + **B** is about:

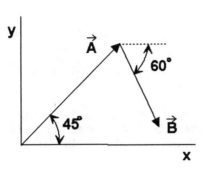

A) 5.5   B) 7.6   *C) 12   D) 14   E) 15

24. A certain vector in the x,y plane has an x component of 4 and a y component of 10. It is rotated in the x,y plane so its x component is doubled. Its new y component is about:

A) 20   *B) 7.2   C) 5.0   D) 4.5   E) 2.2

25. Vectors **A** and **B** each have magnitude L. When drawn tail-to-tail, the angle between them is 30°. The value of **A** ·**B** is:

A) zero   D) $2L^2$
B) L^2 E) none of these
*C)
$\sqrt{3}L^2/2$

26. Let **A** = $2\hat{\imath}$ + $6\hat{\jmath}$ - $3\hat{k}$ and **B** = $4\hat{\imath}$ + $2\hat{\jmath}$ + $\hat{k}$. Then **A** ·**B** equals:

A) $8\hat{\imath}$ + $12\hat{\jmath}$ - $3\hat{k}$ *D) 17
B) $12\hat{\imath}$ - $14\hat{\jmath}$ - $20\hat{k}$ E) none of these
C) 23

27. Two vectors have magnitudes of 10 and 15. The angle between them when they are drawn with their tails at the same point is 65°. The component of the longer vector along the line of the shorter is:

A) 0   B) 4.2   *C) 6.3   D) 9.1   E) 14

28. Let $\mathbf{S} = \hat{\imath} + 2\hat{\jmath} + 2\hat{k}$ and $\mathbf{T} = 3\hat{\imath} + 4\hat{k}$. The angle between these two vectors is given by:

  A) $\cos^{-1}(14/15)$
  B) $\cos^{-1}(11/225)$
  C) $\cos^{-1}(104/225)$
*D) $\cos^{-1}(11/15)$
  E) cannot be found since $\mathbf{S}$ and $\mathbf{T}$ do not lie in the same plane

29. Two vectors lie with their tails at the same point. When the angle between them is increased by 20° their scalar product has the same magnitude but changes from positive to negative. The original angle between them was:

A) 0   B) 60°   C) 70°   *D) 80°   E) 90°

30. If the magnitude of the sum of two vectors is less than the magnitude of either vector, then:

*A) the scalar product of the vectors must be negative
  B) the scalar product of the vectors must be positive
  C) the vectors must be parallel and in opposite directions
  D) the vectors must be parallel and in opposite directions
  E) none of the above

31. If the magnitude of the sum of two vectors is greater than the magnitude of either vector, then:

  A) the scalar product of the vectors must be negative
  B) the scalar product of the vectors must be positive
  C) the vectors must be parallel and in opposite directions
  D) the vectors must be parallel and in opposite directions
*E) none of the above

32. Vectors $\mathbf{A}$ and $\mathbf{B}$ each have magnitude L. When drawn tail-to-tail, the angle between them is 30°. The magnitude of $\mathbf{A} \times \mathbf{B}$ is:

*A) $L^2/2$ D) $2L^2$
  B) L^2 E) none of these
  C)
      $\sqrt{3}L^2/2$

33. Two vectors lie with their tails at the same point. When the angle between them is increased by 20° the magnitude of their vector product has the same magnitude but changes from positive to negative. The original angle between them was:

A) 0   B) 60°   C) 70°   *D) 80°   E) 90°

34. Two vectors have magnitudes of 10 and 15. The angle between them when they are drawn with their tails at the same point is 65°. The component of the longer vector along the line perpendicular to the shorter vector, in the plane of the vectors, is:

A) 0   B) 4.2   C) 6.3   D) 9.1   *E) 14

35. The two vectors $3\hat{\imath} - 7\hat{\jmath}$ and $2\hat{\imath} + 3\hat{\jmath} - 2\hat{k}$ define a plane (it is the plane of the triangle with both tails at one vertex and each head at one of the other vertices). Which of the following vectors is perpendicular to the plane?

*A) $4\hat{\imath} + 6\hat{\jmath} + 13\hat{k}$ D) $4\hat{\imath} + 6\hat{\jmath} - 13\hat{k}$
 B) $-4\hat{\imath} + 6\hat{\jmath} + 13\hat{k}$ E) $4\hat{\imath} + 6\hat{\jmath}$
 C) $4\hat{\imath} - 6\hat{\jmath} + 13\hat{k}$

36. Let $\mathbf{R} = \mathbf{S} \times \mathbf{T}$ and $\theta \neq 90°$, where θ is the angle between $\mathbf{S}$ and $\mathbf{T}$ when they are drawn tail-to-tail. Which of the following is NOT true?

 A) $|\mathbf{R}| = |\mathbf{S}||\mathbf{T}|\sin\theta$ D) $\mathbf{R} \cdot \mathbf{T} = 0$
 B) $-\mathbf{R} = \mathbf{T} \times \mathbf{S}$ *E) $\mathbf{S} \cdot \mathbf{T} = 0$
 C) $\mathbf{R} \cdot \mathbf{S} = 0$

37. The value of $\hat{\imath} \cdot (\hat{\jmath} \times \hat{k})$ is:

A) zero   *B) +1   C) -1   D) 3   E) $\sqrt{3}$

38. The value of $\hat{k} \cdot (\hat{k} \times \hat{\imath})$ is:

*A) zero   B) +1   C) -1   D) 3   E) $\sqrt{3}$

1. Velocity is defined as:

*A) rate of change of position with time
 B) position divided by time
 C) rate of change of acceleration with time
 D) a speeding up or slowing down
 E) change of position

2. Acceleration is defined as:

 A) rate of change of position with time
 B) speed divided by time
*C) rate of change of velocity with time
 D) a speeding up or slowing down
 E) change of velocity

3. Which of the following is a scalar quantity?

*A) speed   D) acceleration
 B) velocity   E) none of these
 C) displacement

4. Which of the following is a vector quantity?

 A) mass   D) temperature
 B) density   *E) none of these
 C) speed

5. Which of the following is NOT an example of accelerated motion?

 A) vertical component of projectile motion
 B) circular motion at constant speed
 C) a swinging pendulum
 D) earth's motion about sun
*E) horizontal component of projectile motion

6. A jet plane in straight horizontal flight passes over your head. When it is directly above you, the sound seems to come from a point behind the plane in a direction 30° from the vertical. The speed of the plane is:

A) the same as the speed of sound
*B) half the speed of sound
C) three-fifths the speed of sound
D) 0.866 times the speed of sound
E) twice the speed of sound

7. A plane traveling north at 200 m/s turns and then travels south at 200 m/s. The change in its velocity is:

A) zero
B) 200 m/s north
C) 200 m/s south
D) 400 m/s north
*E) 400 m/s south

8. Two bodies are falling with negligible air resistance, side by side, above a horizontal plane. If one of the bodies is given an additional horizontal acceleration during its descent, it:

*A) strikes the plane at the same time as the other body
B) has the vertical component of its velocity altered
C) has the vertical component of its acceleration altered
D) follows a hyperbolic path
E) follows a straight line path along the resultant acceleration vector

9. The velocity of a projectile equals its initial velocity added to:

A) a constant horizontal velocity
B) a constant vertical velocity
C) a constantly increasing horizontal velocity
*D) a constantly increasing downward velocity
E) a constant velocity directed at the target

10. A stone thrown from the top of a tall building follows a path that is:

A) circular
B) made of two straight line segments
C) hyperbolic
*D) parabolic
E) a straight line

11. Identical guns fire identical bullets horizontally at the same speed
    from the same height above level planes, one on the earth and one on
    the moon. Which of the following three statements is/are true?
    I.   The horizontal distance traveled by the bullet is greater
         for the moon.
    II. The flight time is less for the bullet on the earth.
    III. The velocity of the bullets at impact are the same.

    A) III only   D) II and III only
    *B) I and II only   E) I, II, III
    C) I and III only

12. A stone is thrown horizontally and follows the path XYZ shown. The
    direction of the acceleration of the stone at point Y is:

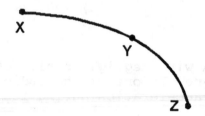

    *A) ↓   B) →   C) ↘   D) ↖   E) ↗

13. A bullet shot horizontally from a gun:

    A) strikes the ground much later than one dropped vertically from the
       same point at the same instant
    B) is brought to rest by air resistance alone
    *C) strikes the ground at approximately the same time as one dropped
       vertically from the same point at the same instant
    D) travels in a straight line
    E) strikes the ground much sooner than one dropped from the same point
       at the same instant

14. A bomber flying in level flight must release its bomb before it is
    over the target. Neglecting air resistance, which one of the
    following is NOT true?

    A) the bomber will be over the target when the bomb strikes
    B) g remains constant for the bomb
    *C) the horizontal velocity of the plane equals the vertical velocity of
       the bomb when it hits the target
    D) the bomb travels in a curved path
    E) the time of flight of the bomb is independent of the horizontal
       speed of the plane

15. The airplane shown is in level flight at an altitude of 0.50 km and
a speed of 150 km/h. At what distance d should it release a heavy
bomb to hit the target X? Take g = 10 m/s^2.

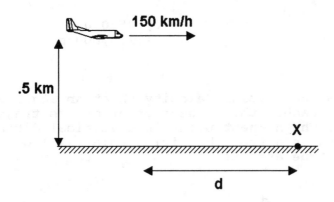

A) 150 m   B) 295 m   *C) 417 m   D) 2550 m   E) 15000 m

16. An object is shot from the back of a truck moving at 30 mph on a
straight horizontal road. The gun is aimed upward, perpendicular to
the bed of the truck. The object falls:

A) in front of the truck
B) behind the truck
*C) on the truck
D) depends on the initial speed of the object
E) depends on the value of g

17. A stone is thrown horizontally from the top of a 20-m high hill. It
strikes the ground at an angle of 45°. With what speed was it
thrown?

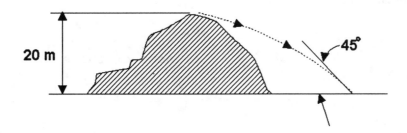

A) 14 m/s   *B) 20 m/s   C) 28 m/s   D) 32 m/s   E) 40 m/s

18. A stone is thrown outward from the top of a 59.4-m high cliff with
an upward velocity component of 19.5 m/s. How many seconds will the
stone be in the air?

A) 4   B) 5   *C) 6   D) 7   E) 8

31

19. A large cannon is fired over level ground at an angle of 30° above the horizontal. The muzzle velocity is 980 m/s. Neglecting air resistance, the projectile will travel what horizontal distance before striking the ground?

A) 4300 m
B) 8500 m
C) 43,000 m

*D) 85,000 m
E) 170,000 m

20. A projectile has an initial velocity v_0 at an angle θ_0 above the horizontal. It reaches the highest point of its trajectory in a time T after launch. The highest point is a vertical distance h_{max} and a horizontal distance d from the firing point. All of the following statements are true except:

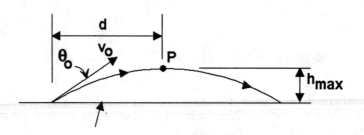

*A) $T = (v_0\cos\theta_0)/g$
B) $d = v_0 T\cos\theta_0$
C) $h_{max} = (v_0\sin\theta_0)2/2g$
D) $v = v_0\cos\theta_0$
E) acceleration = g (in magnitude)

21. A boy on the edge of a vertical cliff 20 m high throws a stone horizontally outwards with a speed of 20 m/s. It strikes the ground at what horizontal distance from the foot of the cliff (use g = 10 m/s^2)?

A) 10 m
*B) 40 m
C) 50 m

D) $50\sqrt{5}$ m
E) none of these

22. Which of the curves on the graph below best represents v_y vs. t for a projectile fired at an angle of 45° above the horizontal?

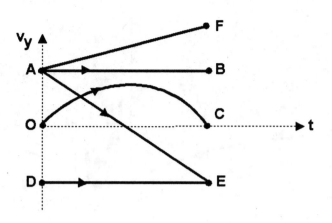

A) OC   B) DE   C) AB   *D) AE   E) AF

23. A cannon fires a projectile as shown. The dashed line shows the trajectory in the absence of gravity; points MNOP correspond to one second intervals. Using g = 10 m/s^2, the lengths X,Y,Z are:

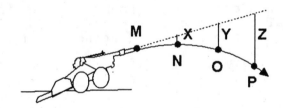

A) 5m, 10m, 15m
*B) 5m, 20m, 45m
C) 10m, 40m, 90m

D) 10m, 20m, 30m
E) 0.2m, 0.8m, 1.8m

33

24. A dart is thrown horizontally toward X at 20 m/s as shown. It hits Y
    0.1 s later. The distance XY is:

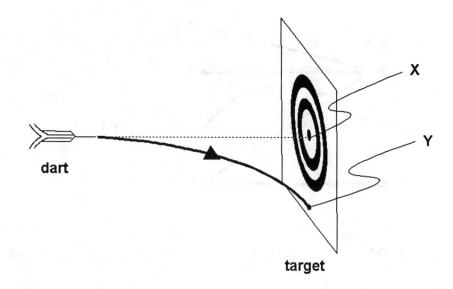

dart

target

A) 2 m   B) 1 m   C) 0.5 m   D) 0.1 m   *E) 0.05 m

25. A projectile is fired over level ground with an initial velocity
    that has a vertical component of 20 m/s and a horizontal component
    of 30 m/s. Using $g = 10$ m/s^2, the distance from launching to landing
    points is

A) 40 m   B) 60 m   C) 80 m   *D) 120 m   E) 180 m

26. An object, tied to a string, moves in a circle at constant speed on
    a horizontal surface as shown. The direction of the displacement of
    this object, as it travels from W to X is:

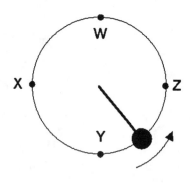

A) ←   B) ↓   C) ↑   D) ↗   *E) ↙

27. An airplane makes a gradual 90° turn while flying at a constant speed of 200 m/s. The process takes 20.0 seconds to complete. For this turn the magnitude of the average acceleration of the plane is

A) zero   B) 40 m/s^2 C) 20 m/s^2 *D) 14 m/s^2 E) 10 m/s^2

28. An airplane is flying north at 500 km/h. It makes a slow 180° turn at constant speed, changing its direction of travel from north through east to south. The process takes 40 seconds. The average acceleration of the plane for this turn (in km/h ·s) is:

A) 12.5 (north)   D) 25 (north)
B) 12.5 (east)   *E) 25 (south)
C) 12.5 (south)

29. An object is moving on a circular path of radius π meters at a constant speed of 4.0 m/s. The time required for one revolution is

A) 2/π^2 s   *B) π^2/2 s   C) π/2 s   D) π^2/4 s   E) 2/π s

30. A particle moves at constant speed in a circular path. The instantaneous velocity and instantaneous acceleration vectors are:

A) both tangent to the circular path
B) both perpendicular to the circular path
*C) perpendicular to each other
D) opposite to each other
E) none of the above

31. A stone is tied to a string and whirled at constant speed in a horizontal circle. The speed is then doubled without changing the length of the string. Afterward, the magnitude of the acceleration of the stone is:

A) the same   D) one fourth as great
B) half as great   E) four times as great
*C) twice as great

32. Two objects are traveling around different circular orbits with constant speed. They both have the same acceleration but object A is traveling twice as fast as object B. The orbit radius for object A is _____ the orbit radius for object B.

A) one fourth   D) twice
B) one half   *E) four times
C) the same as

33. A stone is tied to a 0.50 m string and whirled at a constant speed of 4.0 m/s in a vertical circle. Its acceleration in m/s^2 at the top of the circle is:

A) 9.8, up
B) 9.8, down
C) 12, down

D) 32, up
*E) 32, down

34. A stone is tied to a 0.50 m string and whirled at a constant speed of 4.0 m/s in a vertical circle. The magnitude of its acceleration in m/s^2 at the bottom of the circle is:

A) 9.8, up
B) 9.8, down
C) 12, up

*D) 32, up
E) 32, down

35. A car rounds a 20-m radius curve at 10 m/s. The magnitude of its acceleration in m/s^2 is:

A) 0   B) 0.20   C) 5.0   *D) 40   E) 400

36. For a biological sample in a 1.0-m radius centrifuge to have a centripetal acceleration of 25g its speed in m/s must be:

A) 11   *B) 16   C) 50   D) 122   E) 245

37. A girl on a merry-go-round moves horizontally in a circle at constant speed. She travels one fourth of a revolution, a distance of 25 m along the circumference of the circle, in 5.0 s. The magnitude of her acceleration is:

A) 0.31 m/s^2 B) 1.3 m/s^2 *C) 1.6 m/s^2 D) 3.9 m/s^2 E) 6.3 m/s^2

38. A stone is tied to the end of a string and is swung with constant speed around a horizontal circle with a radius of 1.5 m. If it makes two complete revolutions each second, its acceleration is:

A) 0.24 m/s^2 B) 2.4 m/s^2 C) 24 m/s^2 *D) 240 m/s^2 E) 2400 m/s^2

39. A boat is able to move through still water at 20 m/s. It makes a round trip to a town 3.0 km downstream. If the river flows at 5 m/s, the time required for this round trip is:

A) 120 s   B) 150 s   C) 200 s   D) 300 s   *E) 320 s

40. A boat is traveling upstream at 14 mph with respect to a river that is flowing at 6 mph (with respect to the ground). A man runs directly across the boat, from one side to the other, at 6 mph (with respect to the boat). The velocity of the man with respect to the ground is:

*A) 10 mph   B) 14 mph   C) 18.5 mph   D) 21 mph   E) 26 mph

41. A ferry boat is sailing at 12 mph 30° W of N with respect to a river that is flowing at 6.0 mph E. As observed from the shore, the ferryboat is sailing:

  A) 30° E of N   D) 45° E of N
 *B) due N   E) none of these
  C) 30° W of N

42. A boy wishes to row across a river in the shortest possible time. He can row at 2 m/s in still water and the river is flowing at 1 m/s. At what angle with respect to the water velocity should he point the bow (front) of his boat?

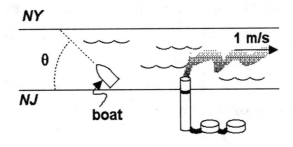

  A) 30°   B) 45°   C) 60°   D) 63°   *E) 90°

43. A girl wishes to row across a river to a point directly opposite as shown. She can row at 2 m/s in still water and the river is flowing at 1 m/s. At what angle with respect to the line joining the starting and finishing points should she point the bow (front) of her boat?

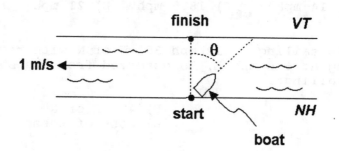

*A) 30°   B) 45°   C) 60°   D) 63°   E) 90°

44. A motor boat can travel at 10 km/h in still water. A river flows at 5 km/h west. A boater wishes to cross from the south bank to a point directly opposite on the north bank. At what angle must the boat be headed?

   A) 27° E of N
*B) 30° E of N
   C) 45° E of N
   D) 60° E of N
   E) depends on the width of the river

45. Two projectiles are in flight at the same time. The acceleration of one relative to the other:

   A) is always 9.8 m/s^2 *D) is zero
   B) can be as large as 19.8 m/s^2 E) none of these
   C) can be horizontal

46. The velocity of a particle, as measured in a certain inertial reference frame, is 0.80c in the positive x direction. Here c is the speed of light. This frame, when viewed from the laboratory, is moving in the positive x direction with a speed of 0.90c. The velocity of particle as measured in the laboratory is:

   A) -0.10c   B) 0.10c   *C) 0.99c   D) 1.7c   E) c

47. The velocity of a particle, as measured in a certain inertial reference frame, is 0.80c in the positive x direction. Here c is the speed of light. This frame, when viewed from the laboratory, is moving in the negative x direction with a speed of 0.90c. The velocity of particle as measured in the laboratory is:

A) -1.7c   *B) -0.36c   C) -0.10c   D) 0.10c   E) c

48. We send a beam of light, traveling at the speed of light c, toward a distant galaxy, which is receding from us with a speed of 0.90c. Observers in the galaxy see the light coming toward them with a speed of:

A) 0   B) 0.10c   *C) c   D) 1.9c   E) 2.0c

49. A space station sends an exploratory spaceship at a speed of 0.80c toward an alien spaceship. Here c is the speed of light. At launch the aliens immediately begin retreating away from the space station at a constant speed of 0.70c. From the point of view of the aliens how fast is the exploratory ship coming toward them?

A) 0.064c   B) 0.10c   *C) 0.23c   D) c   E) 1.5c

1. An example of an inertial reference frame is:

 A) any frame that is not accelerating
*B) a frame attached to a particle on which no forces act
 C) any frame that is at rest
 D) a frame attached to the center of the universe
 E) a frame attached to the earth

2. An object moving at constant velocity in an inertial frame must:

 A) have a net force acting on it
 B) eventually stop due to gravity
 C) not have any force of gravity acting on it
*D) have zero net force acting on it
 E) have no frictional force acting on it

3. In principle, a force is measured by measuring the _____, when the force is applied to it.

 A) velocity of the standard kilogram
 B) speed of the standard kilogram
 C) velocity of any object
*D) acceleration of the standard kilogram
 E) acceleration of any object

4. Which of the following quantities is NOT a vector?

*A) mass   D) acceleration
 B) displacement   E) force
 C) weight

5. A newton is the force

 A) of gravity on a 1 kg body
 B) of gravity on a 1 gram body
 C) that gives a 1 g body an acceleration of 1 cm/s^2
*D) that gives a 1 kg body an acceleration of 1 m/s^2
 E) that gives a 1 kg body an acceleration of 9.8 m/s^2

6. The unit of force called the newton is:

A) $9.8 \text{ kg} \cdot \text{m/s}^2$
*B) 1 kg.m/s^2
C) defined by means of Newton's third law
D) 1 kg of mass
E) 1 kg of force

7. A force of 1 N is:

A) 1 kg/s
B) 1 kg.m/s
*C) 1 kg.m/s^2
D) $1 \text{ kg.m}^2/\text{s}$
E) $1 \text{ kg.m}^2/\text{s}^2$

8. The standard 1-kg mass is attached to a compressed spring and the spring is released. If the mass initially has an acceleration of 5.6 m/s^2, the force of the spring has a magnitude of:

A) 2.8 N
*B) 5.6 N
C) 11.2 N
D) 0
E) an undetermined amount

9. Acceleration is always in the direction:

A) of the displacement
B) of the initial velocity
C) of the final velocity
*D) of the net force
E) opposite to the frictional force

10. The term "mass" refers to the same physical concept as:

A) weight
*B) inertia
C) force
D) acceleration
E) volume

11. The inertia of a body tends to cause the body to:

A) speed up
B) slow down
*C) resist any change in its motion
D) fall toward the earth
E) decelerate due to friction

12. A heavy ball is suspended as shown. A quick jerk on the lower string will break that string but a slow pull on the lower string will break the upper string. The first result occurs because:

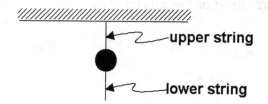

upper string

lower string

  A) the force is too small to move the ball
  B) action and reaction
 *C) the ball has inertia
  D) air friction holds the ball back
  E) the ball has too much energy

13. When a certain force is applied to the 1-kg standard mass its acceleration is 5.0 m/s. When the same force is applied to another object its acceleration is one fifth as much. The mass of the object is:

  A) 0.2 kg   B) 0.5 kg   C) 1.0 kg   *D) 5.0 kg   E) 10 kg

14. Mass differs from weight in that:

  A) all objects have weight but some lack mass
 *B) weight is a force and mass is not
  C) the mass of an object is always more than its weight
  D) mass can only be expressed in the metric system
  E) there is no difference

15. The mass of a body:

  A) is slightly different at different places on the earth
  B) is a vector
 *C) is independent of the acceleration due to gravity
  D) is the same for all bodies of the same volume
  E) can be measured most accurately on a spring scale

16. The mass and weight of a body:

  A) differ by a factor of 9.8
  B) are identical
  C) are the same physical quantities expressed in different units
  D) are both a direct measure of the inertia of the body
 *E) have the same ratio as that of any other body placed at that
     location

17. An object placed on an equal-arm balance requires 12 kg to balance it. When placed on a spring scale, the scale reads 12 kg. Everything (balance, scale, set of masses and object) is now transported to the moon where the force of gravity is one-sixth that on earth. The new readings of the balance and spring scale (respectively) are:

A) 12 kg, 12 kg
B) 2 kg, 2 kg
*C) 12 kg, 2 kg
D) 2 kg, 12 kg
E) 12 kg, 72 kg

18. Two objects, one having three times the mass of the other, are dropped from the same height in a vacuum. At the end of their fall, their velocities are equal because:

A) anything falling in vacuum has constant velocity
B) all objects reach the same terminal velocity
C) the acceleration of the larger object is three times greater than that of the smaller object
D) the force of gravity is the same for both objects
*E) none of the above

19. A feather and a lead ball are dropped from rest in vacuum on the moon. The acceleration of the feather is:

A) more than that of the lead ball
*B) the same as that of the lead ball
C) less than that of the lead ball
D) 9.8 m/s^2
E) zero since it floats in a vacuum

20. Equal forces F act on isolated bodies A and B. The mass of B is three times that of A. The magnitude of the acceleration of A is:

*A) three times that of B
B) 1/3 that of B
C) the same as B
D) nine times that of B
E) 1/9 that of B

21. A car travels east at constant velocity. The net force on the car is:

A) east   B) west   C) up   D) down   *E) zero

22. A constant force of 8.0 N is exerted for 4.0 s on a 16-kg object initially at rest. The change in speed of this object will be:

A) 0.5 m/s   *B) 2 m/s   C) 4 m/s   D) 8 m/s   E) 32 m/s

23. A 6-kg object is moving south. A net force of 12 N north acting on it will result in the object having an acceleration of:

*A) 2 m/s^2, north
 B) 2 m/s^2, south
 C) 6 m/s^2, north
 D) 18 m/s^2, north
 E) 18 m/s^2, south

24. A 2400-lb automobile is pushed along a level road by four students who apply a total forward force of 150 lb. Neglecting friction, the acceleration of the automobile is:

 A) 16 ft/s^2
 B) 8 ft/s^2
 C) 4 ft/s^2
*D) 2 ft/s^2
 E) 1/16 ft/s^2

25. An object rests on a horizontal frictionless surface. A horizontal force of magnitude F is applied. This force produces an acceleration:

 A) only if F is larger than the weight of the object
 B) only while the mass suddenly changes from rest to motion
*C) always
 D) only if the inertia of the object decreases
 E) only if F is increasing

26. A 25-kg chair is pushed across a frictionless horizontal floor with a force of 20 N, directed 20° below the horizontal. The acceleration of the chair is:

 A) 0.27 m/s^2 *B) 0.75 m/s^2 C) 0.80 m/s^2 D) 170 m/s^2 E) 470 m/s^2

27. An 0.25-lb ball is thrown at an angle of 30° above the horizontal with an initial speed of 64 ft/s. At its highest point, the net force on the ball is:

 A) 64 lb, 30° below horizontal
 B) zero
 C) 32 lb, up
 D) 32 lb, down
*E) 0.25 lb, down

28. Two forces are applied to a 5.0-kg object, one is 6.0 N to the north and the other is 8.0 N to the west. The magnitude of the acceleration of the object is:

 A) 0.50 m/s^2 *B) 2.0 m/s^2 C) 2.8 m/s^2 D) 10 m/s^2 E) 50 m/s^2

29. In a tug-of-war, two men each pull on the rope with 100-lb forces, in opposite directions. The tension in the rope is:

*A) 100 lb   B) 200 lb   C) zero   D) 50 lb   E) 141 lb

30. A heavy steel ball B is suspended by a cord from a block of wood W. The entire system is dropped through the air. Neglecting air resistance, the tension in the cord is:

*A) zero
 B) the difference in the masses of B and W
 C) the difference in the weights of B and W
 D) the weight of B
 E) none of these

31. A circus performer of weight W is walking along a "high wire" as shown. The tension in the wire is:

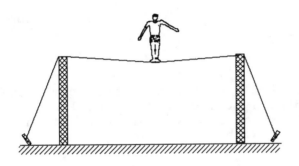

 A) approximately W
 B) approximately W/2
 C) much less than W
*D) much more than W
 E) depends on whether he stands on one or two feet

32. A 1000-kg elevator is rising and its speed is increasing at 3 m/s^2. The tension in the elevator cable is:

 A) 6800 N   B) 1000 N   C) 3000 N   D) 9800 N   *E) 12800 N

33. A 700-kg elevator accelerates downward at 3.0 m/s^2. The force exerted by the cable on the elevator is:

 A) 2.1 kN, up   D) 4.8 kN, down
 B) 2.1 kN, down   E) 9.0 kN, up
*C) 4.8 kN, up

34. A crane operator lowers a 4000-lb steel ball with a downward acceleration of 8 ft/s^2. The tension in the cable is:

 A) 4000 lb
 B) 1000 lb
*C) 3000 lb
 D) 5000 lb
 E) dependent on the velocity of the ball

35. A 1-lb pendulum bob is held at an angle θ from the vertical by a 2-lb horizontal force F as shown. The tension in the string supporting the pendulum bob (in pounds) is:

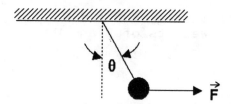

A) cosθ
B) 2/cosθ
*C)
    √5

D) 1
E) none of these

36. A car moves horizontally with a constant acceleration of 13 ft/s². A ball is suspended by a string from the ceiling of the car; the ball does not swing, being at rest with respect to the car. What angle does the string make with the vertical?

*A) 22°
B) 24°
C) 66°
D) 68°
E) cannot be found without knowing string length

37. A man weighing 160 lb is in an elevator that is accelerating upward at 16 ft/s². The force exerted on him by the elevator floor (in pounds) is:

A) 80   B) 160   C) 179   *D) 240   E) 320

38. A physics textbook is suspended on a spring scale in an elevator. Of the following, the scale shows the highest reading when the elevator:

*A) moves upward with increasing speed
 B) moves upward with decreasing speed
 C) remains stationary
 D) moves downward with increasing speed
 E) moves downward at constant speed

39. A physics textbook is suspended on a spring scale in an elevator. Of the following, the scale shows the highest reading when the elevator:

   A) moves downward with increasing speed
   *B) moves downward with decreasing speed
   C) remains stationary
   D) moves upward with decreasing speed
   E) moves upward at constant speed

40. A 150 lb man stands on a spring scale in an elevator that is accelerating upward at 16 ft/s^2. The scale will read (in lbs):

   A) 300   *B) 225   C) 175   D) 150   E) 75

41. A 25-kg chair is pushed across a frictionless horizontal floor with a force of 20 N, directed 20° below the horizontal. The magnitude of the normal force of the floor on the chair is:

   A) 6.8 N   B) 42 N   C) 49 N   *D) 56 N   E) 68 N

42. A block slides down a frictionless plane that makes an angle of 30° with the horizontal. The acceleration of the block (in cm/s^2) is:

   A) 980   B) 566   C) 849   D) zero   *E) 490

43. A 25-N crate slides down a frictionless incline that is 25° above the horizontal. The magnitude of the normal force of the incline on the crate is:

   A) 11 N   *B) 23 N   C) 25 N   D) 100 N   E) 220 N

44. A 25-N crate is held at rest on a frictionless incline by a force that is parallel to the incline. If the incline is 25° above the horizontal the magnitude of the applied force is:

   A) 4.1 N   B) 4.6 N   C) 8.9 N   *D) 11 N   E) 23 N

45. A 25-N crate is held at rest on a frictionless incline by a force that is parallel to the incline. If the incline is 25° above the horizontal the magnitude of the normal force of the incline on the crate is:

   A) 4.1 N   B) 4.6 N   C) 8.9 N   D) 11 N   *E) 23 N

46. A 32-N force, parallel to the incline, is required to push a certain crate at constant velocity up a frictionless incline that is 30° above the horizontal. The mass of the crate is:

A) 3.3 kg   B) 3.8 kg   C) 5.7 kg   *D) 6.5 kg   E) 160 kg

47. When a 40-N force, parallel to the incline and directed up the incline, is applied to a crate on a frictionless incline that is 30° above the horizontal, the acceleration of the crate is 2.0 m/s², down the incline. The mass of the crate is:

A) 3.8 kg   B) 4.1 kg   C) 5.8 kg   D) 6.2 kg   *E) 10 kg

48. When a 40-N force, parallel to the incline and directed up the incline, is applied to a crate on a frictionless incline that is 30° above the horizontal, the acceleration of the crate is 2.0 m/s², up the incline. The mass of the crate is:

A) 3.8 kg   B) 4.1 kg   *C) 5.8 kg   D) 6.2 kg   E) 10 kg

49. The "reaction" force does not cancel the "action" force because:

A) the action force is greater than the reaction force
*B) they act on different bodies
C) they are in the same direction
D) the reaction force exists only after the action force is removed
E) the reaction force is greater than the action force

50. A book rests on a table, exerting a downward force on the table. The reaction to this force is:

A) the force of the earth on the book
*B) the force of the table on the book
C) the force of the earth on the table
D) the force of the book on the earth
E) the inertia of the book

51. A lead block is suspended from your hand by a string. The reaction to the force of gravity on the block is the force exerted by the:

A) string on the block   D) hand on the string
B) block on the string   *E) block on the earth
C) string on the hand

52. A 5-kg concrete block is lowered with a downward acceleration of 2.8 m/s² by means of a rope. The force of the block on the rope is:

A) 14 N, up   *D) 35 N, down
B) 14 N, down   E) 49 N, up
C) 35 N, up

48

53. A 90-kg man stands in an elevator that is moving up at a constant speed of 5.0 m/s. The force exerted by him on the floor is about:

A) zero   B) 90 N   *C) 880 N   D) 450 N   E) 49 N

54. A 90-kg man stands in an elevator that has a downward acceleration of 1.4 m/s². The force exerted by him on the floor is about:

A) zero   B) 90 N   *C) 760 N   D) 880 N   E) 1010 N

55. A 5-kg concrete block is lowered with a downward acceleration of 2.8 m/s² by means of a rope. The force of the block on the earth is:

A) 14 N, up   D) 35 N, down
B) 14 N, down   *E) 49 N, up
C) 35 N, up

56. Two blocks are connected by a string and pulley as shown. Assuming that the string and pulley are massless, the magnitude of the acceleration of each block is:

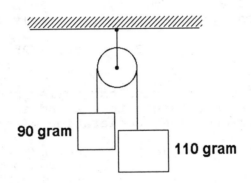

A) 0.049 m/s²   D) 0.54 m/s²
B) 0.020 m/s²   *E) 0.98 m/s²
C) 0.0098 m/s²

57. A 16-lb block and an 8-lb block are connected by a string as shown. If the pulley is massless and the surface is frictionless, the magnitude of the acceleration of the 16-lb block (in ft/s^2) is:

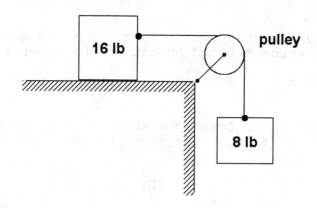

A) 0.33   B) 0.5   C) 16   *D) 10.7   E) 32

58. A 13-lb weight and a 12-lb weight are connected by a massless string over a massless, frictionless pulley. The 13-lb weight has a downward acceleration equal to that of a freely falling body times:

A) 1   B) 1/12   C) 1/13   *D) 1/25   E) 13/25

59. A massless rope passes over a massless pulley suspended from the ceiling. A 4-kg block is attached to one end and a 5-kg block is attached to the other end. The acceleration of the 5-kg block is:

A) g/4   B) 5g/9   C) 4g/9   D) g/5   *E) g/9

60. Two blocks (60 lb and 100 lb) are connected by a string that passes over a massless pulley as shown. The tension in the string is:

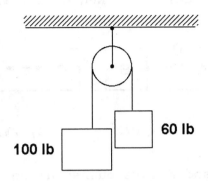

A) 40 lb
B) 60 lb
C) 100 lb

D) 160 lb
*E) none of these

61. Three books (X, Y, and Z) rest on a table. The weight of each book is indicated. The net force acting on book Y is:

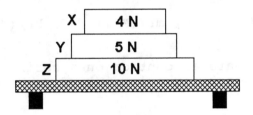

A) 4 N down
B) 5 N up
C) 9 N down

*D) zero
E) none of these

62. Three books (X, Y, and Z) rest on a table. The weight of each book is indicated. The force of book Z on book Y is:

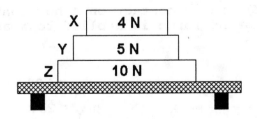

A) 0   B) 5 N   *C) 9 N   D) 14 N   E) 19 N

63. Three blocks (A,B,C), each having mass M, are connected by strings as shown. Block C is pulled to the right by a force **F** that causes the entire system to accelerate. Neglecting friction, the net force acting on block B is:

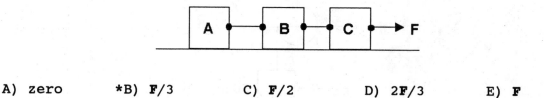

A) zero   *B) **F**/3   C) **F**/2   D) 2**F**/3   E) **F**

64. Two blocks (masses m and M) are pushed along a horizontal frictionless surface by a horizontal applied force **F** as shown. The magnitude of the force that either of these blocks exerts on the other is:

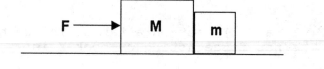

*A) mF/(m+M)   B) mF/M   C) mF/(M-m)   D) MF/(M+m)   E) MF/m

65. Two blocks (X and Y) are in contact on a horizontal frictionless surface. A 36-N constant force is applied to X as shown. The force exerted by X on Y is:

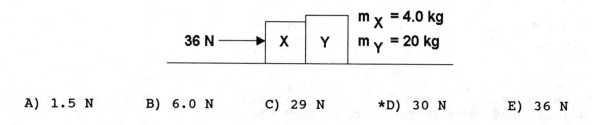

A) 1.5 N   B) 6.0 N   C) 29 N   *D) 30 N   E) 36 N

66. Two blocks (X and Y) are in contact on a horizontal frictionless surface. A 36-N constant force is applied to X as shown. The force exerted by Y on X is:

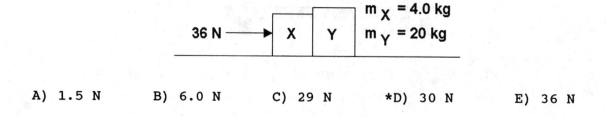

A) 1.5 N   B) 6.0 N   C) 29 N   *D) 30 N   E) 36 N

67. A short 10-g string is used to pull a 50-g toy across a frictionless horizontal surface. If a 3.0×10^{-2}-N force is applied horizontally to the free end, the force of the string on the toy, at the other end, is:

A) 0.15 N
B) 6.0×10^{-3} N
*C) 2.5×10^{-2} N

D) 3.0×10^{-2} N
E) 3.5×10^{-2} N

1. A brick slides on a horizontal surface. Which of the following will increase the frictional force on it?

*A) putting a second brick on top
 B) decreasing the surface area of contact
 C) increasing the surface area of contact
 D) decreasing the mass of the brick
 E) none of the above

2. The coefficient of kinetic friction:

 A) is in the direction of the frictional force
 B) is in the direction of the normal force
 C) is the ratio of force to area
 D) can have units of newtons
*E) none of the above

3. When the brakes of an automobile are applied, the road exerts the greatest retarding force:

 A) while the wheels are sliding
*B) just before the wheels start to slide
 C) when the automobile is going fastest
 D) when the acceleration is least
 E) at the instant when the speed begins to change

4. A forward force of 3 lb is used to pull a 60-lb sled at constant velocity on a frozen pond. The coefficient of friction is:

 A) 0.5   *B) 0.05   C) 2   D) 0.2   E) 20

5. The velocity of a 1.0-lb hockey puck, sliding across a level ice surface, decreases at the rate of 2.0 ft/s^2. The coefficient of kinetic friction between the puck and ice is:

*A) 0.625   B) 0.125   C) 0.5   D) 2.0   E) 32

6. A 3-lb horizontal force is applied to a 10-lb block on a rough horizontal surface. The block is initially at rest. If $\mu_s = 0.5$ and $\mu_k = 0.4$, the frictional force on the block is:

 A) 2 lb   *B) 3 lb   C) 4 lb   D) 5 lb   E) 10 lb

54

7. A 6.0-lb horizontal force is applied to a 10-lb block initially at rest on a rough horizontal surface. If $\mu_s = 0.5$ and $\mu_k = 0.4$, the frictional force on the block is:

A) 2 lb   B) 3 lb   *C) 4 lb   D) 5 lb   E) 10 lb

8. A horizontal shove of at least 50 lb is required to start moving a 200-lb crate initially at rest on a horizontal floor. The coefficient of static friction is:

*A) 0.25   D) 4.00
 B) 0.125   E) none of these
 C) 0.50

9. A force **F** (larger than the largest possible force of static friction) is applied to the left to an object moving to the right on a horizontal surface. Then:

A) the object must be moving at constant speed
B) **F** and the friction force act in opposite directions
*C) the object must be slowing down
D) the object must be speeding up
E) the object must come to rest and remain at rest

10. A block rests on a rough horizontal surface ($\mu_s = 0.50$, $\mu_k = 0.40$). A constant horizontal force, just sufficient to start the block in motion, is applied. The acceleration of the block, in m/s^2 , is:

A) 0   *B) 0.98   C) 3.3   D) 4.5   E) 8.9

11. A car is traveling at 88 ft/s on a horizontal road. The brakes are applied and the car skids to a stop in 4.0 s. The coefficient of kinetic friction between the tires and road is:

A) 0.48   *B) 0.69   C) 0.77   D) 0.92   E) 1.11

12. A boy pulls a wooden box along a rough horizontal floor at constant speed by means of a force **P** as shown. Which of the following must be true (f is the magnitude of the force of friction, N is the magnitude of the normal force, and W is the magnitude of the weight):

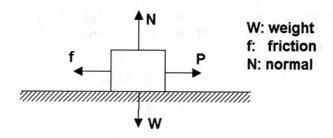

W: weight
f: friction
N: normal

*A) P = f and N = W
 B) P = f and N > W
 C) P > f and N < W

D) P > f and N = W
E) none of these

13. A boy pulls a wooden box along a rough horizontal floor at constant speed by means of a force **P** as shown. Which of the following must be true (f is the magnitude of the force of friction, N is the magnitude of the normal force, and W is the magnitude of the weight):

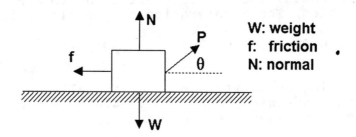

W: weight
f: friction .
N: normal

 A) P = f and N = W
 B) P = f and N > W
*C) P > f and N < W

D) P > f and N = W
E) none of these

14. A 100 lb block is dragged along a rough (μ_k = 0.4) horizontal surface by an applied force **F** as shown. The block moves at constant velocity. The magnitude of **F** is:

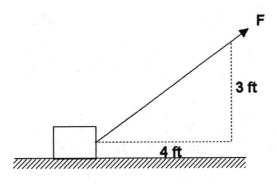

A) 50/32 lb
B) 200/3 lb
*C) 500/13 lb

D) 40 lb
E) 50 lb

15. A block of mass m is pulled at constant velocity along a rough horizontal floor by an applied force **T** as shown. The frictional force is:

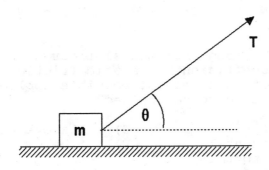

*A) Tcosθ   B) Tsinθ   C) zero   D) mg   E) Tcosθ

57

16. A block of mass m is pulled along a rough horizontal floor by an applied force **T** as shown. The vertical component of the force exerted on the block by the floor is:

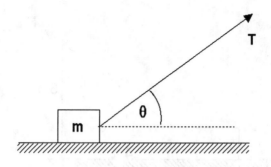

A) mg
B) mg – Tcosθ
C) mg + Tcosθ

*D) mg – Tsinθ
E) mg + Tsinθ

17. A 12-kg crate rests on a horizontal surface and a boy pulls on it with a force that is 30° above the horizontal. If the coefficient of static friction is 0.40, the minimum magnitude force he needs to start the crate moving is:

*A) 44 N   B) 47 N   C) 54 N   D) 56 N   E) 71 N

18. A crate resting on a rough horizontal floor is to be moved horizontally. The coefficient of static friction is 0.40. To start the crate moving with the weakest possible applied force, in what direction should the force be applied?

A) horizontal
B) 24° below the horizontal
*C) 22° above the horizontal

D) 24° above the horizontal
E) 66° below the horizontal

19. A 50-N force is applied to a crate on a horizontal rough floor, causing it to move horizontally. If the coefficient of kinetic friction is 0.50, in what direction should the force be applied to obtain the greatest acceleration?

A) horizontal
B) 60° above the horizontal
C) 30° above the horizontal

*D) 27° above the horizontal
E) 30° below the horizontal

20. A professor holds an eraser against a vertical chalkboard by pushing horizontally on it. He pushes with a force that is much greater than is required to hold the eraser. The force of friction exerted by the board on the eraser increases if he

   A) pushes with slightly greater force
   B) pushes with slightly less force
   C) stops pushing
  *D) raises his elbow so the force he exerts is slightly downward but has the same magnitude
   E) lowers his elbow so the force he exerts is slightly upward but has the same magnitude

21. A horizontal force of 12 N pushes a 0.5-kg block against a vertical wall. The block is initially at rest. If μ_s = 0.6 and μ_k = 0.8 which of the following is true?

  *A) the frictional force is 4.9 N
   B) the frictional force is 7.2 N
   C) the normal force is 4.9 N
   D) the block will start moving and accelerate
   E) if started moving downward, the block will decelerate

22. A horizontal force of 5.0 N pushes a 0.50-kg block against a vertical wall. The block is initially at rest. If μ_s = 0.6 and μ_k = 0.80, the frictional force is:

   A) 0   B) 4.9 N   C) 3.0 N   D) 5.0 N   *E) 4.0 N

23. A horizontal force of 12 N pushes a 0.50-kg block against a vertical wall. The block is initially at rest. If μ_s = 0.6 and μ_k = 0.80, the acceleration of the block in m/s^2 is:

  *A) 0   B) 9.4   C) 9.8   D) 14.4   E) 19.2

24. A horizontal force of 5.0 N pushes a 0.50-kg block against a vertical wall. The block is initially at rest. If μ_s = 0.60 and μ_k = 0.80, the acceleration of the block in m/s^2 is:

   A) 0   *B) 1.8   C) 6.0   D) 8.0   E) 9.8

25. A heavy wooden block is dragged along a rough steel plate as shown. The frictional force in (ii), as compared with that in (i) is:

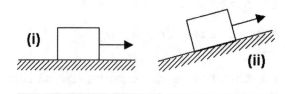

A) the same
B) greater
*C) less
D) less for some angles and greater for others
E) can be less or greater, depending on the magnitude of the applied force.

26. A block is first placed on its long side and then on its short side on the same inclined plane. The block slides down the plane on its short side but remains at rest on its long side. A possible explanation is:

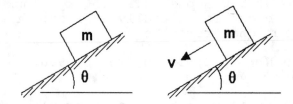

*A) the short side is smoother
B) the frictional force is less because the contact area is less
C) the center of gravity is higher in the second case
D) the normal force is less in the second case
E) the force of gravity is more nearly down the plane in the second case

27. A box rests on a rough board 10 meters long. When one end of the board is slowly raised to a height of 6 meters above the other end, the box begins to slide. The coefficient of static friction is:

A) 0.8   B) 0.25   C) 0.4   D) 0.6   *E) 0.75

28. A block is placed on a rough wooden plane. It is found that when the plane is tilted 30° to the horizontal, the block will slide down at constant speed. The coefficient of kinetic friction of the block with the plane is:

A) 0.500   *B) 0.577   C) 1.73   D) 0.866   E) 4.90

29. A crate is sliding down an incline that is 35° above the horizontal. If the coefficient of kinetic friction is 0.40, the acceleration of the crate is:

A) 0   *B) 2.4 m/s^2 C) 5.8 m/s^2 D) 8.8 m/s^2 E) 10.3 m/s^2

30. A 5.0-kg crate is resting on a horizontal plank. The coefficient of static friction is 0.50 and the coefficient of kinetic friction is 0.40. After one end of the plank is raised so the plank is 25° above the horizontal, the force of friction is:

A) 0   B) 18 N   *C) 21 N   D) 22 N   E) 44 N

31. A 5.0-kg crate is resting on a horizontal plank. The coefficient of static friction is .50 and the coefficient of kinetic friction is 0.40. After one end of the plank is raised so the plank is 30° above the horizontal, the force of friction is:

A) 0   *B) 18 N   C) 21 N   D) 22 N   E) 44 N

32. A 5.0-kg crate is on an incline that is 30° above the horizontal. If the coefficient of static friction is 0.50, the minimum force that can be applied parallel to the plane to hold the crate at rest is:

A) 0   *B) 3.3 N   C) 30 N   D) 46 N   E) 55 N

33. A 5.0-kg crate is on an incline that is 30° above the horizontal. The maximum force that can be applied parallel to the plane without moving the crate is:

A) 0   B) 3.3 N   C) 30 N   *D) 46 N   E) 55 N

34. Block A, with mass m_A, is initially at rest on a horizontal floor. Block B, with mass m_B, is initially at rest on the horizontal top surface of A. The coefficient of static friction between the two blocks is μ_s. Block A is pulled with an increasing force. It begins to slide out from under B when its acceleration reaches:

A) g
*B) $\mu_s g$
C) $m_B \mu_s g$

D) $(m_A/m_B)\mu_s\ g$
E) $(m_B/m_A)\mu_s\ g$

35. The system shown remains at rest. The force of friction on the upper block is:

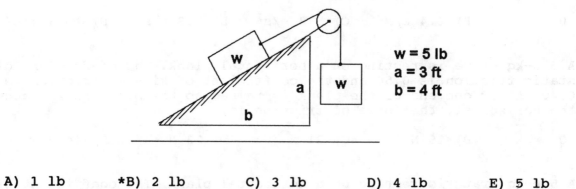

w = 5 lb
a = 3 ft
b = 4 ft

A) 1 lb   *B) 2 lb   C) 3 lb   D) 4 lb   E) 5 lb

36. Block A, with a mass of 50 kg, rests on a horizontal table top. The coefficient of static friction is 0.40. A horizontal string is attached to A and passes over a massless, frictionless pulley as shown. The smallest mass m_B that will start A moving when it is attached to the other end of the string is:

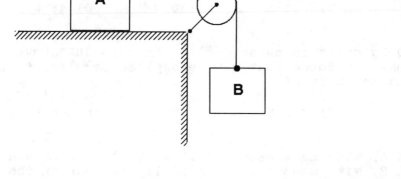

*A) 20 kg   B) 30 kg   C) 40 kg   D) 50 kg   E) 70 kg

62

37. Block A, with a mass of 10 kg, rests on a 35° incline. The coefficient of static friction is 0.40. An attached string is parallel to the incline and passes over a massless, frictionless pulley at the top. The smallest mass m_B, attached to the dangling end, for which A remains at rest is:

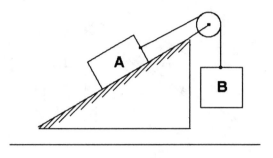

*A) 2.5 kg   B) 3.5 kg   C) 5.9 kg   D) 9.0 kg   E) 10.5 kg

38. Block A, with a mass of 10 kg, rests on a 35° incline. The coefficient of static friction is 0.40. An attached string is parallel to the incline and passes over a massless, frictionless pulley at the top. The largest mass m_B, attached to the dangling end, for which A remains at rest is:

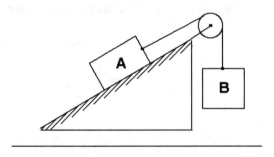

A) 2.5 kg   B) 3.5 kg   C) 5.9 kg   D) 9.0 kg   *E) 10.5 kg

39. Block A, with a mass of 10 kg, rests on a 30° incline. The coefficient of kinetic friction is 0.20. The attached string is parallel to the incline and passes over a massless, frictionless pulley at the top. Block B, with a mass of 8.0 kg, is attached to the dangling end of the string. The acceleration of B is:

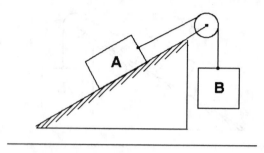

A) 0.69 m/s², up the plane
*B) 0.69 m/s², down the plane
C) 2.6 m/s², up the plane

D) 2.6 m/s², down the plane
E) 0

40. Block A, with a mass of 10 kg, rests on a 30° incline. The coefficient of kinetic friction is 0.20. The attached string is parallel to the incline and passes over a massless, frictionless pulley at the top. Block B, with a mass of 3.0 kg, is attached to the dangling end of the string. The acceleration of B is:

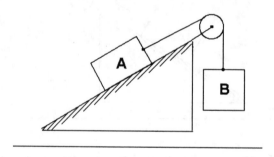

*A) 0.20 m/s², up
B) 0.20 m/s², down
C) 2.8 m/s², up

D) 2.8 m/s², down
E) 0

41. A 1000-kg airplane moves in straight flight at constant speed. The force of air friction is 1800 N. The net force on the plane is:

*A) zero
B) 11800 N
C) 1800 N

D) 9800 N
E) none of these

42. Why do raindrops fall with constant speed during the later stages of their descent?

   A) The gravitational force is the same for all drops
  *B) Air resistance just balances the force of gravity
   C) The drops all fall from the same height
   D) The force of gravity is negligible for objects as small as raindrops
   E) Gravity cannot increase the speed of a falling object to more than 32 ft/s

43. A ball is thrown downward from the edge of a cliff with an initial speed that is greater than the terminal speed. Initially its acceleration is

   A) 0
  *B) upward
   C) downward and greater than g
   D) downward and less than g
   E) downward and equal to g

44. A ball is thrown upward into air with a speed that is greater than terminal speed. On the way up it slows down and after its speed equals the terminal speed but before it gets to the top of its trajectory,

   A) its speed is constant
  *B) it continues to slow down
   C) it speeds up
   D) its motion becomes jerky
   E) none of the above

45. A ball is thrown upward into air with a speed that is greater than terminal speed. It lands at the place where it was thrown. During its flight the force of air resistance is the greatest:

  *A) just after it is thrown
   B) halfway up
   C) at the top of its trajectory
   D) halfway down
   E) just before it lands.

46. Uniform circular motion is the direct consequence of:

   A) Newton's third law
   B) centrifugal force
   C) an acceleration tangent to the path
   D) conservation of energy and momentum
  *E) an acceleration always directed toward the same point

47. An object moving in a circle at constant speed:

   A) must have only one force acting on it
   B) is not accelerating
   C) is held to its path by centrifugal force
  *D) has an acceleration of constant magnitude
   E) has an acceleration that is tangent to the circle

48. An object of mass m and another object of mass 2m are each forced to move along a circle of radius 1.0 m at a constant speed of 1.0 m/s. The magnitudes of their accelerations are:

*A) equal
 B)
    in the ratio of $\sqrt{2}$: 1

C) in the ratio of 2 : 1
D) in the ratio of 4 : 1
E) zero

49. The magnitude of the force (in newtons) required to cause an 0.04-kg object to move at 0.6 m/s in a circle of radius 1.0 m is:

 A) 2.4×10^{-2}
*B) 1.4×10^{-2}
 C) $1.4\pi \times 10^{-2}$

D) $2.4\pi^2 \times 10^{-2}$
E) 3.13

50. 50. A 0.2-kg stone is attached to a string and swung in a circle of radius 0.6 m on a horizontal and frictionless surface. If the stone makes 150 revolutions per minute, the tension on the string is:

A) 0.03 N   B) 0.2 N   C) 0.9 N   D) 1.96 N   *E) 30 N

51. Which of the following five graphs is correct for a particle moving in a circle of radius r at a constant speed of 10 m/s?

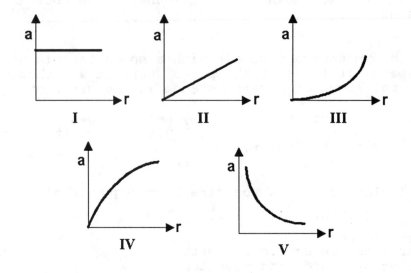

A) I.   B) II.   C) III.   D) IV.   *E) V.

52. An object moves in a circle. If the radius is doubled keeping the speed the same then the centripetal force must be:

 A) twice as great
*B) half as great
 C) four times as great

D) one-fourth as great
E) the same

53. An object moves in a circle. If the mass is tripled, the speed halved and the radius unchanged then the centripetal force must change by a factor of:

A) 3/2   *B) 3/4   C) 9/4   D) 6   E) 12

54. If a satellite moves above the earth's atmosphere in a circular orbit with constant speed, then:

A) its acceleration and velocity are in the same direction
B) the net force on it is zero
C) its velocity is constant
D) it will fall back to earth when its fuel is used up
*E) its acceleration is toward the earth

55. A 200-lb man, sitting next to the driver of a car, presses against the car door with a 50-lb force when the car makes a left turn at 30 mph. The (faulty) door will pop open under a force of 200 lb. Of the following, the least speed for which the man is thrown out of the car is:

A) 32 mph   B) 42 mph   C) 45 mph   *D) 60 mph   E) 120 mph

56. An automobile moves on a level horizontal road in a circle of radius 100 ft. The coefficient of friction between tires and road is 0.50. The maximum speed (in ft/s) with which this car can round this curve is:

A) 10   B) 16   C) 32   *D) 40   E) 44

57. The driver of a 1000-kg car tries to turn through a circle of radius 100 m on an unbanked curve at a speed of 10 m/s. The actual frictional force between the tires and slippery road is 900 N. The car will:

A) slide into the inside of the curve
B) make the turn
C) slow down due to the frictional force
D) make the turn only if it went faster
*E) slide off to the outside of the curve

58. A giant wheel, having a diameter of 40 m, is fitted with a cage a
platform on which a man of mass m stands. The wheel is rotated i
vertical plane at such a speed that the force exerted by the man
the platform is equal to his weight when the cage is at X, as sho
The net force on the man at point X is:

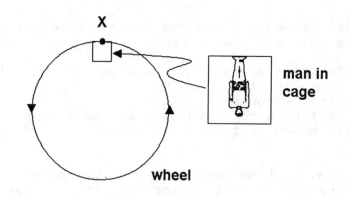

A) zero
B) mg, down
C) mg, up

*D) 2mg, down
E) 2mg, up

59. A giant wheel, 40 m in diameter, is fitted with a cage and platfo
on which a man can stand. The wheel rotates at such a speed that
when the cage is at X (as shown) the force exerted by the man on
platform is equal to his weight. The speed of the man (in m/s) is

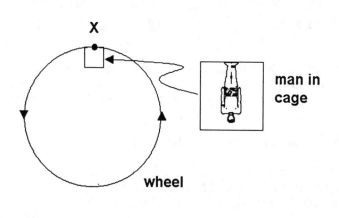

A) 14   *B) 20   C) 28   D) 80   E) 120

60. A person riding a ferris wheel is strapped into her seat by a seat belt. The wheel is spun so that the centripetal acceleration is g. Select the correct combination of forces that act on her when she is at the top. (F_g = gravity force, down; F_b = seat belt force, down; F_s = seat force, up).

	F_g	F_b	F_s				
A)	0	mg	0	D)	mg	mg	0
*B)	mg	0	0	E)	mg	0	mg
C)	0	0	mg				

61. One end of a 1.0-m string is fixed, the other end is attached to a 2.0-kg stone. The stone swings in a vertical circle, passing the bottom point at 4.0 m/s. The string tension (in newtons) at this point is:

A) 0   B) 12   C) 20   D) 32   *E) 52

62. One end of a 1.0-m string is fixed, the other end is attached to a 2.0-kg stone. The stone swings in a vertical circle, passing the top point at 4.0 m/s. The string tension (in newtons) at this point is:

A) 0   *B) 12   C) 20   D) 32   E) 52

63. The iron ball shown is being swung in a vertical circle at the end of a 2-ft string. How slowly, in ft/s, can the ball go through its top position without having the string go slack?

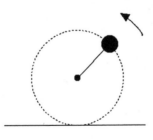

A) 4   B) 6   *C) 8   D) 10   E) 12

64. On some roller coasters each car is suspended below the track by means of a rod that is free to swivel in any direction. When such a car rounds a 45-m radius horizontal curve at 22 m/s (about 50 mph), what angle does the rod make with the vertical?

A) 0   B) 25°   *C) 42°   D) 65°   E) 90°

65. Circular freeway entrance and exit ramps are commonly banked to handle a car moving at 30 mph. To design a similar ramp for 60 mph one should:

A) increase radius by factor of 2
B) decrease radius by factor of 2
*C) increase radius by factor of 4
D) decrease radius by factor of 4
E)

    increase radius by factor of $\sqrt{2}$

1. Which of the following is NOT a correct unit for work?

A) erg
B) ft ·lb
*C) watt

D) newton ·meter
E) joule

2. Which of the following groups does NOT contain a scalar quantity?

A) velocity, force, power
*B) displacement, acceleration, force
C) acceleration, speed, work
D) energy, work, distance
E) pressure, weight, time

3. A boy holds a 10 lb weight at arm's length for 10 s. His arm is 4 ft above the ground. The work (in ft ·lb) done by the boy on the weight while he is holding it is:

*A) 0   B) 4   C) 40   D) 100   E) 400

4. An object moves in a circle at constant speed. The work done by the centripetal force is zero because:

A) the displacement for each revolution is zero
B) the average force for each revolution is zero
C) there is no friction
D) the magnitude of the acceleration is zero
*E) the centripetal force is perpendicular to the velocity

5. An object of mass 1 g is whirled in a horizontal circle of radius 0.5 m at a constant speed of 2 m/s. The work done on the object during one revolution is:

*A) 0   B) 1 J   C) 2 J   D) 4 J   E) 16 J

6. The work done by gravity during the descent of a projectile is:

*A) positive
B) negative
C) zero
D) sign depends on the direction of the y-axis
E) sign depends on the direction of both the x- and y-axes

7. A baseball is hit high into the upper bleachers of left field. Over its entire flight the work done by gravity and the work done by air resistance, respectively, are:

A) positive; positive
B) positive; negative
C) negative; positive
*D) negative; negative
E) unknown since vital information is lacking

8. A fly ball to left field is caught at the same height as it was originally hit. Over its entire flight the work done by gravity and the work done by air resistance, respectively, are:

A) 0; positive
*B) 0; negative
C) positive; negative
D) negative; positive
E) negative; negative

9. A 2 kg object is moving at 3 m/s. A 4 N force is applied in the direction of motion and then removed after the object has traveled an additional 5 m. The work done by this force is:

A) 12 J   B) 15 J   C) 18 J   *D) 20 J   E) 38 J

10. A sledge (including load) weighs 1400 lb. It is pulled on level snow by a dog team exerting a horizontal force on it. The coefficient of kinetic friction between sledge and snow is 0.05. How much work (in ft ·lb) is done by the dog team pulling the sledge 3000 ft at constant speed?

A) 1.4×10^5 *B) 2.1×10^5 C) 8.4×10^7 D) 4.2×10^6 E) 6.7×10^6

11. Camping equipment weighing 6000 N is pulled across a frozen lake by means of a horizontal rope. The coefficient of kinetic friction is 0.05. The work done by the campers in pulling the equipment 1000 m at constant velocity is:

A) 3.1×10^4 J
B) 1.5×10^5 J
*C) 3.0×10^5 J
D) 2.9×10^6 J
E) 6.0×10^6 J

12. Camping equipment weighing 6000 N is pulled across a frozen lake by means of a horizontal rope. The coefficient of kinetic friction is 0.05. How much work is done by the campers in pulling the equipment 1000 m if its speed is decreasing at the constant rate of 0.20 m/s^2?

A) -1.2×10^6 J
*B) 1.8×10^5 J
C) 3.0×10^5 J
D) 4.2×10^5 J
E) 1.2×10^6 J

13. A 1-kg block is lifted vertically 1 m by a boy. The work done by the boy is about:

A) 1 ft ·lb   B) 1 J   *C) 10 J   D) 0.1 J   E) zero

14. A 0.50-kg object moves in a horizontal circular track with a radius of 2.5 m. An external force of 3.0 N, always tangent to the track, causes the object to speed up as it goes around. The work done by the external force as the mass makes one revolution is:

A) 24 J   *B) 47 J   C) 59 J   D) 94 J   E) 120 J

15. A man pulls a 20-lb crate up a frictionless 30° slope 15 ft high as shown. Assuming that the crate moves at constant speed, the work (in ft ·lb) done by the man is:

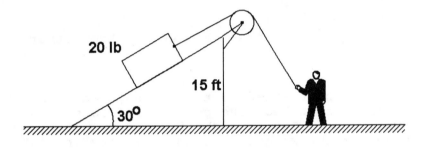

*A) 300   B) 150   C) zero   D) -150   E) -300

16. A man pushes an 80-N crate a distance of 5.0 m upward along a frictionless slope that makes an angle of 30° with the horizontal. The force he exerts is parallel to the slope. If the speed of the crate increases at a rate of 1.5 m/s^2, then the work done by the man is:

A) -200 J   B) 61 J   C) 140 J   D) 200 J   *E) 260 J

17. A man pushes an 80-N crate a distance of 5.0 m upward along a frictionless slope that makes an angle of 30° with the horizontal. The force he exerts is parallel to the slope. If the speed of the crate is constant, then the work done by the man is:

A) -200 J   B) 61 J   C) 140 J   *D) 200 J   E) 260 J

18. A man pushes an 80-N crate at constant speed a distance of 5.0 m upward along a rough slope that makes an angle of 30° with the horizontal. The work done by the force of gravity is:

A) -400 J   *B) -200 J   C) -69 J   D) 200 J   E) 400 J

19. A man pulls a sled along a rough horizontal surface by applying a constant force **F** at an angle θ above the horizontal. In pulling the sled a horizontal distance d, the work done by the man is:

   A) Fd   *B) Fdcosθ   C) Fdsinθ   D) Fd/cosθ   E) Fd/sinθ

20. A man wishes to pull a crate 15 m across a rough floor by exerting a force of 100 N. The coefficient of kinetic friction is 0.25. For the man to do the least work, the angle between the force and the horizontal should be:

   *A) 0   B) 14°   C) 43°   D) 66°   E) 76°

21. A particle moves 5 ft in the +x direction while being acted upon by a constant force $\mathbf{F} = (4\hat{\imath} + 2\hat{\jmath} - 4\hat{k})$ lb. The work (in ft ·lb) done on the particle by this force is:

   *A) 20   D) 30
   B) 10   E) need to know other forces
   C) -20

22. A spring, with a pointer attached to its end, hangs next to a scale. With a 100-N weight attached, the pointer indicates "40" on the scale as shown. Using a 200-N weight instead results in "60" on the scale. Using an unknown weight X instead results in "30" on the scale. The weight of X is:

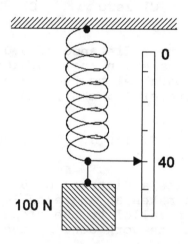

   A) 10 N   B) 20 N   C) 30 N   D) 40 N   *E) 50 N

23. Three identical springs (X,Y,Z) are arranged as shown. When a 4.0-kg mass is hung on X, the mass descends 3.0 cm. When a 6.0-kg mass is hung on Y, the mass descends:

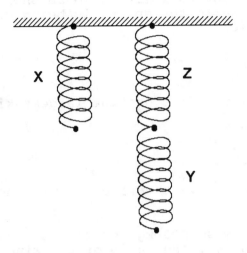

A) 2.0 cm   B) 4.0 cm   C) 4.5 cm   D) 6.0 cm   *E) 9.0 cm

24. When a certain rubber band is stretched a distance x, it exerts a restoring force of magnitude $F = Ax$, where A is a constant. The work done by a person in stretching this rubber band from x = 0 to x = L is:

A) AL^2 B) $A + 2L$ C) $A + 2L^2$ D) A/L *E) $AL^2/2$

25. When a certain rubber band is stretched a distance x, it exerts a restoring force $F = ax + bx^2$, where a and b are constants. The work done is stretching this rubber band from x = 0 to x = L is:

A) $aL^2 + bLx^3$
B) $aL + 2bL^2$
C) $a + 2bL$
D) bL
*E) $aL^2/2 + bL^3/3$

26. An ideal spring is hung vertically from the ceiling. When a 2.0-kg mass hangs at rest from it the spring is extended 6.0 cm. A downward external force is now applied to the mass to extend the spring an additional 10 cm. While the spring is being extended by the force, the work done by the spring is:

*A) −3.6 J
B) −3.3 J
C) -3.4×10^{-5} J
D) 3.3 J
E) 3.6 J

27. An ideal spring is hung vertically from the ceiling. When a 2.0-kg mass hangs at rest from it the spring is extended 6.0 cm from its equilibrium length. A upward external force is then applied to the mass to compress the spring so it is 10 cm shorter than its equilibrium length. While the spring is being compressed the work done by the spring is:

*A) -1.0 J   B) -0.52 J   C) -0.26 J   D) 0.52 J   E) 1.0 J

28. Which of the following bodies has the largest kinetic energy?

  A) mass 3M and speed V
  B) mass 3M and speed 2V
*C) mass 2M and speed 3V
  D) mass M and speed 4V
  E) all four of the above have the same kinetic energy

29. Two trailers, X with mass 500 kg and Y with mass 2000 kg, are being pulled at the same speed. The ratio of the kinetic energy of Y to that of X is:

A) 1:1   B) 2:1   *C) 4:1   D) 9:1   E) 1500:1

30. A 4000-lb car is traveling at 88 ft/s (60 mph) along a horizontal road when the brakes are applied. The car skids to a stop in 4.0 s. How much kinetic energy (in ft ·lb) does the car lose in this time?

A) 1.5×10^7 *B) 4.84×10^5 C) 2.42×10^5 D) 1.21×10^5 E) 46

31. An object is constrained by a cord to move in a circular path of radius 0.5 m on a horizontal frictionless surface. The cord will break if its tension exceeds 16 N. The maximum kinetic energy of the object is:

*A) 4 J   B) 8 J   C) 16 J   D) 32 J   E) 64 J

32. The weight of an object on the moon is one-sixth of its weight on the earth. The ratio of the kinetic energy of a body on the earth moving with speed V to that of the same body moving with speed V on the moon is:

A) 6:1   B) 36:1   *C) 1:1   D) 1:6   E) 1:36

33. Which of the following is the correct combination of dimensions for the quantity "energy"?

A) MLT   B) LT^2/m *C) ML^2/T^2 D) M^2L^3T E) ML/T^2

34. The amount of work required to stop a moving object is equal to the:

   A) velocity of the object
  *B) kinetic energy of the object
   C) mass of the object times its acceleration
   D) mass of the object times its velocity
   E) square of the velocity of the object

35. A 5.0 kg cart is moving horizontally at 6.0 m/s. In order to change its speed to 10.0 m/s, the net work done on the cart must be:

   A) 40 J   B) 90 J   *C) 160 J   D) 400 J   E) 550 J

36. A particle is initially at rest on a horizontal frictionless table. It is acted upon by a constant horizontal force F. Which of the following five graphs is a correct plot of work W as a function of particle speed v?

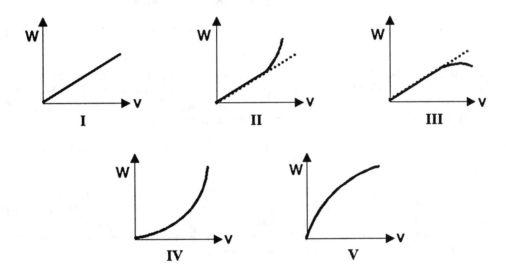

   A) I.   B) II.   C) III.   *D) IV.   E) V.

37. An 8-lb block slides down an incline. It has an initial speed of 7 ft/s. The work (in ft ·lb) done by the resultant force on this block is:

   A) 3
   B) 6
   C) 56
  *D) not enough information is given
   E) none of these

38. A 4-kg cart starts up an incline with a speed of 3 m/s and comes to rest 2 m up the incline. The total work done on the cart is:

A) 6 J
B) 8 J
C) 12

*D) 18 J
E) not enough information given

39. Two masses, m_1 and m_2, have the same kinetic energy and are both moving to the right. The same constant force F is applied to the left to both masses. If $m_1 = 4m_2$, the ratio of the stopping distance of m_1 to that of m_2 is:

A) 1:4   B) 4:1   C) 1:2   D) 2:1   *E) 1:1

40. A Boston Red Sox baseball player catches a ball of mass m which is moving toward him with speed v. While bringing the ball to rest, his hand moves back a distance d. Assuming constant deceleration, the horizontal force exerted on the ball by his hand is:

A) mv/d   B) mvd   C) mv^2/d D) 2mv/d   *E) $mv^2/(2d)$

41. A 0.50-kg object moves in a horizontal circular track with a radius of 2.5 m. An external force of 3.0 N, always tangent to the track, causes the object to speed up as it goes around. If it starts from rest its speed at the end of one revolution is:

A) 9.8 m/s   *B) 14 m/s   C) 15 m/s   D) 19 m/s   E) 21 m/s

42. A 0.50-kg object moves on a horizontal frictionless circular track with a radius of 2.5 m. An external force of 3.0 N, always tangent to the track, causes the object to speed up as it goes around. If it starts from rest, then at the end of one revolution the radial component of the force of the track on it is:

A) 19 N   *B) 38 N   C) 47 N   D) 75 N   E) 96 N

43. A 2-kg particle on the end of an ideal spring is pulled out 0.5 m and released from rest. When it passes the equilibrium point its speed is:

A) 0   B) 0.05 m/s   *C) 5 m/s   D) 10 m/s   E) 100 m/s

44. At time $t = 0$ a particle starts moving along the x axis. If its kinetic energy increases uniformly with t the net force acting on it must be:

A) constant
B) proportional to t
C) inversely proportional to t
D) proportional to $\sqrt{t}$

*E) proportional to $1/\sqrt{t}$

45. At time $t = 0$ a 2-kg particle has a velocity in m/s of $4\hat{\imath} - 3\hat{\jmath}$. At $t = 3$ s its velocity in m/s is $2\hat{\imath} + 3\hat{\jmath}$. During this time the work done on it was:

A) 4 J
B) -4 J
*C) -12 J

D) -40 J
E) $4\hat{\imath} + 36\hat{\jmath}$ J

46. A particle starts from rest at time $t = 0$ and moves along the x axis. If the net force on it is proportional to t, its kinetic energy is proportional to:

A) t
B) t^2
*C) t^4

D) $1/t^2$
E) none of the above

47. A 1.5 kg crate falls from a height of 2.0 m onto an industrial spring scale with a spring constant of 1.5×10^5 N/m. At its greatest compression the reading on the scale is:

A) 15 N
B) 30 N
C) 1.5×10^3 N

D) 2.1×10^3 N
*E) 3.0×10^3 N

48. A particle moving along the x axis is acted upon by a single force $F = F_o e^{-kx}$, where F_o and k are constants. The particle is released from rest at $x = 0$. It will attain a maximum kinetic energy of:

*A) F_o/k B) F_o/e^k C) kF_o D) $1/2(kF_o)^2$ E) $ke^k F_o$

49. The mechanical advantage of any machine is:

A) the efficiency of the machine
B) the work done by the machine
C) the ratio of the work done by the machine to the work expended on it
*D) the ratio of the force exerted by the machine to the force applied to it
E) the ratio of the force applied to the machine to the force exerted by it

50. In raising an object to a given height by means of an inclined plane, as compared with raising the object vertically, there is a reduction in:

   A) work required
   B) distance pushed
   C) friction
   *D) force required
   E) value of the acceleration due to gravity

51. A watt is:

   A) $kg \cdot m/s^3$ B) $kg \cdot m^2/s$ *C) $kg \cdot m^2/s^3$ D) $kg \cdot m/s$ E) $kg \cdot m^2/s^2$

52. Power has the dimensions of:

   A) ML^2/T^2
   B) MT/L^2
   C) ML/T^2

   *D) ML^2/T^3
   E) none of these

53. Which of the following five units represents a quantity that is NOT the same as the other four?

   A) joule
   B) erg
   *C) watt

   D) foot $\cdot$ pound
   E) newton $\cdot$ meter

54. Which of the following five quantities is NOT an expression for energy? Here m is a mass, g is the acceleration due to gravity, h and d are distances, F is a force, v is a speed, a is an acceleration, P is power, and t is time.

   A) mgh   B) Fd   C) $1/2mv^2$ *D) ma   E) Pt

55. A watt $\cdot$ second is a unit of:

   A) force
   B) power
   C) displacement

   D) speed
   *E) energy

56. A horsepower per hour is a unit of:

   A) energy
   B) power
   C) force

   D) acceleration
   *E) none of these

57. A kilowatt hour is a unit of:

A) power
B) energy/time
*C) work

D) power/time
E) force/distance

58. A man moves the 10-g object shown in a vertical plane from position X to position Y along a circular track of radius 20 m. The process takes 0.75 min. The work done by the man is about:

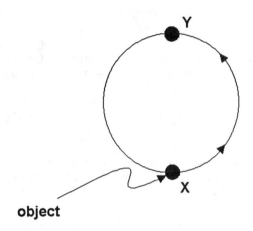

A) 1 J   B) 2 J   *C) 4 J   D) 6 J   E) 12 J

59. A woman lifts a barbell 2.0 m in 5.0 s. If she lifts it the same distance in 10 s, the work done by her is:

A) four times as great
B) two times as great
*C) the same

D) half as great
E) one fourth as great

60. An escalator is used to move 20 people (60 kg each) per minute from the first floor of a department store to the second floor, 5 m above. The power required is approximately:

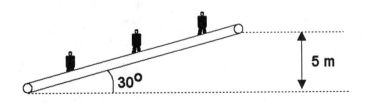

A) 100 W   B) 200 W   *C) 1000 W   D) 2000 W   E) 60,000 W

81

61. A person holds a 20-lb weight two feet above the floor for 30 seconds. The power required to do this is:

A) 80 ft.lb/s
B) 40 ft.lb/s
C) 20 ft.lb/s
D) 10 ft.lb/s
*E) none of these

62. A 50-N force acts on a 2-kg particle that starts from rest. When the force has been acting for 2 s the rate at which it is doing work is:

A) 75 W B) 100 W C) 1000 W *D) 2500 W E) 5000 W

63. A 50-N force acts on a 2-kg particle that starts from rest. At the instant the particle has gone 2 m the rate at which the force is doing work is:

A) 2.5 W B) 25 W C) 75 W D) 100 W *E) 1000 W

64. A particle starts from rest and is acted on by a net force that does work at a rate that is proportional to the time t. The speed of the particle is proportional to:

*A) $\sqrt{t}$ B) t C) t^2 D) $1/\sqrt{t}$ E) 1/t

65. If a proton (mass = 1.67×10^{-27} kg) travels at 0.95 times the speed of light ($c = 3.00 \times 10^{-8}$ m/s), then its kinetic energy is:

A) 6.8×10^{-11} J
B) 1.5×10^{-10} J
C) 2.2×10^{-10} J
*D) 3.3×10^{-10} J
E) 4.3×10^{-10} J

66. If a particle has a kinetic energy that is 9 times the value given by $1/2mv^2$, its speed is:

A) 9c B) 3c C) c/9 D) c/3 *E) 0.98c

1. A force acting on a particle is called conservative if:

*A) its work is zero when the particle moves exactly once around any closed path
 B) its work equals the change in the kinetic energy of the particle
 C) it obeys Newton's second law
 D) it obeys Newton's third law
 E) it is not a frictional force

2. A non-conservative force:

 A) violates Newton's second law
 B) violates Newton's third law
 C) cannot do any work
 D) must be perpendicular to the velocity of the particle on which it acts
*E) none of the above

3. The sum of the kinetic and potential energies of a system of objects is conserved:

 A) only when no external force acts on the objects
 B) only when the objects move along closed paths
 C) only when the work done by the resultant external force is zero
 D) always
*E) none of the above

4. A force acting on a particle is conservative if:

 A) its work equals the change in the kinetic energy of the particle
 B) it obeys Newton's second law
 C) it obeys Newton's third law
*D) its work depends on the end points of the motion, not the path between
 E) it is not a frictional force

5. Two particles interact by conservative forces only and they complete round trips, ending at the points where they started. Over this trip:

 A) the kinetic energy might change
 B) the potential energy might change
 C) the total mechanical energy might change
 D) heat might be generated
*E) none of the above

6. Two objects interact with each other and with no other objects. Initially object A has a speed of 5 m/s and object B has a speed of 10 m/s. In the course of their motion they return to their initial positions. Then A has a speed of 4 m/s and B has a speed of 7 m/s. We can conclude:

A) the potential energy changed from the beginning to the end of the trip
B) mechanical energy was increased by non-conservative forces
*C) mechanical energy was decreased by non-conservative forces
D) mechanical energy was increased by conservative forces
E) mechanical energy was decreased by conservative forces

7. A good example of kinetic energy is provided by:

A) a wound-up clock spring
B) the raised weights of a grandfather's clock
*C) a tornado
D) a gallon of gasoline
E) an automobile storage battery

8. No kinetic energy is possessed by:

A) a shooting star
B) a rotating propeller on a moving airplane
C) a pendulum at the bottom of its swing
*D) an elevator standing at the fifth floor
E) a cyclone

9. The wound-up spring of a clock possesses:

A) kinetic but no potential energy
*B) potential but no kinetic energy
C) both potential and kinetic energy
D) neither potential nor kinetic energy
E) depends on the system of units

10. A body at rest is capable of doing work if:

A) the potential energy is positive
B) the potential energy is negative
C) it is free to move in such a way as to decrease its kinetic energy
*D) it is free to move in such a way as to decrease the potential energy
E) it is free to move in such a way as to increase the potential energy

11. Which one of the following five quantities CANNOT be used as a unit of potential energy?

A) watt ·second
*B) gram ·cm/s$_2$
C) joule

D) slug ·ft^2/s^2
E) ft ·lb

84

12. Suppose that the fundamental dimensions are taken to be: force (F), velocity (V) and time (T). The dimensions of potential energy are then:

   A) F/T   *B) FVT   C) FV/T   D) F/T^2 E) FV^2/T^2

13. A golf ball is struck by a golf club and falls on a green eight feet above the tee. The potential energy of the earth-ball system is greatest:

   A) just before the ball is struck
   B) just after the ball is struck
   C) just after the ball lands on the green
   D) when the ball comes to rest on the green
   *E) when the ball reaches the highest point in its flight

14. A ball is held at a height H above a floor. It is then released and
    falls to the floor. If air resistance can be ignored which of the
    five graphs below correctly gives the mechanical energy E of the
    earth-ball system as a function of the altitude y of the ball?

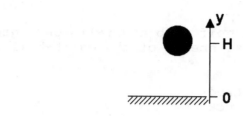

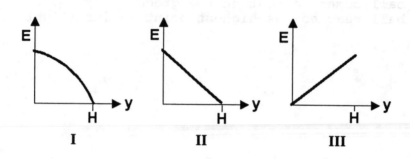

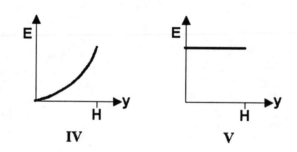

   A) I.   B) II.   C) III.   D) IV.   *E) V.

15. A 6.0-kg block is released from rest 80 m above the ground. When it
    has fallen 60 m its kinetic energy is approximately:

   A) 4800 J   *B) 3500 J   C) 1200 J   D) 120 J   E) 60 J

16. A 2-kg block is thrown upward from a point 20 m above the earth's
    surface. At what height above the earth's surface will the
    gravitational potential energy of the earth-block system have
    increased by 500 J?

   A) 5 m   B) 25 m   *C) 45 m   D) 70 m   E) 270 m

17. An elevator is rising at constant speed. Consider the following
    statements:
     I. the upward cable force is constant
    II. the kinetic energy of the elevator is constant
   III. the gravitational potential energy of the earth-elevator
       system is constant
    IV. the acceleration of the elevator is zero
     V. the mechanical energy of the earth-elevator system is
    constant

A) all five are true   D) only I, II, and III are true
B) only II and V are true   *E) only I, II, and IV are true
C) only IV and V are true

18. A projectile of mass 0.50 kg is fired with an initial speed of
    10 m/s at an angle of 60° above the horizontal. The potential energy
    (relative to ground level) of the projectile at its highest point
    is:

A) 25 J   D) 6.25 J
*B) 18.75 J   E) none of these
C) 12.5 J

19. For a block of mass m to slide without friction up the rise of
    height h shown, it must have a minimum initial speed of:

A) $\overline{1/2\sqrt{gh}}$ B) $\sqrt{gh/2}$ *C) $\sqrt{2gh}$ D) $2\sqrt{2gh}$ E) $2\sqrt{gh}$

20. A 2.2-kg block starts from rest on a rough inclined plane that makes
    an angle of 25° with the horizontal. The coefficient of kinetic
    friction is 0.25. As the block goes 2.0 m down the plane, the
    mechanical energy of the earth-block system changes by:

A) 0   *B) -9.8 J   C) 9.8 J   D) -18 J   E) 18 J

21. A simple pendulum consists of a 2.0 kg mass attached to a string. It is released from rest at X as shown. Its speed at the lowest point Y is:

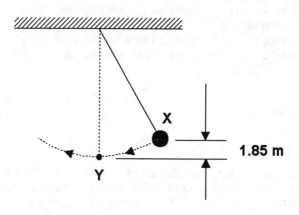

A) 0.90 m/s   B) $\sqrt{3.6}$ m/s   C) 3.6 m/s   *D) 6.0 m/s   E) 36 m/s

22. The long pendulum shown is drawn aside until the ball has risen 1.0 ft. It is then released from rest. The speed of the ball at its lowest position is:

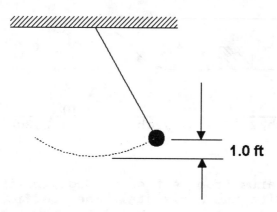

A) 4 ft/s   B) 5 ft/s   C) 6 ft/s   D) 7 ft/s   *E) 8 ft/s

23. A particle moves along the x axis under the influence of a stationary object. The force exerted on the particle is given by $F = 8x^3$, where F is in newtons and x is in meters. If x = 0 is taken to be the zero of potential energy, then the potential energy in joules is given by:

A) $2x^4$ *B) $-2x^4$ C) $24x^2$ D) $-24x^2$ E) $5 - 2x^4$

24. A 0.20-kg particle moves along the x axis under the influence of a stationary object. The potential energy is given by $U(x) = 8x^2 + 2x^4$, where U is in joules and x is in meters. If the particle has a speed of 5.0 m/s when it is at x = 1.0 m, its speed when it is at the origin is:

A) 0   B) 2.5 m/s   C) 5.7 m/s   *D) 7.9 m/s   E) 11 m/s

25. Which of the five graphs correctly shows the potential energy of a spring as a function of its elongation x?

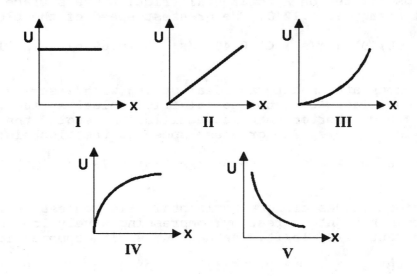

A) I.   B) II.   *C) III.   D) IV.   E) V.

26. A force of 10 N holds a spring with a 20-N/m spring constant in compression. The potential energy stored in the spring is:

A) 0.5 J   *B) 2.5 J   C) 5 J   D) 10 J   E) 200 J

27. An ideal spring is used to fire a 15.0-g block horizontally across a frictionless table top. The spring has a spring constant of 20 N/m and is initially compressed by 7.0 cm. The speed of the block as it leaves the spring is:

A) 0
B) 1.9×10^{-3} m/s
C) 2.6×10^{-2} m/s
D) 0.39 m/s
*E) 2.6 m/s

28. A 0.50-kg block attached to an ideal spring with a spring constant
    of 80 N/m oscillates on a horizontal frictionless surface. The total
    mechanical energy is 0.12 J. The greatest extension of the spring
    from its equilibrium length is:

    A) 1.5×10^{-3} m   *D) 0.054 m
    B) 3.0×10^{-3} m   E) 18 m
    C) 0.039 m

29. A 0.50-kg block attached to an ideal spring with a spring constant
    of 80 N/m oscillates on a horizontal frictionless surface. The total
    mechanical energy is 0.12 J. The greatest speed of the block is:

    A) 0.15 m/s   B) 0.24 m/s   C) 0.49 m/s   *D) 0.69 m/s   E) 1.46 m/s

30. A 0.50-kg block attached to an ideal spring with a spring constant
    of 80 N/m oscillates on a horizontal frictionless surface. When the
    spring is 4.0 cm shorter than its equilibrium length, the speed of
    the block is 0.50 m/s. The greatest speed of the block is:

    A) 0.23 m/s   B) 0.32 m/s   C) 0.55 m/s   *D) 0.78 m/s   E) 0.93 m/s

31. A 4.0-lb block slides along a horizontal frictionless surface at
    8 ft/s. It is brought to rest by compressing a very long spring of
    spring constant (1/8) lb/ft. The maximum spring compression is:

    A) 4 ft   *B) 8 ft   C) 16 ft   D) 2 ft   E) 45 ft

32. A block of mass m is initially moving to the right on a horizontal
    frictionless surface at a speed v. It then compresses a spring of
    spring constant k. At the instant when the kinetic energy of the
    block is equal to the potential energy of the spring, the spring is
    compressed a distance of:

    *A)   D) $mv^2/4k$
       $v\sqrt{m/2k}$ E)
    B) $(1/2)mv^2$ $(1/4)\sqrt{mv/k}$
    C) $(1/4)mv^2$

33. A 200-lb man jumps out of a window into a fire net 30 ft below. The
    net stretches 6 ft (vertically) before bringing the man to rest and
    tossing him back into the air. The maximum potential energy
    (in ft ·lb) of the net is:

    *A) 7200   B) 6000   C) 1800   D) 1200   E) 600

34. A toy cork gun contains a spring whose spring constant is 10.0 N/m. The spring is compressed 5 cm and then used to propel a 6.00 gram cork. The cork, however, sticks to the spring for 1.00 cm beyond its unstretched length before separation occurs. The muzzle velocity of this cork is:

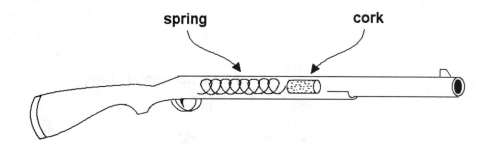

spring   cork

A) 1.02 m/s   B) 1.41 m/s   *C) 2.00 m/s   D) 2.04 m/s   E) 4.00 m/s

35. A small object of mass m, on the end of a light cord, is held horizontally at a distance r from a fixed support as shown. The object is then released. What is the tension in the cord when the object is at the lowest point of its swing?

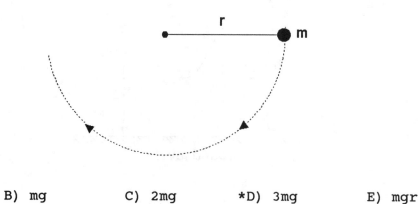

r   m

A) mg/2   B) mg   C) 2mg   *D) 3mg   E) mgr

36. The string in the figure is 50 cm long. When the ball is released from rest, it will swing along the dotted arc. How fast, in m/s, will it be going at the lowest point in its swing?

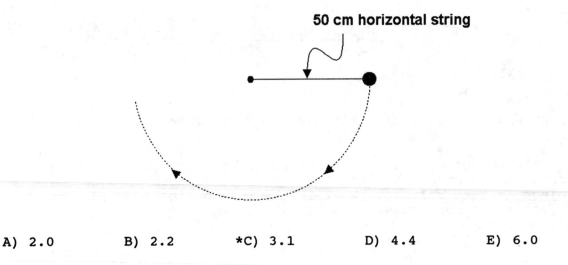

50 cm horizontal string

A) 2.0   B) 2.2   *C) 3.1   D) 4.4   E) 6.0

37. A block at point P is released from rest and slides along the frictionless track shown. At point Q, its speed is:

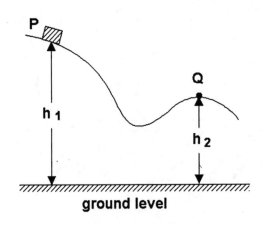

ground level

*A)
    $2g\sqrt{h_1-h_2}$
B) $2g(h_1-h_2)$
C) $(h_1-h_2)/2g$

D)
    $\sqrt{2g(h_1-h_2)}$
E) $(h_1-h_2)^2/2g$

38. A small object of mass m slides along the frictionless loop-the-loop track of radius R as shown. What is the smallest value of Y such that the object will slide without losing contact with the track?

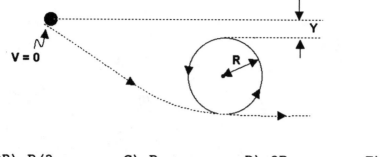

A) R/4   *B) R/2   C) R   D) 2R   E) zero

39. The bicyclist shown coasting down the slope had hopes to loop-the-loop in a circle of diameter 14 ft. What minimum speed must he have at the top of the loop?

A) 40 ft/s   B) 32 ft/s   C) 24 ft/s   D) 20 ft/s   *E) 15 ft/s

40. A rectangular block is moving along a frictionless path when it encounters the circular loop as shown. The block passes points 1,2,3,4,1 before returning to the horizontal track. At point 3:

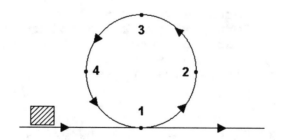

A) its mechanical energy is a minimum
B) the forces on it are balanced
C) it is not accelerated
*D) its speed is a minimum
E) it experiences a net upward force

41. A ball of mass m, at one end of a string of length L, rotates in a vertical circle just fast enough to prevent the string from going slack at the top of the circle. The speed of the ball at the bottom of the circle is:

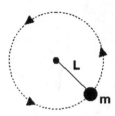

A) $\sqrt{2gL}$ B) $\sqrt{3gL}$ C) $\sqrt{4gL}$ *D) $\sqrt{5gL}$ E) $\sqrt{7gL}$

42. A particle is released from rest at the point x = a and moves along the x axis subject to the potential energy function U(x) shown. The particle:

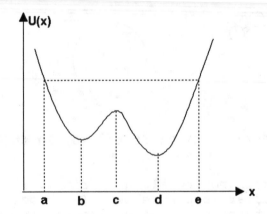

*A) oscillates back and forth between x = a and x = e
 B) oscillates back and forth between x = a and x = c
 C) moves to infinity at varying speed
 D) moves to x = e where it remains at rest
 E) moves to x = b where it remains at rest

43. The potential energy of a particle moving along the x axis is given by U(x) = $8x^2 + 2x^4$, where U is in joules and x is in meters. If the total mechanical energy is 9.0 J, the limits of motion are:

*A) -0.96 m; +0.96 m   D) -0.96 m; +2.2 m
 B) -2.2 m; +2.2 m   E) -0.96 m; +1.6 m
 C) -1.6 m; +1.6 m

94

44. The potential energy of a 0.20 kg particle moving along the x axis is given by $U(x) = 8x^2 + 2x^4$, where U is in joules and x is in meters. When the particle is at x = 1.0 m it is traveling in the positive x direction with a speed of 5.0 m/s. It next stops momentarily to turn around at x =

A) 0   B) -1.1 m   *C) 1.1 m   D) -2.3 m   E) 2.3 m

45. Given a potential energy function U(x). The corresponding force **F** is in the positive x direction if:

 A) U is positive
 B) U is negative
 C) U is an increasing function of x
*D) U is a decreasing function of x
 E) it is impossible to obtain the direction of **F** from U

46. The first graph shows the potential energy U(x) for a particle moving on the x axis. Which of the following five graphs correctly gives the force F exerted on the particle?

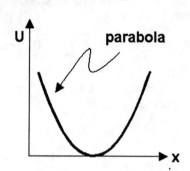

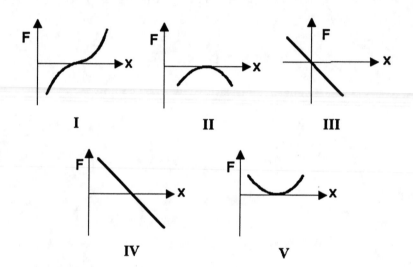

A) I.   B) II.   C) III.   *D) IV.   E) V.

47. The diagram shows a plot of the potential energy as a function of x for a particle moving along the x axis. The points of <u>stable</u> equilibrium are:

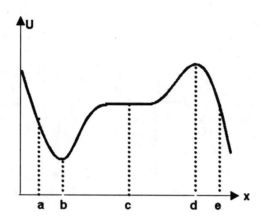

A) only a   *B) only b   C) only c   D) only d   E) b and d

48. The diagram shows a plot of the potential energy as a function of x for a particle moving along the x axis. The points of <u>unstable</u> equilibrium are:

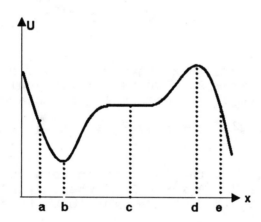

A) only a   B) only b   C) only c   *D) only d   E) b and d

97

49. The diagram shows a plot of the potential energy as a function of x for a particle moving along the x axis. The points of <u>neutral</u> equilibrium are:

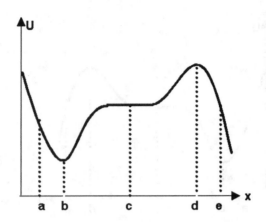

A) only a   B) only b   *C) only c   D) only d   E) b and d

50. The potential energy of a body of mass m is given by $U = -mgx + 1/2kx^2$. The corresponding force is:

A) $-mgx^2/2 + kx^3/6$

B) $mgx^2/2 - kx^3/6$

C) $-mg + kx/2$

D) $-mg + kx$

*E) $mg - kx$

51. The potential energy of a 0.20-kg particle moving along the x axis is given by $U(x) = 8x^2 - 2x^4$, where U is in joules and x is in meters. When the particle is at x = 1.0 m its acceleration is:

A) 0   B) -8 m/s^2 C) 8 m/s^2 *D) -40 m/s^2 E) 40 m/s^2

52. The potential energy for the interaction between the two atoms in a diatomic molecule is $U = A/x^{12} - B/x^6$ where A and B are constants and x is the interatomic distance. The force that one atom exerts on the other is:

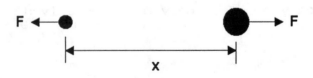

*A) $12A/x^{13} - 6B/x^7$

B) $72A/x^{12} - 72B/x^6$

C) $-13A/x^{13} + 7B/x^7$

D) $A/x^{13} - B/x^7$

E) $-11A/x^{11} + 5B/x^5$

98

53. The internal energy of a system consisting of a thrown ball, the earth, and the air is most closely associated with:

  A) the interaction of the earth and the ball
  B) the kinetic energy of the ball as a whole
  C) motions of the individual particles within the ball
 *D) motions of individual particles within the ball and the air
  E) the kinetic energy of the earth as a whole

54. Objects A and B interact with each other via both conservative and non-conservative forces. Let K_A and K_B be the kinetic energies, U be the potential energy, and E_{int} be the internal energy. If no external agent does work on the objects then:

  A) $K_A + U$ is conserved
  B) $K_A + U + E_{int}$ is conserved
  C) $K_A + K_B + E_{int}$ is conserved
  D) $K_A + K_B + U$ is conserved
 *E) $K_A + K_B + U + E_{int}$ is conserved

55. A block slides across a rough horizontal table top. The work done by friction changes:

  A) only the kinetic energy
  B) only the potential energy
  C) only the internal energy
  D) only the kinetic and potential energies
 *E) only the kinetic and internal energies

56. A 25-g ball is released from rest 80 m above the surface of the earth. Just before it hits the surface its speed is 20 m/s. During the fall the internal energy of the ball and air changed by:

 *A) + 15 J   B) -15 J   C) +5 J   D) -5 J   E) 0

57. A 5 kg projectile is fired over level ground with a velocity of 200 m/s at an angle of 25° above the horizontal. Just before it hits the ground its speed is 150 m/s. Over the entire trip the change in the internal energy of the projectile and air is:

  A) +19,000 J   D) -44,000 J
  B) -19,000 J   E) 0
 *C) +44,000 J

58. A 0.75-kg block slides on a rough horizontal table top. Just before it hits a horizontal ideal spring its speed is 3.5 m/s. It hits the spring and compresses it 5.7 cm before coming to rest. If the spring constant is 1200 N/m, the internal energy of the block and the table top must have increased by:

  A) 0   B) 1.9 J   *C) 2.6 J   D) 4.6 J   E) 6.5 J

59. Two atoms interact with each other via a spring-like force. Their energy is quantized. This means:

*A) energy can be gained or lost only in discrete amounts
 B) a numerical value can be assigned the energy lost or gained
 C) the energy can be doubled but not tripled
 D) energy is a valid physical quantity
 E) none of the above

60. A proton (mass = 1.67×10^{-27} kg) interacts with a heavy molecule via a spring-like force with a spring constant of 75 N/m. The energy of the system can change by:

A) 5.6×10^{-21} J
B) 1.1×10^{-20} J
C) 1.7×10^{-20} J

*D) 2.2×10^{-20} J
E) 2.8×10^{-20} J

1. Which one of the following statements is true?

A) the center of mass of an object must lie within the object
B) all the mass of an object is actually concentrated at its center of mass
C) the center of mass of an object cannot move if there is zero net force on the object
D) the center of mass of a cylinder must lie on its axis
*E) none of the above

2. The (x,y) coordinates in meters of the center of mass of the 3 particle system shown below are:

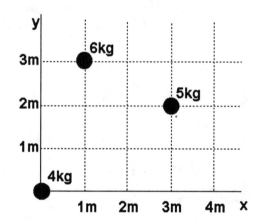

A) (0, 0)
B) (1.3, 1.7)
*C) (1.4, 1.9)

D) (1.9, 2.5)
E) (1.4, 2.5)

3. The center of mass of a uniform disc of radius R is located:

A) somewhere on a circle R from the disc center
B) somewhere on a circle R/2 from the disc center
C) somewhere on a circle R/3 from the disc center
D) somewhere on a circle 2R/3 from the disc center
*E) at the disc center

4. The center of mass of the system consisting of the earth, the sun, and the planet Mars is:

A) closer to the earth than to either of the other bodies
*B) closer to the sun than to either of the other bodies
C) closer to Mars than to either of the other bodies
D) at the geometric center of the triangle formed by the three bodies
E) at the center of the line joining the earth and Mars

5. The center of mass of the earth's atmosphere is

A) a little less than halfway between the earth's surface and the outer boundary of the atmosphere
B) near the surface of the earth
C) near the outer boundary of the atmosphere
*D) near the center of the earth
E) none of the above

6. A thick uniform wire is bent into the shape of the letter "U" as shown. Which point indicates the location of the center of mass of this wire?

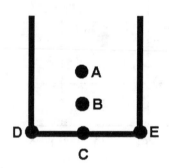

A) A   *B) B   C) C   D) D   E) E

7. Block A, with a mass of 4 kg, is stationary while block B, with a mass of 8 kg, is moving at 3 m/s. The center of mass of the two block system has a speed in m/s of:

A) 0   B) 1.5   *C) 2   D) 3   E) 12

8. At the same instant that a 0.50-kg ball is dropped from 25 m above the earth, a second ball, with a mass of 0.25 kg, is thrown straight upward from the earth's surface with an initial velocity of 15 m/s. They move along nearby lines but pass each other without colliding. At the end of 2.0 s the height above the earth's surface of the center of mass of the two-ball system is:

A) 2.9 m   B) 4.0 m   C) 5.0 m   *D) 7.1 m   E) 10.4 m

9. At the same instant that a 0.50 kg ball is dropped from 25 m above
   the earth, a second ball, with a mass of 0.25 kg, is thrown straight
   upward from the earth's surface with an initial velocity of 15 m/s.
   They move along nearby lines but pass without colliding. At the end
   of 2.0 s the velocity of the center of mass of the two ball system
   is:

   A) 11 m/s, down   D) 15 m/s, up
   B) 11 m/s, up   E) 20 m/s, down
  *C) 15 m/s, down

10. At the same instant that a 0.50 kg ball is dropped from 25 m above
    the earth, a second ball, with a mass of 0.25 kg, is thrown straight
    upward from the earth's surface with an initial velocity of 15 m/s.
    They move along nearby lines but pass without colliding. At the end
    of 2.0 s the acceleration of the center of mass of the two ball
    system is:

    A) 0.25g   B) 0.50g   C) 0.75g   *D) g   E) g/0.75

11. At the same instant that a 0.50 kg ball is dropped from a high
    building, a second ball, with a mass of 0.25 kg, is thrown straight
    upward from the earth's surface with an initial velocity of
    19.6 m/s. They move along nearby lines but pass without colliding.
    When the second ball is at its highest point the velocity of the
    center of mass of the two ball system is:

    A) 0   *D) 27 m/s, down
    B) 10 m/s, down   E) 40 m/s, down
    C) 20 m/s, down

12. A light rope passes over a light frictionless pulley attached to the
    ceiling. A large mass is tied to one end and a smaller mass is tied
    to the other. Starting from rest the larger mass moves downward and
    the smaller moves upward with the same acceleration. Which of the
    following statements is true for the system consisting of the two
    masses?

    A) The center of mass remains at rest.
    B) The net external force is zero.
    C) The velocity of the center of mass is a constant.
    D) The acceleration of the center of mass is g, downward.
   *E) None of the above statements are true.

13. Two 4.0-kg blocks are tied together with a compressed spring between them. They are thrown from the ground with an initial velocity of 35 m/s, 45° above the horizontal. At the highest point of the trajectory they become untied and spring apart. About how far below the highest point is the center of mass of the two block system 2.0 s later, before either fragment has hit the ground?

 A) 12 m
*B) 20 m
 C) 31 m
 D) Can't tell because the velocities of the fragments are not given.
 E) Can't tell because the coordinates of the highest point are not given.

14. The center of mass of a system of particles has a constant velocity if:

 A) the forces exerted by the particles on each other sum to zero
*B) the external forces acting on particles of the system sum to zero
 C) the velocity of the center of mass is initially zero
 D) the particles are distributed symmetrically around the center of mass
 E) the center of mass is at the geometric center of the system

15. The center of mass of a system of particles remains at the same place if:

*A) it is initially at rest and the external forces sum to zero
 B) it is initially at rest and the internal forces sum to zero
 C) the sum of the external forces is less than the maximum force of static friction
 D) no friction acts internally
 E) none of the above

16. A man sits in the back of a canoe in still water. He then moves to the front of the canoe and sits there. Afterwards the canoe

 A) is forward of its original position and moving forward
 B) is forward of its original position and moving backward
 C) is rearward of its original position and moving forward
 D) is rearward of its original position and moving backward
*E) is rearward of its original position and not moving

17. A 160 lb hunter gets a rope around a 800 lb polar bear. They are stationary, 60 ft apart, on frictionless level ice. When the hunter pulls the polar bear to him, the polar bear will move:

*A) 10 ft   B) 12 ft   C) 30 ft   D) 48 ft   E) 50 ft

18. Two boys (40 kg and 60 kg) stand on a horizontal frictionless
    surface holding the ends of a light 10-m long rod. The boys pull
    themselves together along the rod. When they meet the 40-kg boy will
    have moved what distance?

    A) 4 m
    B) 5 m
  *C) 6 m
    D) 10 m
    E) need to know the forces they exert

19. The center of mass of a system of particles obeys an equation
    similar to Newton's second law $\mathbf{F} = m\mathbf{a}_{cm}$, where

    A) $\mathbf{F}$ is the total internal force and m is the total mass of the system
    B) $\mathbf{F}$ is the total internal force and m is the mass acting on the system
  *C) $\mathbf{F}$ is the total external force and m is the total mass of the system
    D) $\mathbf{F}$ is the force of gravity and m is the mass of the earth
    E) $\mathbf{F}$ is the force of gravity and m is the total mass of the system

20. A large wedge rests on a horizontal frictionless surface, as shown.
    A block starts from rest and slides down the inclined surface of the
    wedge, which is rough. During the motion of the block the center of
    mass of the block and wedge:

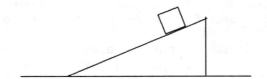

    A) does not move
    B) moves horizontally with constant speed
    C) moves horizontally with increasing speed
  *D) moves vertically with increasing speed
    E) moves both horizontally and vertically

21. A large wedge with a mass of 10 kg rests on a horizontal
    frictionless surface, as shown. A block with a mass of 5.0 kg starts
    from rest and slides down the inclined surface of the wedge, which
    is rough. At one instant the wedge is moving to the left with a
    speed of 3.0 m/s. At that instant the horizontal component of the
    velocity of the block is:

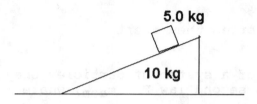

A) 3.0 m/s left   D) 6.0 m/s, left
B) 3.0 m/s, right   E) 17 m/s, right
*C) 6.0 m/s, right

22. A 2.0 kg mass is attached to one end of a spring with a spring
    constant of 100 N/m and a 4.0 kg mass is attached to the other end.
    The masses are placed on a horizontal frictionless surface and set
    into motion. At one instant the 2.0 kg mass is observed to be
    traveling to the right with a speed of 0.50 m/s and the 4.0 kg mass
    is observed to be traveling to the left with a speed of 0.30 m/s.
    Since the only forces acting are the force of gravity, the normal
    force of the surface, and the force of the spring, we conclude that:

A) the spring is compressed at the time of the observation
B) the spring is not compressed at the time of observation
C) the motion was started with the masses at rest
*D) the motion was started with at least one of masses moving
E) the motion was started by compressing the spring

23. A 2.0 kg mass is attached to one end of a spring with a spring
    constant of 100 N/m and a 4.0 kg mass is attached to the other end.
    The masses are placed on a horizontal frictionless surface and the
    spring is compressed 10 cm. The spring is then released with the
    masses at rest and the masses oscillate. When the spring has its
    equilibrium length the speeds of the masses are:

A) 0 and 0.29 m/s   D) 0.14 and 0.29 m/s
B) 0 and 0.58 m/s   E) 0.58 and 1.2 m/s
*C) 0.29 and 0.58 m/s

24. Momentum may be expressed in:

A) kg/m   D) kg/(m ·s)
B) gram ·s   E) N/s
*C) N ·s

25. The momentum of an object at a given instant is independent of its:

A) inertia
B) mass
C) speed
D) velocity
*E) acceleration

26. If two different masses have the same kinetic energy, their momenta are:

A) proportional to their masses
B) proportional to the square of their masses
*C) proportional to the square root of their masses
D) inversely proportional to their masses
E) inversely proportional to the square root of their masses

27. Two bodies, A and B, have equal kinetic energies. The mass of A is nine times that of B. The ratio of the momentum of A to that of B is:

A) 1:9   B) 1:3   C) 1:1   *D) 3:1   E) 9:1

28. Two objects, P and Q, have the same momentum. Q can have more kinetic energy than P if it:

A) weighs more than P
*B) is moving faster than P
C) weighs the same as P
D) is moving slower than P
E) is moving at the same speed as P

29. Which of the following five objects requires the greatest change in momentum to stop moving?

A) electron   mass = 10^{-30} kg   speed = 10^7 m/s
*B) oil tanker   mass = 10^8 kg   speed = 10^{-1} m/s
C) rain drop   mass = 10^{-4} kg   speed = 10 m/s
D) snail   mass = 10^{-2} kg   speed = 10^{-4} m/s
E) satellite   mass = 10 kg   speed = 10^4 m/s

30. Which of the following quantities can have a numerical value independent of the frame of reference in which it is evaluated?

A) velocity
B) momentum
C) kinetic energy
D) displacement
*E) none of these

31. A 0.20 kg rubber ball is dropped from the window of a building. It strikes the sidewalk below at 30 m/s and rebounds at 20 m/s. The change in momentum of the ball as a result of the collision with the sidewalk is (in kg ·m/s):

*A) 10   B) 6.0   C) 4.0   D) 2.0   E) 1.0

32. A 1.0 kg ball moving at 2.0 m/s perpendicular to a wall rebounds from the wall at 1.5 m/s. The gain in momentum of the ball is:

A) zero
B) 0.5 N ·s away from wall
C) 0.5 N ·s toward wall
*D) 3.5 N ·s away from wall
E) 3.5 N ·s toward wall

33. A ball is thrown into the air. As it rises, there is an increase in its:

A) acceleration
B) velocity
C) kinetic energy
*D) potential energy
E) momentum

34. If the total momentum of a system is changing:

A) particles of the system must be exerting forces on each other
B) the system must be under the influence of gravity
C) the center of mass must have constant velocity
*D) a net external force must be acting on the system
E) none of the above

35. When you step on the accelerator to increase the speed of your car, the force that accelerates the car is:

A) the force of your foot on the accelerator
*B) the force of friction of the road on the tires
C) the force of the engine on the drive shaft
D) the normal force of the road on the tires
E) none of the above

36. When you step on the brake pedal to stop your car, the force that decelerates the car is:

A) the force of your foot on the brake pedal
B) the force of the brakeshoes on the brake disk
*C) the force of friction of the road on the tires
D) the normal force of the road on the tires
E) none of the above

37. A 2.5 kg stone is released from rest and falls toward the earth. after 4.0 s, its momentum (in kg ·m/s) is:

*A) 98   B) 78   C) 39   D) 24   E) zero

38. In a tug-of-war game the winning team stood its ground. It pulled the rope through its hands without moving along the ground. The losing team did not let the rope slip but dragged its feet along the ground as it moved with constant velocity. For the system composed of the two teams and the rope which of the following statements is true while the losing team is moving?

 A) External forces are doing positive work.
 B) External forces are doing zero work.
*C) Internal forces are doing positive work
 D) Internal forces are doing zero work
 E) None of the above statements are true.

39. A 1000 kg automobile starts from rest and accelerates to 20 m/s in a distance of 500 m, over a horizontal road. If the tires do not skid on the road which of the following statements is NOT true?

*A) The work done by the road on the car is at least $2.0x10^5$ J.
 B) The work done by the engine is at least $2.0x10^5$ J.
 C) The work done by the normal force of the road on the tires is zero.
 D) The total frictional force of the road on the tires is at least 400 N.
 E) The total frictional force of the tires on the road is at least 400 N.

40. A man, standing at rest on a horizontal frictionless floor, might get himself moving by:

 A) walking   D) crawling slowly
 B) rolling   *E) throwing a shoe horizontally
 C) exhaling vertically

41. A 140 lb woman stands on frictionless level ice. She kicks a 0.2 lb stone backwards with her foot so that the stone acquires a velocity of 3.5 ft/s. The velocity (in ft/s) acquired by the woman is:

 A) 3.5 forward   D) 3.5 backward
 B) 0.005 backward   E) none of these
*C) 0.005 forward

42. A man is marooned at rest on level frictionless ice. In desperation, he hurls his shoe to the right at 45 ft/s. If the man weighs 180 lb and the shoe weighs 1.0 lb, the man moves to the left at approximately:

   A) 1 ft/s
  *B) 0.25 ft/s
   C) 32 ft/s

   D) 4 ft/s
   E) 9 ft/s

43. A rifle of mass M is initially at rest but free to recoil. It fires a bullet of mass m and velocity v (relative to the ground). After firing, the velocity of the rifle (relative to the ground) is:

   A) −mv   B) −Mv/m   *C) −mv/M   D) −v   E) mv/M

44. Bullets from two revolvers are fired with the same velocity. The bullet from gun #1 is twice as heavy as the bullet from gun #2. Gun #1 weighs three times as much as gun #2. The ratio of the momentum imparted to gun #1 to that imparted to gun #2 is:

   A) 2:3   B) 3:2   *C) 2:1   D) 3:1   E) 6:1

45. A 5-kg object can move along the x axis. It is subjected to a force F in the positive x direction; a graph of F as a function of time t is shown below. Over the time the force is applied the change in the velocity of the object is:

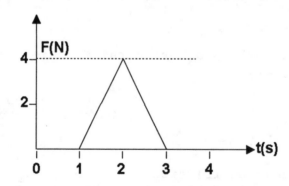

  *A) 0.8 m/s   B) 1.1 m/s   C) 1.6 m/s   D) 2.3 m/s   E) 4.0 m/s

46. Force:

   A) equals the negative integral (with respect to distance) of the potential energy function
   B) is the ability to do work
   C) is the rate of change of doing work
  *D) equals the time rate of change of momentum
   E) has dimensions of momentum multiplied by time

47. Cart A, with a mass of 0.2 kg, travels on a horizontal air track at
    3 m/s and hits cart B, which has a mass of 0.4 kg and is initially
    at rest. After the collision the center of mass of the two cart
    system has a speed in m/s of:

    A) 0
    *B) 1
    C) 2
    D) 3
    E) can't tell without knowing the energy

48. A 500 kg sack of coal is dropped on a 2000 kg railroad flatcar which
    was initially moving at 3 m/s as shown. After the sack rests on the
    flatcar, the speed of the flatcar is:

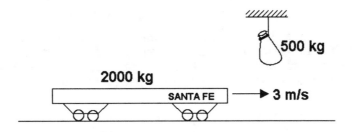

    A) 0.6 m/s   B) 1.2 m/s   C) 1.8 m/s   *D) 2.4 m/s   E) 3.6 m/s

49. Sand is dropped straight down on a moving conveyor belt at the rate
    of 3.0 kg/s. If friction in the bearings can be ignored the power
    that must be expended to keep the belt moving at 2.0 m/s is:

    A) 0   B) 3.0 W   C) 6.0 W   D) 9.0 W   *E) 12 W

50. A cart loaded with sand slides along a horizontal frictionless
    track. As the cart moves, sand trickles out at a constant rate
    through a hole in the back of the cart. The speed of the cart will:

    A) decrease at a constant rate   D) decrease at a variable rate
    B) increase at a constant rate   E) increase at a variable rate
    *C) remain the same

51. The thrust of a rocket is

    A) a gravitational force acting on the rocket
    *B) the force of the exiting fuel gases on the rocket
    C) any force that is external to the rocket-fuel system
    D) a force that arises from the reduction in mass of the rocket-fuel
       system
    E) none of the above

111

52. At one instant of time a rocket is traveling in outer space at 2500 m/s and is exhausting fuel at a rate of 100 kg/s. If the speed of the fuel as it leaves the rocket is 1500 m/s, relative to the rocket, the thrust is:

A) 0
B) 1.0×10^5 N
*C) 1.5×10^5 N
D) 2.9×10^5 N
E) 2.5×10^5 N

53. A rocket exhausts fuel with a velocity of 1500 m/s, relative to the rocket. It starts from rest in outer space with fuel comprising 80 per cent of the total mass. When all the fuel has been exhausted its speed is:

A) 3600 m/s   *B) 2400 m/s   C) 1200 m/s   D) 880 m/s   E) 400 m/s

54. A 1000 kg space probe is motionless in space. To start moving, its main engine is fired for 5 s during which time it ejects exhaust gases at 5000 m/s. At the end of this process it is moving at 20 m/s. The approximate mass of the ejected gas is:

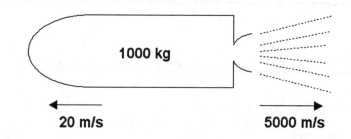

1000 kg

20 m/s   5000 m/s

A) 0.8 kg   *B) 4 kg   C) 5 kg   D) 20 kg   E) 25 kg

55. Why does a rocket accelerate when it is fired horizontally?

A) exhaust gases push against outside air
*B) exhaust gases, which the rocket pushes backwards, push the rocket forward
C) outside air exerts more force on the back of the rocket than on the front
D) exhaust speed is greater than the rocket speed
E) atmospheric pressure at the back of the rocket is reduced

56. A proton (mass = 1.67×10^{-27} kg) is traveling at 2.5×10^8 m/s, an appreciable fraction of the speed of light. The magnitude of its momentum is:

A) 1.1×10^{-10} kg $\cdot$m/s
B) 1.9×10^{-10} kg $\cdot$m/s
C) 3.6×10^{-15} kg $\cdot$m/s
D) 4.2×10^{-19} kg $\cdot$m/s
*E) 7.6×10^{-19} kg $\cdot$m/s

57. The magnitude of the momentum of a proton
    (mass = 1.67×10^{-27} kg) is 6.5×10^{-18} kg $\cdot$m/s. This is larger than mc,
    so the kinetic energy of the proton is:

A) 1.5×10^{-10} J   D) 1.3×10^{-8} J
*B) 1.8×10^{-9} J   E) 5.7×10^{-8} J
C) 2.0×10^{-9} J

1. The physical quantity "impulse" has the same dimensions as that of:

 A) force   B) power   C) energy   *D) momentum   E) work

2. The law of conservation of momentum applies to a system of colliding objects only if:

 A) there is no change in kinetic energy of the system
 B) the coefficient of restitution is one
 C) the coefficient of restitution is zero
 *D) the net external impulse is zero
 E) the collisions are all elastic

3. Sphere X, of mass 2 kg, is moving to the right at 10 m/s. Sphere Y, of mass 4 kg, is moving to the left at 10 m/s. The two spheres collide head-on. The ratio of the magnitude of the impulse exerted by X on Y to that exerted by Y on X is:

 A) 1/4
 B) 1/2
 C)
    $1/(\sqrt{2})$
 *D) 1
 E) need to know whether the collision is elastic or inelastic

4. Two bodies of unequal mass, placed on a frictionless surface, are acted on by equal horizontal forces for equal times. Just after these forces are removed, the body of greater mass will have:

 A) the greater speed
 B) the greater acceleration
 C) the smaller momentum
 D) the greater momentum
 *E) the same momentum as the other body

5. A 0.2 kg rubber ball is dropped from the window of a building. It strikes the sidewalk below at 30 m/s and rebounds up at 20 m/s. The magnitude of the impulse due to the collision with the sidewalk is:

 *A) 10 N ·s   D) 19.6 N ·s
 B) 6.0 N ·s   E) 9.8 N ·s
 C) 2.0 N ·s

6. A 10 kg block of ice is at rest on a frictionless horizontal
   surface. A 1.0 N force is applied in an easterly direction for
   1.0 s. During this time interval, the block:

 A) acquires a speed of 1 m/s
 B) moves 10 cm
*C) acquires a momentum of 1.0 kg ·m/s
 D) acquires a kinetic energy of 0.1 J
 E) none of the above

7. A uniform narrow bar, resting on ice, is given a transverse
   horizontal impulse **J** at one end as shown. The center of mass of the
   bar CM will then:

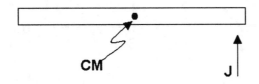

 A) remain at rest   D) move in a parabola
 B) move in a circle   E) move along some other curve
*C) move in a straight line

8. What impulse will give a 2.0 kg object a momentum change of
   + 50 kg ·m/s?

 A) +25 N ·s   D) -50 N ·s
 B) -25 N ·s   E) +100 N ·s
*C) +50 N ·s

9. A 2-kg object is acted upon by a single force in the x direction in a manner described by the graph shown. The momentum acquired by the object is:

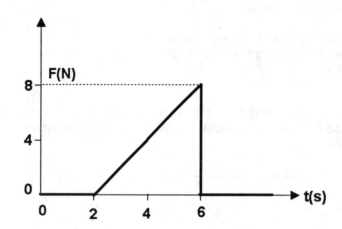

*A) 16 N ·s   B) 30 N ·s   C) 32 N ·s   D) 40 N ·s   E) 48 N ·s

10. A golf ball of mass m is hit by a golf club so that the ball leaves the tee with speed v. The club is in contact with the ball for time T. The average force on the club on the ball during the time T is:

A) mvT
*B) mv/T
C) $(1/2)mv^2T$

D) $mv^2/(2T)$
E) $mT^2/(2v)$

11. A 2-kg puck is moving north at 3 m/s on a horizontal smooth ice surface. The puck is then pushed east by a constant 4-N force. After how many seconds is the puck moving exactly northeast?

A) $1.5/(\sqrt{2})$ B) $1.5\sqrt{2}$ *C) 1.5   D) 2.75   E) 4.25

12. A 160 pound acrobat falls 16 feet from rest into a net. The net tosses him back up with the same speed he had just before he hit the net. The average upward force exerted on him by the net during this collision is:

A) 16 lb
B) 32 lb
C) 64 lb
D) 160 lb
*E) impossible to determine from given data

13. Whenever an object strikes a stationary object of equal mass:

   A) the two objects cannot stick together
   B) the collision must be elastic
   C) the first object must stop
   D) momentum is not necessarily conserved
  *E) none of the above

14. In which case is the momentum of the CAPITALIZED SYSTEM conserved?

   A) a BALL falling freely in a vacuum
   B) a RUBBER BALL as it bounces from the floor
   C) a CAR making a turn at constant speed
  *D) TWO BALLS colliding at right angles
   E) a BULLET AND THE GUN from which it was fired when the gun is firmly
      held

15. An event in which a particle at rest decays into two different
    particles, only one of which remains at rest, would be extremely
    surprising because:

   A) energy cannot be conserved in such a decay
   B) mass cannot be conserved in such a decay
   C) angular momentum cannot be conserved in such a decay
  *D) momentum cannot be conserved in such a decay
   E) charge cannot be conserved in such a decay

16. A particle at rest decays into two other particles, which move away
    from the decay site. Which of the following statements is true?

   A) The product particles might move in the same direction.
   B) The product particles might move at a right angle to each other.
   C) The product particles together might be more massive than the
      original particle.
  *D) The product particles together must be less massive than the
      original particle.
   E) None of the above are true.

17. For a two-body collision a frame of reference for which the total
    momentum is zero is one which, from the point of view of laboratory,
    has the same velocity as:

  *A) the center of mass
   B) the incident object
   C) the target object
   D) the average of the two bodies, before the collision
   E) the average of the two bodies, after the collision

117

18. An inelastic collision is one in which:

   A) momentum is not conserved but kinetic energy is conserved
   B) total mass is not conserved but momentum is conserved
   C) neither kinetic energy nor momentum is conserved
  *D) momentum is conserved but kinetic energy is not conserved
   E) the total impulse is equal to the change in kinetic energy

19. A 5-ton freight car, moving at 4 mph, collides and couples with an
    8-ton freight car which was initially at rest. The common final
    speed of these two cars is:

   A) 1 mph   B) 1.31 mph   *C) 1.54 mph   D) 2.5 mph   E) 4 mph

20. A one-pound puck is traveling at 10 ft/s. It strikes a two-pound
    puck which is stationary. The two pucks stick together. Their common
    final speed is:

   A) 5 ft/s   B) $\sqrt{50}$ ft/s   C) 3.33 ft/s   D) $\sqrt{10}$ ft/s   E) 2.5 ft/s

Ans. c

21. A 3.00-gram bullet traveling horizontally at 400 m/s hits a 3.00-kg
    wooden block which is initially at rest on a smooth horizontal
    table. The bullet buries itself in the block without passing
    through. The speed of the block after the collision is:

   A) 133 cm/s   D) 4000 cm/s
  *B) 40 cm/s   E) 16000 cm/s
   C) 1200 cm/s

22. A cart of mass m, traveling on a horizontal air track with speed v,
    collides with a stationary cart of mass 2m. The carts stick
    together. The impulse exerted by one cart on the other has
    magnitude:

   A) 0   *B) 2mv/3   C) mv   D) 3mv/2   E) 2mv

23. A 4-ton freight car moving at 3 mph bumps into a stationary 6-ton freight car. The two cars couple together. Their speed just after impact is:

A) zero   *B) 1.2 mph   C) 1.9 mph   D) 2.0 mph   E) 3.0 mph

24. A 3-gram bullet is fired horizontally into a 10-kg block of wood suspended by a rope from the ceiling. The block swings in an arc, rising 3 mm above its lowest position. The kinetic energy of the block at the bottom of its swing is approximately:

*A) 0.3 J
 B) 0.0003 J
 C) need to know how much heat was generated in the collision
 D) zero
 E) 30 J

25. A 3-gram bullet is fired horizontally into a 10-kg block of wood suspended by a rope from the ceiling. The block swings in an arc, rising 3 mm above its lowest position. The velocity of the bullet was:

 A) need to know how much heat was generated in the collision
*B) 8×10^4 cm/s
 C) 2400 cm/s
 D) 800 cm/s
 E) 2.4×10^6 cm/s

26. A 3-kg and a 2-kg cart approach each other on a horizontal air track in such a way that their center of mass has a speed of 4 m/s. They collide and stick together. After the collision their total kinetic energy in joules is:

A) 16   *D) 40
B) 20   E) can't tell from the given data
C) 24

27. Blocks A and B are moving toward each other. A has a mass of 2.0 kg and a velocity of 50 m/s, while B has a mass of 4.0 kg and a velocity of -25 m/s. They suffer a completely inelastic collision. The kinetic energy dissipated during the collision is:

A) 0   B) 2500 J   C) 5000 J   *D) 7500 J   E) 10000 J

28. For a completely inelastic two-body collision the kinetic energy retained by the objects is the same as:

    A) the total kinetic energy before the collision
    B) the difference in the kinetic energies of the objects before the collision
 *C) $\frac{1}{2}Mv_{cm}^2$, where M is the total mass and v_{cm}^2 is the velocity of the center of mass
    D) the kinetic energy of the more massive body before the collision
    E) the kinetic energy of the less massive body before the collision

29. Two spacemen are floating together with zero speed in a gravity-free region of space. The mass of spaceman A is 120 kg and that of spaceman B is 90 kg. Spaceman A pushes B away from him with B attaining a final speed of 0.5 m/s. The final recoil speed of A is:

    A) zero   *B) 0.38 m/s   C) 0.5 m/s   D) 0.67 m/s   E) 1.0 m/s

30. A 75 kg man is riding in a 30 kg cart at 2.0 m/s. He jumps off in such a way as to land on the ground with no horizontal velocity. The resulting change in speed of the cart is:

    A) zero   B) 2.0 m/s   C) 3.0 m/s   *D) 5.0 m/s   E) 7.0 m/s

31. An unstable nucleus has mass M and is initially at rest. It ejects a particle of mass m with speed v. The recoil speed of the remaining nucleus is:

    A) v   B) mv/M   C) mv/(m+M)   D) (m+M)v/m   *E) mv/(M-m)

32. A horizontal moving walkway is moving at 3 m/s. On the average, during each second, four stationary people step onto it and four people step off it. Assuming each person's mass is 60 kg, what average driving force must be exerted on the walkway to keep it moving?

    A) 45 N   B) 80 N   *C) 720 N   D) 1080 N   E) 2400 N

33. An elastic collision is one in which:

    A) momentum is not conserved but kinetic energy is conserved
    B) total mass is not conserved but momentum is conserved
 *C) kinetic energy and momentum are both conserved
    D) momentum is conserved but kinetic energy is not conserved
    E) the total impulse is equal to the change in kinetic energy

34. Object A strikes the stationary object B head-on in an elastic collision. The mass of A is fixed, you may choose the mass of B appropriately. Then:

   A) for B to have the greatest recoil speed, choose $m_A = m_B$
   B) for B to have the greatest recoil momentum, choose $m_B << m_A$
   C) for B to have the greatest recoil kinetic energy, choose $m_B >> m_A$
   D) for B to have the least recoil speed, choose $m_B = m_A$
   *E) for B to have the greatest recoil kinetic energy, choose $m_B = m_A$

35. Block A, with a mass of 2.0 kg, moves along the x axis with a velocity of 5.0 m/s (in the positive x direction). It suffers an elastic collision with block B, initially at rest, and the blocks leave the collision along the x axis. If B is much more massive than A, the velocity of A after the collision is:

   A) 0   B) +5.0 m/s   *C) -5.0 m/s   D) +10 m/s   E) -10 m/s

36. Block A, with a mass of 2.0 kg, moves along the x axis with a velocity of 5.0 m/s (in the positive x direction). It suffers an elastic collision with block B, which initially has a velocity of -2.0 m/s (in the negative x direction). The blocks leave the collision along the x axis. If B is much more massive than A, the velocity of A after the collision is:

   A) 0   B) -3.0 m/s   C) -5.0 m/s   D) -7.0 m/s   *E) -9.0 m/s

37. A very massive object traveling at 10 m/s strikes a light object, initially at rest, and the light object moves off in the direction of travel of the heavy object. Its speed is:

   A) 5.0 m/s
   B) 10 m/s
   C) 15 m/s
   *D) 20 m/s
   E) Can't tell from the information given.

38. A 5.0 gram ball is moving downward at 100 cm/s. It undergoes an elastic collision with a heavy horizontal plate which is fixed to the earth. The change in momentum of the ball due to this collision is:

   A) 500 gm ·cm/s, up   D) 500 gm ·cm/s, down
   *B) 1000 gm ·cm/s, up   E) 1000 gm ·cm/s, down
   C) zero

39. Sphere A has mass m and is moving with velocity v. It makes a head-on elastic collision with a stationary sphere B of mass 2m. After the collision their speeds (v_A, v_B) are:

A) 0, v/2
*B) −v/3, 2v/3
C) −v, v

D) −2v/3, v/3
E) none of these

40. Blocks A and B are moving toward each other along the x axis. A has a mass of 2.0 kg and a velocity of 50 m/s (in the positive x direction), while B has a mass of 4.0 kg and a velocity of −25 m/s (in the negative x direction). They suffer an elastic collision and move off along the x axis. After the collision the velocities of A and B, respectively, are:

*A) −50 and 25 m/s
B) 50 and −25 m/s
C) −25 and 50 m/s

D) 25 and −50 m/s
E) −25 and −50 m/s

41. Blocks A and B move toward each other along the x axis. A has a mass of 2.0 kg and a velocity of 10 m/s (in the positive x direction); B has a mass of 3.0 kg and a velocity of −5.0 m/s (in the negative x direction). They suffer an elastic collision and go off along the x axis. After the collision the velocities of A and B, respectively, are:

A) −10 and +5.0 m/s
*B) −8.0 and +7.0 m/s
C) −9.0 and +6.0 m/s

D) −5.0 and +10 m/s
E) +5.0 and −10 m/s

42. Blocks A and B are moving toward each other along the x axis. A has a mass of 2.0 kg and a velocity of 50 m/s, while B has a mass of 4.0 kg and a velocity of −25 m/s. They suffer an elastic collision and move off along the x axis. The kinetic energy transferred from A to B during the collision is:

*A) 0   B) 2500 J   C) 5000 J   D) 7500 J   E) 10000 J

43. When a particle suffers a head-on elastic collision with another particle, initially at rest, the greatest fraction of kinetic energy is transferred if:

A) the incident particle is initially traveling very fast
B) the incident particle is traveling very slowly
C) the incident particle is much more massive than the target particle
D) the incident particle is much less massive than the target particle
*E) the incident and target particle have the same mass

44. Two objects, X and Y, are held at rest on a horizontal frictionless
    surface. A spring is compressed between X and Y. The mass of X is
    2/5 times the mass of Y. When the objects are released, the ratio of
    the kinetic energy of X to that of Y is:

A) 2/5   B) 4/25   C) 25/4   *D) 5/2   E) 1

45. Two carts (A and B), having spring bumpers, collide as shown. Cart A
    has a mass of 2 kg and is initially moving to the right. Cart B has
    a mass of 3 kg and is initially stationary. When the separation
    between the carts is a minimum:

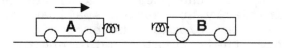

  A) cart B is still at rest
  B) cart A has come to rest
  C) both carts have the same momentum
  D) both carts have the same kinetic energy
 *E) the kinetic energy of the system is at a minimum

46. Two blocks (1 kg and 3 kg) are joined by a thread and travel
    together over a horizontal frictionless surface at speed v as shown.
    The thread is then cut. Their final speeds (V_1 and V_3) are:

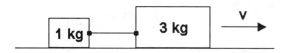

  A) $V_1 = 2v/3$, $V_3 = v/3$ D) $V_1 = 3v/4$, $V_3 = v/4$
  B) $V_1 = v/3$, $V_3 = 2v/3$ *E) none of these
  C) $V_1 = v/4$, $V_3 = 3v/4$

47. Two identical carts travel at 1 m/s on a common surface. They
    collide head-on and are reported to rebound, each with a speed of
    2 m/s. Then:

  A) momentum was not conserved, therefore the report must be false
 *B) if potential energy were changed to kinetic during the collision,
     the report could be true
  C) if the collision were elastic, the report could be true
  D) if the surface were inclined, the report could be true
  E) if the duration of the collision were short enough, the report could
     be true

48. A projectile in flight explodes into several fragments. The total momentum of the fragments immediately after this explosion:

 *A) is the same as the momentum of the projectile immediately before the explosion
  B) has been changed into kinetic energy of the fragments
  C) is less than the momentum of the projectile immediately before the explosion
  D) is more than the momentum of the projectile immediately before the explosion
  E) has been changed into radiant energy

49. A block moves at 5 m/s in the positive x direction and hits an identical block, initially at rest. A small amount of gunpowder had been placed on one of the blocks. The explosion does not harm the blocks but it doubles their total kinetic energy. After the explosion the blocks move along the x axis and the incident block has a speed in m/s of:

 *A) 1.8   B) 5.0   C) 6.8   D) 7.1   E) 11.8

50. A He^4 nucleus (atomic weight 4) moving with speed v breaks up into a neutron (atomic weight 1) and a He^3 nucleus. The neutron moves off at right angles to the original He^4 as shown. It the neutron speed is 3v, the final speed of the He^3 nucleus is:

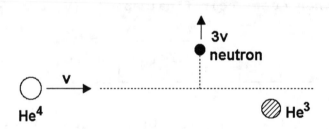

  A) zero   *D) 5v/3
  B) v   E) none of these
  C) 4v/3

51. A stream of gas consists of n molecules. Each molecule has mass m and speed v. The stream is reflected elastically from a rigid surface as shown. The magnitude of the total change in momentum of the stream is:

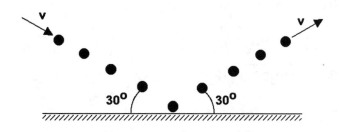

A) 2mnv
B) 2mnv sin 60°
C) mnv sin 60°

D) mnv cos 60°
*E) mnv

52. In a nuclear reaction the total kinetic energy of the products is greater than the total initial kinetic energy if:

A) one or more of the products is in an excited state
*B) the total mass of the products is less than the original total mass
C) the total mass of the products is greater than the original total mass
D) the collision is elastic
E) none of the above occur

53. Particle A, initially at rest, decays into particles B and C. To find the momenta of the decay products the correct relativistic equations to use are $p_B = -p_C$ and:

A) $0 = \sqrt{(P_B c)^2 + (m_B c^2)} + \sqrt{(P_C c) + (m_C c^2)^2}$

B) $m_A c^2 = \sqrt{(P_B c)^2 + (m_B c^2)^2} + \sqrt{(P_C c)^2 + (m_C c^2)^2}$

C) $0 = \sqrt{(P_B c)^2 + (m_B c)^2} + \sqrt{(P_C c)^2 + (m_C c^2)^2} + m_B c^2 + m_C c^2$

D) $M_A c^2 = \sqrt{(P_B c)^2 + (m_B c^2)^2} + \sqrt{(P_C c)^2 + (m_C c^2)^2} + m_B c^2 + m_C c^2$

E) $m_A c^2 = \sqrt{(P_B c)^2 + (m_B c^2)^2} + \sqrt{(P_C c)^2 + (m_C c^2)^2} - m_B c^2 - m_C c^2$

Ans. b

1. A radian is about:

A) 25°   B) 37°   C) 45°   *D) 57°   E) 90°

2. One revolution is about the same as:

A) 1 rad   B) 57 rad   C) π/2 rad   D) π rad   *E) 2π rad

3. One revolution per minute is about:

A) 0.0524 rad/s   D) 1.57 rad/s
*B) 0.105 rad/s   E) 6.28 rad/s
C) 0.95 rad/s

4. If a wheel turns with constant angular speed then:

A) each point on its rim moves with constant velocity
B) each point on its rim moves with constant acceleration
*C) the wheel turns through equal angles in equal times
D) the angle through which the wheel turns in each second increases as
   time goes on
E) the angle through which the wheel turns in each second decreases as
   time goes on

5. If a wheel is turning at 3.0 rad/s, the time it takes to complete
   one revolution is about:

A) 0.33 s   B) 0.67 s   C) 1.0 s   D) 1.3 s   *E) 2.1 s

6. If wheel turning at a constant rate completes 100 revolutions in
   10 s its angular speed is:

A) 0.31 rad/s   D) 31 rad/s
B) 0.63 rad/s   *E) 63 rad/s
C) 10 rad/s

7. The angular speed in rad/s of the second hand of a watch is:

A) π/1800   B) π/60   *C) π/30   D) 2π   E) 60

8. The angular speed in rad/s of the minute hand of a watch is:

A) 60/π   B) 1800/π   C) π   *D) π/1800   E) π/60

9. A flywheel, initially at rest, has a constant angular acceleration. After 9 seconds the flywheel has rotated 450 rad. Its angular acceleration in rad/s^2 is:

A) 100   B) 1.77   C) 50   *D) 11.1   E) 15.9

10. Ten seconds after the switch of an electric fan is turned on, the fan rotates at 300 rev/min. Its average angular acceleration is:

*A) 3.14 rad/s^2 D) 50 rev/min^2
B) 30 rad/s^2 E) 1800 rev/s^2
C) 30 rev/s^2

11. A wheel rotates with a constant angular acceleration of π rad/s^2. During the time interval from t_1 to t_2 its angular displacement is π rad. At time t_2 its angular velocity is 2π rad/s. Its angular velocity in rad/s at time t_1 is:

A) zero   B) 1   C) π *D) $\pi\sqrt{2}$ E) 2π

12. A flywheel rotating at 12 rev/s is brought to rest in 6 s. The magnitude of the average angular acceleration in rad/s^2 of the wheel during this process is:

A) 1/π B) 2   C) 4   *D) 4π E) 72

13. A phonograph turntable, rotating at 0.75 rev/s, slows down and stops in 30 s. The magnitude of its average angular acceleration in rad/s^2 for this process is:

A) 1.5   B) 1.5π C) $\pi/40$ *D) $\pi/20$ E) 0.75

14. The angular velocity of a rotating wheel increases 2 revolutions per second every minute. The angular acceleration, in rad/s^2 of this wheel is:

A) 4π^2 B) 2π C) 1/30   *D) 2π/30   E) 4π

15. A wheel initially has an angular velocity of 18 rad/s but it is slowing at a rate of 2.0 rad/s^2. The time it takes to stop is:

A) 3.0 s   D) 12 s
B) 6.0 s   E) never stops
*C) 9.0 s

128

16. A wheel rotating with constant angular acceleration initially has an angular velocity of 36 rad/s but after 6.0 s its angular velocity is 24 rad/s. Its angular acceleration is:

A) 2.0 rad/s^2
*B) -2.0 rad/s^2
C) 3.0 rad/s^2

D) -3.0 rad/s^2
E) 6.0 rad/s^2

17. A wheel rotating with constant angular acceleration initially has an angular velocity of -36 rad/s but after 6.0 s its angular velocity is -24 rad/s. Its angular acceleration is:

*A) 2.0 rad/s^2
B) -2.0 rad/s^2
C) 3.0 rad/s^2

D) -3.0 rad/s^2
E) -6.0 rad/s^2

18. A wheel initially has an angular velocity of 18 rad/s but it is slowing at a rate of 2.0 rad/s^2. By the time it stops it will have turned through:

*A) 13 rev   B) 26 rev   C) 39 rev   D) 52 rev   E) 65 rev

19. A wheel starts from rest and has an angular acceleration of 4.0 rad/s^2. When it has made 10 revolutions its angular velocity is:

A) 16 rad/s
*B) 22 rad/s
C) 32 rad/s

D) 250 rad/s
E) 500 rad/s

20. A wheel starts from rest and has an angular acceleration of 4.0 rad/s^2. The time it takes to make 10 revolutions is:

A) 0.50 s   B) 0.71 s   C) 1.4 s   *D) 1.8 s   E) 3.1 s

21. A wheel starts from rest and has an angular acceleration that is given by $\alpha(t) = 6t^2$. The angle through which it turns in time t is given by:

A) $(1/8)t^4$ B) $(1/4)t^4$ *C) $(1/2)t^4$ D) t^4 E) 12

22. A wheel starts from rest and has an angular acceleration that is given by $\alpha(t) = 6t^2$. The time it takes to make 10 revolutions is:

A) 2.8 s   B) 3.4 s   *C) 4.0 s   D) 4.7 s   E) 5.3 s

23. A wheel starts from rest and has an angular acceleration that is given by $\alpha(t) = 6t^2$. After it has turned through 10 revolutions its angular velocity is:

   A) 63 rad/s
   *B) 75 rad/s
   C) 89 rad/s

   D) 130 rad/s
   E) 210 rad/s

24. A wheel is spinning at 27 rad/s but is slowing with an acceleration that has a magnitude given by $3t^2$, in rad/s^2 for t in seconds. It stops in a time of:

   A) 1.7 s   B) 2.6 s   *C) 3.0 s   D) 4.4 s   E) 7.3 s

25. If the angular velocity vector of a spinning body points out of the page then, when viewed from above the page, the body is spinning:

   A) clockwise about an axis that is perpendicular to the page
   *B) counterclockwise about an axis that is perpendicular to the page
   C) about an axis that is parallel to the page
   D) about an axis that is changing orientation
   E) about an axis that is getting longer

26. The angular velocity vector of a spinning body points out of the page. If the angular acceleration vector points into the page then:

   *A) the body is slowing down
   B) the body is speeding up
   C) the body is starting to turn in the opposite direction
   D) the axis of rotation is changing orientation
   E) none of the above

27. A child, riding on a large merry-go-round, travels a distance of 3000 m in a circle of diameter 40 m. The total angle in radians through which she revolves is:

   A) 50
   B) 75
   *C) 150

   D) 314
   E) none of these

28. The figure shows a cylinder of radius 0.7 m rotating about its axis at 10 rad/s. The speed of the point P is:

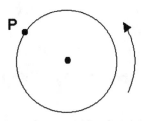

*A) 7.0 m/s
 B) 14π rad/s
 C) 7π rad/s

D) 0.7 m/s
E) none of these

29. The fan shown has been turned on and is speeding up as it rotates clockwise. The direction of the acceleration of the point X on the fan tip could be:

A) ✓   B) ↘   *C) ↓   D) ←   E) →

30. A wheel of diameter 8 inches has a 12-foot cord wrapped around its periphery. Starting from rest, the wheel is given a constant angular acceleration of 2 rad/s^2. The cord will unwind in:

*A) 6 s   B) 12 s   C) 3 s   D) 60 s   E) 20 s

31. A particle moves in a circular path of radius 0.10 m with a constant angular speed of 5 rev/s. The acceleration of the particle is:

A) 0.10π m/s^2
B) 0.50 m/s^2
C) 500π m/s^2

D) $1000\pi^2$ m/s^2
*E) $10\pi^2$ m/s^2

32. A car travels north at constant velocity. It goes over a piece of mud which sticks to the tire. The initial acceleration of the mud, as it leaves the ground, is:

 *A) vertically upward
  B) horizontally to the north
  C) horizontally to the south
  D) zero
  E) upward and forward at 45° to the horizontal

33. String is wrapped around the periphery of a 5.0-cm radius cylinder, free to rotate on its axis. If the string is pulled out at a constant rate of 10 cm/s and does not slip on the cylinder, the angular velocity of the cylinder is:

 *A) 2.0 rad/s   D) 25 rad/s
  B) 5.0 rad/s   E) 50 rad/s
  C) 10 rad/s

34. String is wrapped around the periphery of a 5.0-cm radius cylinder, free to rotate on its axis. The string is pulled straight out at a constant rate of 10 cm/s and does not slip on the cylinder. As each small segment of string leaves the cylinder, its acceleration changes by:

  A) 0   D) 0.10 rad/s^2
  B) 0.010 rad/s^2 *E) 0.20 rad/s^2
  C) 0.020 rad/s^2

35. A flywheel of diameter 4.0 ft has a constant angular acceleration of 5.0 rad/s^2. The tangential acceleration of a point on its rim is:

  A) 10 rad/s^2 B) 20 rad/s^2 C) 5 ft/s^2 *D) 10 ft/s^2 E) 20 ft/s^2

36. For a wheel spinning with constant angular acceleration on an axis through its center, the ratio of the speed of a point on the rim to the speed of a point halfway between the center and the rim is:

  A) 1   *B) 2   C) 1/2   D) 4   E) 1/4

37. For a wheel spinning on an axis through its center, the ratio of the tangential acceleration of a point on the rim to the tangential acceleration of a point halfway between the center and the rim is:

  A) 1   *B) 2   C) 1/2   D) 4   E) 1/4

38. For a wheel spinning on an axis through its center, the ratio of the radial acceleration of a point on the rim to the radial acceleration of a point halfway between the center and the rim is:

A) 1   *B) 2   C) 1/2   D) 4   E) 1/4

39. Two wheels are identical but wheel B is spinning with twice the angular velocity of wheel A. The ratio of the radial acceleration of a point on the rim of B to the radial acceleration of a point on the rim of A is:

A) 1   B) 2   C) 1/2   *D) 4   E) 1/4

40. A wheel starts from rest and spins with a constant angular acceleration. As time goes on the acceleration vector for a point on the rim:

  A) decreases in magnitude and becomes more nearly tangent to the rim
  B) decreases in magnitude and becomes more nearly radial
  C) increases in magnitude and becomes more nearly tangent to the rim
 *D) increases in magnitude and becomes more nearly radial
  E) increases in magnitude but retains the same angle with the tangent to the rim

41. The acceleration of a point on a spinning wheel is increased by a factor of 4 if:

  A) the angular velocity and the angular acceleration are each increased by a factor of 4
  B) the angular velocity is increased by a factor of 4 and the angular acceleration is not changed
  C) the angular velocity and the angular acceleration are each increased by a factor of 2
  D) the angular velocity in increased by a factor of 2 and the angular acceleration is not changed
 *E) the angular velocity is increased by a factor of 2 and the angular acceleration is increased by a factor of 4

42. Four equal point masses m are arranged in the x-y plane as shown. They are connected by light sticks to form a rigid body. If m = 2.0 kg and a = 1.0 m, the rotational inertia about the y-axis of this array is:

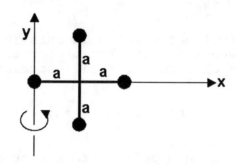

A) 4.0 kg $\cdot$m^2
*B) 12 kg $\cdot$m^2
C) 9.6 kg $\cdot$m^2

D) 4.8 kg $\cdot$m^2
E) none of these

43. Three identical objects of mass M are fastened to a massless rod of length L as shown. The rotational inertia about one end of the rod of this array is:

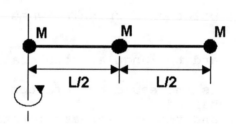

A) $ML^2/2$ B) ML^2 C) $3ML^2/2$ *D) $5ML^2/4$ E) $3ML^2$

44. The rotational inertia of a thin cylindrical shell of mass M, radius R, and length L about its symmetry axis is:

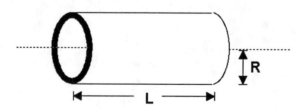

A) $MR^2/2$
B) $ML^2/2$
C) ML^2

*D) MR^2
E) none of these

45. The rotational inertia of a wheel about its axle does not depend upon its:

A) diameter
B) mass
C) distribution of mass

*D) speed of rotation
E) material composition

46. Consider four objects, each having the same mass and the same radius:
   A. a solid sphere
   B. a hollow sphere
   C. a flat disk in the x-y plane
   D. a hoop in the x-y plane
The order of increasing rotational inertia (about an axis through the center of mass and parallel to the z-axis) is:

A) ABCD   B) DCBA   *C) ACBD   D) DBCA   E) CABD

47. A and B are two solid cylinders made of aluminum. Their dimensions are shown. The ratio of the rotational inertia of B to that of A (about the common axis X-X') is:

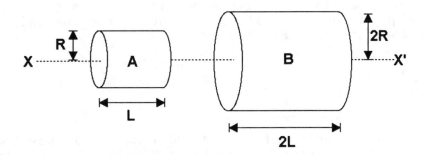

A) 2   B) 4   C) 8   D) 16   *E) 32

48. Two circular disks having the same mass and the same thickness are made from different materials. The disk with the smaller rotational inertia is:

*A) that made from the more dense material
B) that made from the less dense material
C) neither - both rotational inertias are the same
D) the disk with the larger angular velocity
E) the disk with the larger torque

49. A solid cylinder made of lead has the same mass and the same length as a solid cylinder made of wood. The rotational inertia of the lead cylinder compared to the wooden one is:

   A) greater
   *B) less
   C) same
   D) unknown unless the radii are given
   E) unknown unless both the masses and the radii are given

50. To increase the rotational inertia of a solid disk about its axis without changing its mass:

   A) drill holes near the rim and put the material near the axis
   *B) drill holes near the axis and put the material near the rim
   C) drill holes at points on a circle near the rim and put the material at points between the holes
   D) drill holes at points on a circle near the axis and put the material at points between the holes
   E) do none of the above (the rotational inertia cannot be changed without changing the mass)

51. The rotational inertia of a disk about its axis is 0.70 kg·m^2. When a 2.0 kg weight is added to its rim, 0.40 m from the axis, the rotational inertia becomes:

   A) 0.38 kg ·m^2 D) 0.86 kg ·m^2
   B) 0.54 kg ·m^2 *E) 1.0 kg ·m^2
   C) 0.70 kg ·m^2

52. When a thin uniform stick of mass M and length L is pivoted about its midpoint, its rotational inertia is $ML^2/12$. When pivoted about a parallel axis through one end, its rotational inertia is:

   A) $ML^2/12$ B) $ML^2/6$ *C) $ML^2/3$ D) $7ML^2/12$ E) $13ML^2/12$

53. The rotational inertia of a sphere about a diameter is $(5/2)MR^2$, where M is its mass and R is its radius. If the sphere is pivoted about an axis that is tangent to its surface, its rotational inertia is:

   A) MR^2 B) $(1/2)MR^2$ C) $(3/2)MR^2$ D) $(5/2)MR^2$ *E) $(7/2)MR^2$

54. A force with a given magnitude is to be applied to a wheel. The torque can be maximized by:

   A) applying the force near the axle, radially outward from the axle
   B) applying the force near the rim, radially outward from the axle
   C) applying the force near the axle, parallel to a tangent to the wheel
   *D) applying the force at the rim, tangent to the rim
   E) applying the force at the rim, at 45° to the tangent

55. A rod is pivoted about its center. A 5 N force is applied 4 m from the pivot and another 5 N force is applied 2 m from the pivot, as shown. The magnitude of the total torque about the pivot (in N ·m) is:

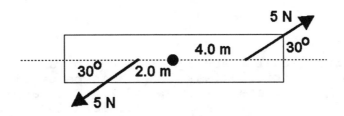

A) 0   *B) 5   C) 8.7   D) 15   E) 26

56. As a particle starts from rest and moves with constant angular acceleration around a circular orbit, the point of application of the force acting on it does not change. This must mean:

A) the torque acting on it is increasing in magnitude
B) the torque acting on it is decreasing in magnitude
C) the force acting on it is increasing in magnitude
D) the force acting on it is decreasing in magnitude
*E) none of the above

57. $\tau = I\alpha$ for object rotating about a fixed axis, where τ is the net torque acting on it, I is its rotational inertia, and α is its angular acceleration. This expression:

A) is the definition of torque
B) is the definition of rotational inertia
C) is the definition of angular acceleration
*D) follows directly from Newton's second law
E) depends on a principle of physics that is unrelated to Newton's second law

58. A disk is free to rotate on a fixed axis. A force of given magnitude F, in the plane of the disk, is to be applied. Of the following alternatives the greatest angular acceleration is obtained if the force is:

A) applied tangentially halfway between the axis and the rim
*B) applied tangentially at the rim
C) applied radially halfway between the axis and the rim
D) applied radially at the rim
E) applied at the rim but neither radially nor tangentially

59. A cylinder is 0.10 m in radius and 0.20 in length. Its rotational inertia, about the cylinder axis on which it is mounted, is 0.020 kg $\cdot m^2$. A string is wound around the cylinder and pulled with a force of 1.0 N. The angular acceleration in rad/s^2 of the cylinder is:

A) 2.5   *B) 5.0   C) 10   D) 15   E) 20

60. A disk with a rotational inertia of 5.0 kg $\cdot m^2$ and a radius of 0.25 m rotates on a frictionless fixed axis perpendicular to the disk and through its center. A force of 2.0 N is applied tangentially to the rim. The angular acceleration of the disk is:

*A) 0.40 rad/s^2 D) 2.5 rad/s^2
 B) 0.4 rad/s^2 E) 10 rad/s^2
 C) 1.0 rad/s^2

61. A disk with a rotational inertia of 5.0 kg $\cdot m^2$ and a radius of 0.25 m rotates on a frictionless fixed axis perpendicular to the disk and through its center. A force of 2.0 N is applied parallel to the axis. The angular acceleration of the disk is:

*A) 0   D) 1.0 rad/s^2
 B) 0.40 rad/s^2 E) 2.5 rad/s^2
 C) 0.4 rad/s^2

62. A disk with a rotational inertia of 5.0 kg $\cdot m^2$ and a radius of 0.25 m rotates on a frictionless fixed axis perpendicular to the disk and through its center. A force of 2.0 N is applied tangentially to the rim. If the disk starts at rest, then after it has turned through half a revolution its angular velocity is:

 A) 0.57 rad/s   D) 1.6 rad/s
 B) 0.64 rad/s   E) 3.2 rad/s
*C) 0.80 rad/s

63. A thin circular hoop of mass 1.0 kg and radius 2.0 m is rotating about an axis through its center and perpendicular to its plane. It is slowing down at the rate of 7.0 rad/s^2. The net torque, in kg $\cdot m^2/s^2$, acting on it is:

 A) 7.0   D) 44.0
 B) 14.0   E) none of these
*C) 28.0

138

64. A certain wheel has a rotational inertia of 12 kg ·m^2. As it turns through 5.0 revolutions its angular velocity increases from 5.0 rad/s to 6.0 rad/s. If the net torque is constant its value is:

A) 0.016 N ·m
*B) 0.18 N ·m
C) 0.57 N ·m
D) 1.1 N ·m
E) 3.6 N ·m

65. A 32 lb block is attached to a cord that is wrapped around the rim of a flywheel of diameter 1 ft and hangs vertically, as shown. The rotational inertia of the flywheel is 0.5 slug ·ft^2. When the block is released and the cord unwinds, the acceleration of the block is:

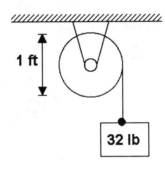

*A) g/3   B) g   C) 2g/3   D) g/32   E) g/16

66. A 8.0 cm radius disk with a rotational inertia of 0.12 kg ·m^2 is free to rotate on a horizontal axis. A string is fastened to the surface of the disk and a 10-kg mass hangs from the other end. The mass is raised by using a crank to apply a 9.0-N ·m torque to the disk. The acceleration of the mass is:

*A) 0.50 m/s^2 B) 1.7 m/s^2 C) 6.2 m/s^2 D) 12 m/s^2 E) 20 m/s^2

67. A 0.70-kg disk with a rotational inertia given by MR^2/2 is free to rotate on a fixed horizontal axis suspended from the ceiling. A string is wrapped around the disk and a 2.0-kg mass hangs from the free end. If the string does not slip then as the mass falls and the cylinder rotates the suspension holding the cylinder pulls up on the cylinder with a force of:

*A) 10 N   B) 13 N   C) 16 N   D) 26 N   E) 29 N

68. A small disk of radius R_1 is mounted coaxially with a larger disk of radius R_2. The disks are securely fastened to each other and the combination is free to rotate on a fixed axle that is perpendicular to a horizontal frictionless table top. The rotational inertia of the combination is I. A string is wrapped around the larger disk and attached to a block of mass m, on the table. Another string is wrapped around the smaller disk and is pulled with a force **F** as shown. The acceleration of the block is:

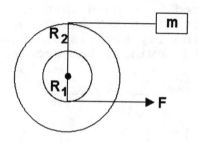

A) R_1F/mR_2

B) $R_1R_2F/(I - mR_2^2)$

*C) $R_1R_2F/(I + mR_2^2)$

D) $R_1R_2F/(I - mR_1R_2)$

E) $R_1R_2F/(I + mR_1R_2)$

69. A small disk of radius R_1 is fastened coaxially to a larger disk of radius R_2. The combination is free to rotate on a fixed axle, which is perpendicular to a horizontal frictionless table top. The rotational inertia of the combination is I. A string is wrapped around the larger disk and attached to a block of mass m, on the table. Another string is wrapped around the smaller disk and is pulled with a force **F** as shown. The tension in the string pulling the block is:

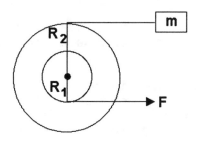

A) R_1F/R_2

B) $mR_1R_2F/(I - mR_2^2)$

*C) $mR_1R_2F/(I + mR_2^2)$

D) $mR_1R_2F/(I - mR_1R_2)$

E) $mR_1R_2F/(I + mR_1R_2)$

70. A block is attached to each end of a rope that passes over a pulley suspended from the ceiling. The blocks do not have the same mass. If the rope does not slip on the pulley, then at any instant after the blocks start moving the rope:

*A) pulls on both blocks, but exerts a greater force on the heavier block

B) pulls on both blocks, but exerts a greater force on the lighter block

C) pulls on both blocks and exerts the same non-zero force on both

D) does not pull on either block

E) pulls only on the lighter block

71. A pulley with a radius of 3.0 cm and a rotational inertia of 4.5×10^{-3} kg $\cdot m^2$ is suspended from the ceiling. A rope passes over it with a 2.0-kg block attached to one end and a 4.0-kg block attached to the other. The rope does not slip on the pulley. When the velocity of the heavier block is 2.0 m/s the total kinetic energy of the pulley and blocks is:

A) 2.0 J   B) 4.0 J   C) 14 J   *D) 22 J   E) 28 J

72. A pulley with a radius of 3.0 cm and a rotational inertia of 4.5×10^{-3} kg ·m^2 is suspended from the ceiling. A rope passes over it with a 2.0-kg block attached to one end and a 4.0-kg block attached to the other. The rope does not slip on the pulley. At any instant after the blocks start moving the object with the greatest kinetic energy is:

  A) the heavier block
  B) the lighter block
 *C) the pulley
  D) either block (the two blocks have the same kinetic energy)
  E) none (all three objects have the same kinetic energy)

73. A disk with a rotational inertia of 5.0 kg ·m^2 and a radius of 0.25 m rotates on a fixed axis perpendicular to the disk and through its center. A force of 2.0 N is applied tangentially to the rim. As the disk turns through half a revolution the work done by the force is:

 *A) 1.6 J   B) 2.5 J   C) 6.3 J   D) 10 J   E) 40 J

74. A grinding wheel, used to sharpen tools, is powered by a motor. A knife held against the wheel exerts a torque of 0.80 N ·m. If the wheel rotates with a constant angular velocity of 20 rad/s the work done on the wheel by the motor in 1.0 min is:

  A) 0   B) 480 J   *C) 960 J   D) 1400 J   E) 1800 J

75. A disk has a rotational inertia of 6.0 kg ·m^2 and a constant angular acceleration of 2.0 rad/s^2. If it starts from rest the work done during the first 5.0 s by the net torque acting on it is:

  A) 0   B) 30 J   C) 60 J   *D) 300 J   E) 600 J

76. A disk starts from rest and rotates around a fixed axis, subject to a constant net torque. The work done by the torque during the second 5 s is _____ as the work done during the first 5 s.

  A) the same   *D) four times as much
  B) twice as much   E) one fourth as much
  C) half as much

77. A disk starts from rest and rotates about a fixed axis, subject to a constant net torque. The work done by the torque during the second revolution is _____ as the work done during the first revolution.

 *A) the same   D) four times as much
  B) twice as much   E) one fourth as much
  C) half as much

142

1. A wheel rolls along a horizontal road as shown. The velocity of the center of the wheel is represented by →. Point P is painted on the rim of the wheel. The instantaneous velocity of point P is:

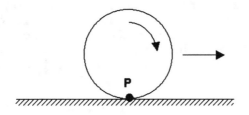

A) →   B) ←   C) ↑   D) ↗   *E) zero

2. A wheel of radius 0.5 m rolls without slipping on a horizontal surface as shown. Starting from rest, the wheel moves with constant angular acceleration 6 rad/s^2. The distance in m traveled by the center of the wheel from t = 0 to t = 3 s is:

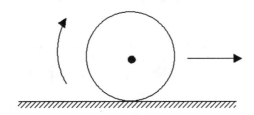

A) zero   D) 18
B) 27   E) none of these
*C) 13.5

3. A forward force acting on the axle pulls a rolling wheel on a horizontal surface. If the wheel does not slip the frictional force of the surface on the wheel:

A) is zero
B) is in the forward direction and does zero work on the wheel
C) is in the forward direction and does positive work on the wheel
*D) is in the backward direction and does zero work on the wheel
E) is in the backward direction and does positive work on the wheel

143

4. When the speed of a rear-drive car is increasing on a horizontal road the direction of the frictional force on the tires is:

A) forward for all tires
B) backward for all tires
C) forward for the front tires and backward for the rear tires
*D) backward for the front tires and forward for the rear tires
E) zero

5. A 3.0-kg solid wheel, rolling without slipping on a horizontal surface, has a rotational inertia about its axis given by $MR^2/2$, where M is its mass and R is its radius. A force is applied to the axle and the center of mass has an acceleration of 2.0 m/s^2. The magnitudes of the applied force and the frictional force of the surface, respectively, are:

A) 6.0 N, 0   *D) 9.0 N, 3.0 N
B) 0. 6.0 N   E) 12 N, 3.0 N
C) 3.0 N, 9.0 N

6. The coefficient of static friction between a certain cylinder and a horizontal floor is 0.40. If the rotational inertia of the cylinder about its symmetry axis is given by $I = (1/2)MR^2$, then the maximum acceleration the cylinder can have without slipping is:

A) 0.1 g   B) 0.2 g   C) 0.4 g   *D) 0.8 g   E) g

7. A thin-walled hollow tube rolls without slipping along the floor. The ratio of its translational kinetic energy to its rotational kinetic energy (about an axis through its center of mass) is:

*A) 1   B) 2   C) 3   D) 1/2   E) 1/3

8. A sphere and a cylinder of equal mass and radius are simultaneously released from rest on the same inclined plane. Then:

A) the sphere reaches the bottom first because it has the greater inertia
B) the cylinder reaches the bottom first because it picks up more rotational energy
C) the sphere reaches the bottom first because it picks up more rotational energy
D) they reach the bottom together
*E) none of the above is true

144

9. A hoop has a mass of 200 grams and a radius of 25 cm. It rolls
   without slipping along the ground at 500 cm/s. Its total kinetic
   energy is:

   A) 2.5 J
   *B) 5 J
   C) 10 J
   D) 250 J
   E) need to know the angular velocity

10. A yo-yo, arranged as shown, rests on a frictionless surface. When a
    force **F** is applied to the string as shown, the yo-yo:

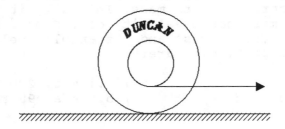

    A) moves to the left and rotates counterclockwise
   *B) moves to the right and rotates counterclockwise
    C) moves to the left and rotates clockwise
    D) moves to the right and rotates clockwise
    E) moves to the right and does not rotate

11. We may apply conservation of energy to a cylinder rolling down an
    incline without slipping and exclude friction because:

    A) there is no friction present
    B) the angular velocity of the center of mass about the point of
       contact is zero
    C) the coefficient of kinetic friction is zero
   *D) the linear velocity of the point of contact (relative to the
       inclined surface) is zero
    E) the coefficient of static and kinetic friction are equal

12. Two uniform cylinders have different masses and different rotational
    inertias. They simultaneously start from rest at the top of an
    inclined plane and roll without slipping down the plane. The
    cylinder that gets to the bottom first is:

    A) the one with the larger mass
    B) the one with the smaller mass
    C) the one with the larger rotational inertia
    D) the one with the smaller rotational inertia
   *E) neither (they arrive together)

13. A 5000-gram ball rolls from rest down an inclined plane. A 4900-gram block, mounted on roller bearings totaling 100 grams, rolls from rest down the same plane. At the bottom, the block has the:

 *A) greater speed
  B) smaller speed
  C) same speed as the ball
  D) depends on the angle of inclination
  E) depends on the radius of the ball

14. A cylinder of radius R = 6.0 cm is resting on a rough surface. The coefficient of kinetic friction between the cylinder and the surface is 0.30 and the rotational inertia for rotation about the axis is given by $MR^2/2$, where M is its mass. Initially it is not rotating but its center of mass has a velocity of 7.0 m/s. After 2.0 s the velocity of its center of mass and its angular velocity about its center of mass, respectively, are:

  A) 1.1 m/s, 0   *D) 1.1 m/s, 200 rad/s
  B) 1.1 m/s, 19 rad/s   E) 5.9 m/s, 98 rad/s
  C) 1.1 m/s, 98 rad/s

15. The fundamental dimensions of angular momentum are:

  A) MLT^{-1} D) ML^2T^{-2}
  B) $ML^{-2}T^{-2}$ E) none of these
 *C) ML^2T^{-1}

16. Typical units of angular momentum are:

  A) kg $\cdot$m/s   *D) kg $\cdot$m^2/s
  B) kg $\cdot$m^2/s^2 E) none of these
  C) kg $\cdot$m/s^2

17. The unit kg $\cdot$m^2/s can be used for:

 *A) angular momentum   D) torque
  B) rotational kinetic energy   E) power
  C) rotational inertia

18. The newton $\cdot$second is a unit of:

  A) work   *D) linear momentum
  B) angular momentum   E) none of these
  C) power

19. A 2.0-kg block travels around a 0.50-m radius circle with an angular velocity of 12 rad/s. It angular momentum about the center of the circle is:

*A) 6.0 kg ·m²/s   D) 72 kg ·m²/s²
 B) 12 kg ·m/s   E) 576 kg/m ·s²
 C) 48 kg/m ·s

20. The angular momentum vector of the earth, due to its daily rotation, is directed:

 A) tangent to the equator toward the east
 B) tangent to the equator toward the west
*C) due north
 D) due south
 E) toward the sun

21. A 6-kg particle moves to the right at 4 m/s as shown. Its angular momentum in kg ·m²/s² about the point O is:

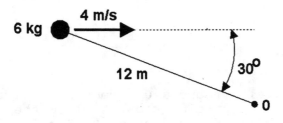

 A) zero   B) 288   *C) 144   D) 24   E) 249

22. Two objects are moving in the x-y plane as shown. The magnitude of their total angular momentum (about the origin O) is (in kg ·m²/s):

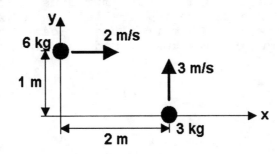

 A) zero   *B) 6   C) 12   D) 30   E) 78

147

23. A 2.0-kg block starts from rest on the x axis 3.0 m from the origin and thereafter has an acceleration given by $\mathbf{a} = 4.0\hat{\imath} - 3.0\hat{\jmath}$ in m/s^2. At the end of 2.0 s its angular momentum about the origin is:

A) 0
*B) $-36\ \hat{k}\ $ kg $\cdot$m^2/s
C) $48\ \hat{k}\ $ kg $\cdot$m^2/s
D) $-96\ \hat{k}\ $ kg $\cdot$m^2/s
E) $+96\ \hat{k}\ $ kg $\cdot$m^2

24. A 15-g paper clip is attached to the rim of a phonograph record with a radius of 30 cm, spinning at 3.5 rad/s. Its angular momentum in kg $\cdot$m2/s is:

A) 1.4×10^{-3}
*B) 4.7×10^{-3}
C) 1.6×10^{-2}
D) 3.2×10^{-1}
E) 1.1

25. A 2.0-kg block travels around a 0.50 m radius circle with an angular speed of 12 rad/s. The circle is parallel to the xy plane and is centered on the z axis, 0.75 m from the origin. The magnitude of the angular momentum around the origin is:

A) 6.0 kg $\cdot$m^2/s
B) 9.0 kg $\cdot$m^2/s
*C) 11 kg $\cdot$m^2/s
D) 14 kg $\cdot$m^2/s
E) 20 kg $\cdot$m^2/s

26. A 2.0-kg block travels around a 0.50 m radius circle with an angular speed of 12 rad/s. The circle is parallel to the xy plane and is centered on the z axis, a distance of 0.75 m from the origin. The z component of the angular momentum around the origin is:

*A) 6.0 kg $\cdot$m^2/s
B) 9.0 kg $\cdot$m^2/s
C) 11 kg $\cdot$m^2/s
D) 14 kg $\cdot$m^2/s
E) 20 kg $\cdot$m^2/s

27. A 2.0-kg block travels around a 0.50 m radius circle with an angular speed of 12 rad/s. The circle is parallel to the xy plane and is centered on the z axis, 0.75 m from the origin. The component in the xy plane of the angular momentum around the origin has magnitude:

A) 0
B) 6.0 kg $\cdot$m^2/s
*C) 9.0 kg $\cdot$m^2/s
D) 11 kg $\cdot$m^2/s
E) 14 kg $\cdot$m^2/s

28. A uniform disk has radius R and mass M. When it is spinning with angular velocity ω about an axis through its center and perpendicular to its face its angular momentum is $I\omega$. When it is spinning about a parallel axis a distance h away its angular momentum is

A) $I\omega$
*B) $(I + Mh^2)\omega$
C) $(I - Mh^2)\omega$
D) $(I + MR^2)\omega$
E) $(I - MR^2)\omega$

29. A pulley with radius R and rotational inertia I is free to rotate on a horizontal fixed axis through its center. A string passes over the pulley. Mass m_1 is attached to one end and mass m_2 is attached to the other. At one time m_1 is moving downward with speed v. If the string does not slip on the pulley the magnitude of the total angular momentum, about the pulley center, of the masses and pulley, considered as a system, is given by:

A) $(m_1 - m_2)vR + Iv/R$
*B) $(m_1 + m_2)vR + Iv/R$
C) $(m_1 - m_2)vR - Iv/R$
D) $(m_1 + m_2)vR - Iv/R$
E) none of the above

30. A rod rests on frictionless ice. While forces that are equal in magnitude and opposite in direction are simultaneously applied to its ends as shown, the quantity that vanishes is its:

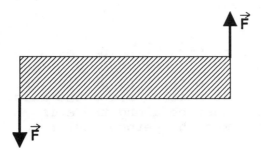

A) angular momentum
B) angular acceleration
*C) total linear momentum
D) kinetic energy
E) rotational inertia

31. A 2.0-kg stone is tied to a 0.50-m string and swung around a circle at a constant angular velocity of 12 rad/s. The torque on the stone about the center of the circle is:

*A) 0   B) 6.0 N ·m   C) 12 N ·m   D) 72 N ·m   E) 140 N ·m

32. A 2.0-kg stone is tied to a 0.50 m string and swung around a circle at a constant angular velocity of 12 rad/s. The circle is parallel to the xy plane and is centered on the z axis, 0.75 m from the origin. The magnitude of the torque about the origin is:

*A) 0   B) 9.8 N ·m   C) 15 N ·m   D) 26 N ·m   E) 39 N ·m

33. A 2.0-kg block starts from rest on the x axis 3.0 m from the origin and thereafter has an acceleration given by $\mathbf{a} = 4.0\hat{\imath} - 3.0\hat{\jmath}$ in m/s^2. The torque, relative to the origin, acting on it at the end of 2.0 s is:

A) 0
*B) -12 $\hat{k}$ N ·m
C) 24 $\hat{k}$ N ·m
D) -144 $\hat{k}$ N ·m
E) $+144$ $\hat{k}$ N ·m

34. A pulley with radius R is free to rotate on a horizontal fixed axis through its center. A string passes over the pulley. Mass m_1 is attached to one end and mass m_2 is attached to the other. The portion of the string attached to m_1 has tension T_1 and the portion attached to m_2 has tension T_2. The magnitude of the total external torque, about the pulley center, acting on the masses and pulley, considered as a system, is given by:

*A) $|m_1 - m_2|gR$
B) $(m_1 + m_2)gR$
C) $|m_1 - m_2|gR + (T_1 + T_2)R$
D) $(m_1 + m_2)gR + (T_1 - T_2)R$
E) $|m_1 - m_2|gR + (T_2 - T_1)R$

35. If a body is spinning about a principal axis then:

A) the torque acting on it must be perpendicular to the axis
B) the torque acting on it must be along the axis
*C) its angular momentum must be along the axis
D) its angular momentum must he perpendicular to the axis
E) none of the above

36. If a body is spinning about a principal axis then:

A) the torque and angular momentum are in the same direction
B) the force and angular momentum are in the same direction
C) the angular velocity vector and the torque are in the same direction
*D) the angular velocity vector and the angular momentum are in the same direction
E) the torque and angular velocity vector are in the same direction

37. An ice skater with rotational inertia I_0 is spinning with angular speed ω_0. She pulls her arms in, decreasing her rotational inertia to $I_0/3$. Her angular speed becomes:

A) $\omega_0/3$ B) $\omega_0/\sqrt{3}$ C) ω_0 D) $\sqrt{3}\omega_0$ *E) $3\omega_0$

150

38. A man, with his arms at his sides, is spinning on a light frictionless turntable. When he extends his arms:

  A) his angular velocity increases
  B) his angular velocity remains the same
  C) his rotational inertia decreases
  D) his rotational kinetic energy increases
 *E) his angular momentum remains the same

39. A man, holding a weight in each hand, stands at the center of a horizontal frictionless rotating turntable. The effect of the weights is to double the rotational inertia of the system. As he is rotating, the man opens his hands and drops the two weights. They fall outside the turntable. Then:

  A) his angular velocity doubles
 *B) his angular velocity remains about the same
  C) his angular velocity is halved
  D) the direction of his angular momentum vector changes
  E) his rotational kinetic energy increases

40. A uniform sphere of radius R rotates about a diameter with angular momentum L. Under the action of internal forces the sphere collapses to a uniform sphere of radius R/2. Its new angular momentum is:

  A) L/4   B) L/2   *C) L   D) 2L   E) 4L

41. When a man on a frictionless rotating stool extends his arms horizontally, his rotational kinetic energy:

  A) must increase
 *B) must decrease
  C) must remain the same
  D) may increase or decrease depending on his initial angular velocity
  E) may increase or decrease depending on his gravitational potential energy

42. When a woman on a frictionless rotating turntable extends her arms out horizontally, her angular momentum

  A) must increase
  B) must decrease
 *C) must remain the same
  D) may increase or decrease depending on her initial angular velocity
  E) tilts away from the vertical

43. Two disks are mounted on low friction bearings on a common shaft.
The first disc has rotational inertia I and is spinning with angular
velocity ω. The second disc has rotational inertia 2I and is
spinning (in the same direction as the first disc) with angular
velocity 2ω as shown. The two disks are slowly forced toward each
other along the shaft until they couple and have a final common
angular velocity of:

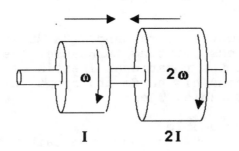

A) $5\omega/3$ B) $\omega\sqrt{3}$ C) $\omega\sqrt{7/3}$ D) ω E) 3ω

Ans. a

44. A wheel, mounted on a vertical shaft of negligible rotational
inertia, is rotating at 500 rpm. Another identical (but not
rotating) wheel is suddenly dropped onto the same shaft as shown.
The resultant combination of the two wheels and shaft will rotate
at:

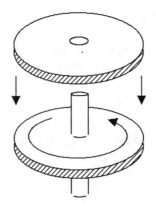

*A) 250 rpm   B) 354 rpm   C) 500 rpm   D) 707 rpm   E) 1000 rpm

45. A phonograph record is dropped onto a freely spinning turntable. Then:

   A) neither angular momentum nor mechanical energy is conserved because of the frictional forces between record and turntable
   B) the frictional force between record and turntable increases the total angular momentum
   C) the frictional force between record and turntable decreases the total angular momentum
  *D) the total angular momentum remains constant
   E) the sum of the angular momentum and rotational kinetic energy remains constant

46. A playground merry-go-round has a radius of 3.0 m and a rotational inertia of 600 kg $\cdot m^2$. When the merry-go-round is at rest, a 20-kg child runs at 5.0 m/s along a line tangent to the rim and jumps on. The angular velocity of the merry-go-round is then:

  *A) 0.38 rad/s   D) 0.56 rad/s
   B) 0.45 rad/s   E) 1.2 rad/s
   C) 0.71 rad/s

47. A playground merry-go-round has a radius of 3.0 m and a rotational inertia of 600 kg $\cdot m^2$. It is initially spinning at 0.80 rad/s when a 20-kg child crawls from the center to the rim. When the child reaches the rim the angular velocity of the merry-go-round is:

  *A) 0.61 rad/s   D) 0.89 rad/s
   B) 0.73 rad/s   E) 1.1 rad/s
   C) 0.80 rad/s

48. Two pendulum bobs of unequal mass are made of perfectly elastic material. They are suspended from the same fixed point by strings of equal length. The lighter bob is drawn aside and then released so that it collides with the other bob on reaching the vertical position. What quantities are conserved in this collision?

  *A) both kinetic energy and angular momentum of the system
   B) only kinetic energy
   C) only angular momentum
   D) angular speed of lighter bob
   E) none of the above

49. A particle, held by a string whose other end is attached to a fixed point C, moves in a circle on a horizontal frictionless surface. the string is cut, the angular momentum of the particle about the point C:

   A) increases
   B) decreases
  *C) does not change
   D) changes direction but not magnitude
   E) none of these

50. An object M, on the end of a string, moves in a circle on a horizontal frictionless table as shown. As the string is slowly pulled through a small hole in the table:

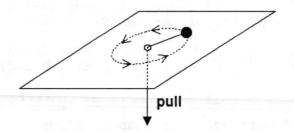

pull

  *A) the angular momentum of M remains constant
   B) the angular momentum of M decreases
   C) the kinetic energy of M remains constant
   D) the kinetic energy of M decreases
   E) none of the above

51. A top spinning on the floor precesses because the torque due to gravity, about the point of contact of the top with the floor, is

   A) parallel to the angular momentum
   B) parallel to the angular velocity vector
   C) parallel to the axis of rotation
   D) perpendicular to the floor
  *E) none of the above

52. The precessional angular velocity of a spinning top increases if:

   A) its spin angular velocity increases
   B) it leans at a larger angle to the vertical
   C) it leans at a smaller angle to the vertical
   D) its rotational inertia increases without a change in mass
  *E) its rotational inertia decreases without a change in mass

1. A torque applied to a rigid object always tends to produce:

A) linear acceleration
B) rotational equilibrium
*C) rotational acceleration
D) precession
E) none of these

2. The conditions that the sum of forces and the sum of the torques both vanish:

*A) hold for every solid body in equilibrium
B) hold only for elastic solid bodies in equilibrium
C) hold for every solid body
D) are always sufficient to calculate the forces on a solid object in equilibrium
E) are sufficient to calculate the forces on a solid object in equilibrium only if the object is elastic

3. For an object in equilibrium the sum of the torques acting on it vanishes only if each torque is calculated about:

A) the center of mass
B) the center of gravity
C) the geometrical center
D) the point of application of the force
*E) the same point

4. A body is in equilibrium under the combined action of several forces. Then:

A) all the forces must be applied at the same point
B) all of the forces are composed of pairs of equal and opposite forces
*C) the sum of the components of all the forces in any direction must equal zero
D) any two of these forces must be balanced by a third force
E) the lines of action of all the forces must pass through the center of gravity of the body

5. A body is in equilibrium under the combined action of several forces. Then:

A) all the forces must be applied at the same point
B) all of the forces are composed of pairs of equal and opposite forces
C) any two of these forces must be balanced by a third force
*D) the sum of the torques about any point must equal zero
E) the lines of action of all the forces must pass through the center of gravity of the body

6. To determine if a rigid body is in equilibrium the vector sum of the gravitational forces acting on the particles of the body can be replaced by a single force acting at:

A) the center of mass
B) the geometrical center
*C) the center of gravity
D) a point on the boundary
E) none of the above

7. The center of gravity coincides with the center of mass:

A) always
B) never
C) if the center of mass is at the geometrical center of the body
*D) if the acceleration due to gravity is uniform over the body
E) if the body has a uniform distribution of mass

8. The location of which of the following points within an object might depend on the orientation of the object?

A) Its center of mass
*B) Its center of gravity
C) Its geometrical center
D) Its center of momentum
E) None of the above

9. A cylinder placed so it can roll on a horizontal table top, with its center of gravity above its geometrical center, is:

A) in stable equilibrium
*B) in unstable equilibrium
C) in neutral equilibrium
D) not in equilibrium
E) none of the above

10. A cylinder placed so it can roll on a horizontal table top, with its center of gravity below its geometrical center, is:

*A) in stable equilibrium
B) in unstable equilibrium
C) in neutral equilibrium
D) not in equilibrium
E) none of the above

11. A cube balanced with one edge in contact with a table top and with its center of gravity directly above the edge is in _____ equilibrium with respect to rotation about the edge and in _____ equilibrium with respect to rotation about a horizontal axis that is perpendicular to the edge.

A) stable, stable
B) stable, unstable
*C) unstable, stable
D) unstable, unstable
E) unstable, neutral

12. A 40-lb child sits in a light swing and is pulled sideways and held with a horizontal force of 25 lb. The tension in each of the two supporting ropes is:

A) 47.2 lb   B) 65.0 lb   C) 15.0 lb   *D) 23.6 lb   E) 31.2 lb

13. A picture P of weight W is hung by two strings as shown. The total upward pull of the strings on the picture is:

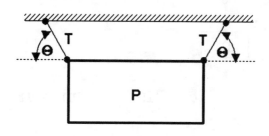

A) 2W cosθ   B) T sinθ   C) T cosθ   *D) 2T sinθ   E) 2T cosθ

14. A picture can be hung on a wall in three different ways as shown. The tension in the string is:

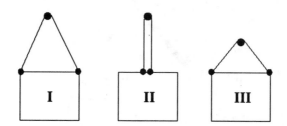

A) least in I
B) least in III
C) greatest in I

D) greatest in III
*E) greatest in II

15. A uniform plank XY is supported by two equal 120-N forces at X and Y, as shown. The support at X is then moved to Z (half-way to the plank center). The supporting force at Y then becomes:

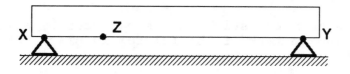

A) 240 N   B) 160 N   *C) 80 N   D) 60 N   E) 40 N

16. A uniform rod AB is 3 ft long and weighs 4 lb. It is suspended by strings AC and BD as shown. A block P weighing 24 lb is attached at E, 3/4 ft from A. The tension in the string BD is:

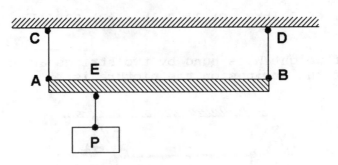

A) 20 lb   *B) 8 lb   C) 2 lb   D) 6 lb   E) 12 lb

17. A 5-ft weightless strut, hinged to a wall, is used to support a 200-lb block as shown. The tension in the horizontal rope is:

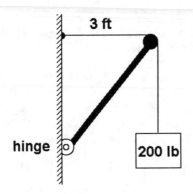

A) 100 lb   *B) 150 lb   C) 200 lb   D) 250 lb   E) 300 lb

18. A uniform plank is 12 ft long and weighs 20 lb. It is balanced on a sawhorse at its center. An additional 40 lb weight is now placed on the left end of the plank. To keep the plank balanced, it must be moved what distance to the right?

*A) 4 ft   B) 3 ft   C) 2 ft   D) 3.43 ft   E) 1 ft

19. A uniform 240-gram meter stick can be balanced by a 240-gram weight placed at the 100-cm mark if the fulcrum is placed at the point marked:

*A) 75 cm   B) 60 cm   C) 50 cm   D) 40 cm   E) 80 cm

20. A ladder leans against a wall. If the ladder is not to slip, which one of the following must be true?

  A) the coefficient of friction between the ladder and the wall must not be zero
*B) the coefficient of friction between the ladder and the floor must not be zero
  C) both a and b
  D) either a or b
  E) neither a nor b

21. A 240-lb man stands halfway up a 13-ft ladder of negligible weight. The base of the ladder is 5 ft from the wall as shown. Assuming that the wall-ladder contact is frictionless, the wall pushes against the ladder with a force of:

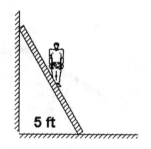

5 ft

A) 26 lb   *B) 50 lb   C) 67 lb   D) 78 lb   E) 100 lb

22. A 20-lb uniform plank leans against a frictionless wall as shown.
    The torque (about point P) applied to the plank by the wall is:

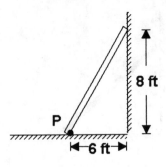

A) 20 lb ·ft
*B) 60 lb ·ft
C) 120 lb ·ft

D) 30 lb ·ft
E) 40 lb ·ft

23. A uniform ladder is 30 ft long and weighs 100 lb. It rests with its
    upper end against a frictionless vertical wall. Its lower end rests
    on the ground and is prevented from slipping by a peg driven into
    the ground. The ladder makes a 30° angle with the horizontal. The
    force exerted on the wall by the ladder is:

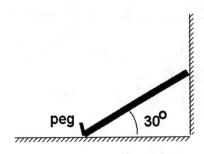

*A) 86.6 lb   B) 12 lb   C) 18.3 lb   D) 150 lb   E) 28.9 lb

24. A window washer attempts to lean a ladder against a frictionless
    wall. He finds that the ladder slips on the ground when it is placed
    at an angle of less than 75° to the ground but remains in place when
    the angle is greater than 75°. The coefficient of static friction
    between the ladder and the ground:

*A) is about 0.13
 B) is about 1.0
 C) is about 1.3
 D) depends on the mass of the ladder
 E) depends on the length of the ladder

25. The 150-lb ball shown is suspended on a string AC and rests against the frictionless vertical wall AB. The string makes an angle of 30° with the wall. The tension in the string is:

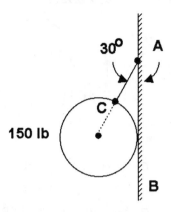

*A) 173 lb
 B) 520 lb
 C) 300 lb

D) 600 lb
E) none of these

26. The 150-lb ball shown is suspended on a string AC and rests against the frictionless vertical wall AB. The string makes an angle of 30° with the wall. The ball presses against the wall with a force of:

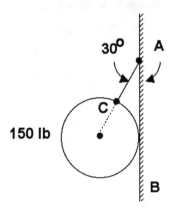

A) 30 lb   B) 75 lb   *C) 87 lb   D) 150 lb   E) 173 lb

27. A 60-lb weight is hung from two ropes as shown. The tension in the horizontal rope is:

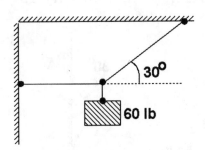

   A) zero   B) 164 lb   C) 120 lb   *D) 104 lb   E) 44 lb

28. A 240-lb block is suspended as shown. The beam AB is weightless and is hinged to the wall at A. The tension in the cable BC is:

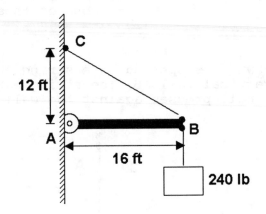

A) 300 lb   *D) 400 lb
B) 320 lb   E) none of these
C) 180 lb

162

29. A horizontal beam of weight W is supported by a hinge and cable as shown. The force exerted on the beam by the hinge has a vertical component which must be:

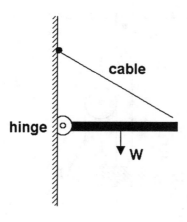

*A) nonzero and up
 B) nonzero and down
 C) nonzero but not enough information given to know whether up or down
 D) zero
 E) equal to W

30. A 100-lb uniform vertical boom is attached to the ceiling by a hinge, as shown. A 200-lb weight W and a horizontal guy wire are attached to the lower end of the boom as indicated. The tension T in the horizontal guy wire is:

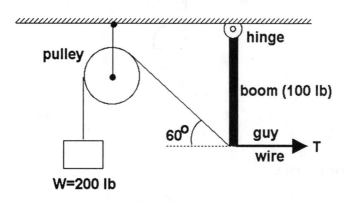

A) 86 lb   *B) 100 lb   C) 172 lb   D) 200 lb   E) 300 lb

163

31. The pull P is just sufficient to keep the 14-lb block and the weightless pulleys in equilibrium as shown. The tension T in the upper cable is:

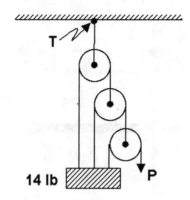

A) 14 lb   B) 28 lb   *C) 16 lb   D) 9.33 lb   E) 18.7 lb

32. The ideal mechanical advantage (i.e. the ratio of the weight W to the pull P for equilibrium) of the combination of pulleys shown is:

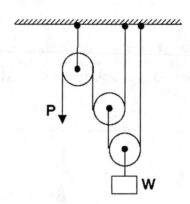

A) 1   B) 2   C) 3   *D) 4   E) 5

33. Stress can be measured in:

*A) N/m^2 D) $N \cdot m$
 B) $N \cdot m^2$ E) none of these (it is unitless)
 C) N/m

34. Strain can be measured in:

 A) N/m^2 D) $N \cdot m$
 B) $N \cdot m^2$ *E) none of these (it is unitless)
 C) N/m

164

35. Young's modulus can be correctly given in:

   A) ft ·lb
   B) lb/ft^2
   C) ft ·lb/s

   *D) newton/meter
   E) joule

36. Young's modulus is a proportionality constant that relates the force per unit area applied perpendicularly at the surface of an object to:

   A) the shear
   B) the fractional change in volume
   *C) the fractional change in length
   D) the pressure
   E) the spring constant

37. Young's modulus can be used to calculate the strain for a stress that is:

   A) just below the ultimate strength
   B) just above the ultimate strength
   *C) well below the yield strength
   D) well above the yield strength
   E) none of the above

38. The ultimate strength of a sample is the stress at which the sample:

   A) returns to its original shape when the stress is removed
   B) remains underwater
   *C) breaks
   D) bends 180°
   E) does none of these

39. A certain wire stretches 1 cm when a force F is applied to it. The same force is applied to a wire of the same material but with twice the diameter and twice the length. The second wire stretches:

   A) 0.25 cm   *B) 0.5 cm   C) 1 cm   D) 2 cm   E) 4 cm

40. A force of 5000 N is applied outwardly to each end of a 5.0-m long rod with a radius of 34.0 cm and a Young's modulus of 125x10^8 N/m^2. The elongation in mm of the rod is:

   A) 0.0020   B) 0.0040   C) 0.14   *D) 0.71   E) 1.42

41. A 4.0 m steel beam with a cross sectional area of 1.0×10^{-2} m^2 and a Young's modulus of 2.0×10^{11} N/m^2 is wedged horizontally between two vertical walls. In order to wedge the beam, it is compressed by 0.020 mm. If the coefficient of static friction between the beam and the walls is 0.70, the maximum mass (including its own) it can bear without slipping is:

A) 0
B) 1.1×10^4 kg
*C) 2.3×10^4 kg
D) 3.3×10^4 kg
E) 4.6×10^4 kg

42. Two supports, made of the same material and initially of equal length, are 2.0 m apart. A stiff board with a length of 4.0 m and a mass of 10 kg is placed on the supports, with one support at the left end and the other at the midpoint. A 20-kg block is placed on the board in such a way that the board is horizontal. The distance from the left end of the board to the block is:

A) 0   *B) 0.5 m   C) 1.0 m   D) 1.5 m   E) 2.0 m

43. The bulk modulus is a proportionality constant that relates the pressure acting on an object to:

A) the shear
*B) the fractional change in volume
C) the fractional change in length
D) Young's modulus
E) the spring constant

44. A cube with edges exactly 2 cm long is made of material with a bulk modulus of 3.5×10^9 N/m^2. When it is subjected to a pressure of 3.0×10^5 Pa its volume in cm^3 is:

A) 7.31
*B) 7.99931
C) 8.00069
D) 8.69
E) none of these

45. A cube with 2.0-cm sides is made of material with a bulk modulus of 4.7×10^5 N/m^2. When it is subjected to a pressure of 2.0×10^5 Pa the length in cm of its any of its sides is:

A) 0.85
B) 1.15
*C) 1.66
D) 2.0
E) none of these

46. To shear a cube-shaped object, forces of equal magnitude and
    opposite directions might be applied:

   A) to opposite faces, perpendicular to the faces
  *B) to opposite faces, parallel to the faces
   C) to adjacent faces, perpendicular to the faces
   D) to adjacent faces, neither parallel or perpendicular to the faces
   E) to a single face, in any direction

47. A shearing force of 50 N is applied to an aluminum rod with a cross
    section area of 1.0×10^{-5} m and a shear modulus of 2.5×10^{10} N/m^2. As
    a result the rod is sheared through an angle (in degrees) of:

   A) 0   *B) 1.1×10^{-2} C) 0.11   D) 1.1   E) 11

1. In simple harmonic motion, the restoring force must be proportional to the:

A) amplitude
B) frequency
C) velocity
*D) displacement
E) displacement squared

2. An oscillatory motion must be simple harmonic if:

A) the amplitude is small
B) the potential energy is equal to the kinetic energy
C) the motion is along the arc of a circle
*D) the acceleration varies sinusoidally with time
E) the derivative, dU/dx, of the potential energy is negative

3. In simple harmonic motion, the magnitude of the acceleration is:

A) constant
*B) proportional to the displacement
C) inversely proportional to the displacement
D) greatest when the velocity is greatest
E) never greater than g

4. A particle oscillating in simple harmonic motion is:

A) never in equilibrium because it is in motion
B) never in equilibrium because there is a force
C) in equilibrium at the ends of its path because its velocity is zero there
*D) in equilibrium at the center of its path because the acceleration is zero there
E) in equilibrium at the ends of its path because the acceleration is zero there

5. An object is undergoing simple harmonic motion. Throughout one complete cycle it:

A) has constant speed
B) has varying amplitude
C) has varying period
*D) has varying acceleration
E) has varying mass

6. When a body executes simple harmonic motion, its acceleration at the ends of its path must be:

A) zero
B) less than g
C) more than g

D) suddenly changing in sign
*E) none of these

7. An object attached to one end of a spring makes 20 vibrations in 10 seconds. Its period is:

A) 2 Hz   B) 10 s   C) 0.05 Hz   D) 2 s   *E) 0.50 s

8. An object attached to one end of a spring makes 20 vibrations in 10 seconds. Its frequency is:

*A) 2 Hz   B) 10 s   C) 0.05 Hz   D) 2 s   E) 0.50 s

9. An object attached to one end of a spring makes 20 vibrations in 10 seconds. Its angular frequency is:

A) 0.79 rad/s
B) 1.57 rad/s
C) 2.0 rad/s

D) 6.3 rad/s
*E) 12.6 rad/s

10. Frequency f and angular frequency ω are related by

A) $f = \pi\omega$ B) $f = 2\pi\omega$ C) $f = \omega/\pi$ *D) $f = \omega/2\pi$ E) $f = 2\omega/\pi$

11. A block attached to a spring oscillates in simple harmonic motion along the x axis. The limits of its motion are x = 10 cm and x = 50 cm and it goes from one of these extremes to the other in 0.25 s. Its amplitude and frequency are:

A) 40 cm, 2 Hz
*B) 20 cm, 4 Hz
C) 40 cm, 2 Hz

D) 25 cm. 4 Hz
E) 20 cm, 2 Hz

12. A weight suspended from an ideal spring oscillates up and down. If the amplitude of the oscillation is doubled, the period will:

*A) remain the same
B)
   increase by a factor of $\sqrt{2}$
C) double

D) halve
E)
   decrease by a factor of $\sqrt{2}$

169

13. In simple harmonic motion, the magnitude of the acceleration is greatest when the:

  A) displacement is zero   D) force is zero
*B) displacement is maximum   E) none of these
  C) velocity is maximum

14. In simple harmonic motion, the displacement is maximum when the:

  A) acceleration is zero   D) kinetic energy is maximum
  B) velocity is maximum   E) momentum is maximum
*C) velocity is zero

15. In simple harmonic motion:

*A) the acceleration is greatest at the maximum displacement
  B) the velocity is greatest at the maximum displacement
  C) the period depends on the amplitude
  D) the acceleration is constant
  E) the acceleration is greatest at zero displacement

16. The amplitude and phase constant of an oscillator are determined by:

  A) the frequency
  B) the angular frequency
  C) the initial displacement alone
  D) the initial velocity alone
*E) both the initial displacement and velocity

17. Two identical undamped oscillators have the same amplitude of oscillation only if:

  A) they are started with the same displacement x_o
  B) they are started with the same velocity v_o
  C) they are started with the same phase
*D)
    they are started so the combination $\omega^2 x_o^2 + v_o^2$ is the same

  E)
    they are started so the combination $x_o^2 + \omega^2 v_o^2$ is the same

18. The amplitude of any oscillator can be doubled by:

  A) doubling only the initial displacement
  B) doubling only the initial speed
  C) doubling the initial displacement and halving the initial speed
  D) doubling the initial speed and halving the initial displacement
*E) doubling both the initial displacement and the initial speed

19. It is impossible for two particles, each executing simple harmonic motion, to remain in phase with each other if they have different:

  A) masses
  *B) periods
  C) amplitudes

  D) spring constants
  E) kinetic energies

20. The acceleration of a body executing simple harmonic motion leads the velocity by what phase?

  A) 0   B) $\pi/8$ rad   C) $\pi/4$ rad   *D) $\pi/2$ rad   E) π rad

21. The displacement of a mass oscillating on a spring is given by $x(t) = x_m\cos(\omega t + \Phi)$. If the initial displacement is zero and the initial velocity is in the negative x direction, then the phase constant Φ is:

  A) 0
  *B) $\pi/2$ radians
  C) π radians

  D) $3\pi/2$ radians
  E) 2π radians

22. The displacement of a mass oscillating on a spring is given by $x(t) = x_m\cos(\omega t + \Phi)$. If the mass is initially displaced in the negative x direction and given a positive initial velocity, then the phase constant Φ is between:

  A) 0 and $\pi/2$ radians
  B) $\pi/2$ and π radians
  C) π and $3\pi/2$ radians
  *D) $3\pi/2$ and 2π radians
  E) none of the above (Φ is exactly 0, $\pi/2$, π, or $3\pi/2$ radians)

23. A certain spring elongates 9 mm when it is suspended vertically and a block of mass M is hung on it. The natural frequency of this mass-spring system is:

  A) 0.014
  *B) 5.3 Hz
  C) 31.8 Hz

  D) 181.7 Hz
  E) need to know M

24. Mass m oscillating on the end of a spring with spring constant k has amplitude A. Its maximum speed is:

$$A) A\sqrt{k/m} \quad B) A^2k/m \quad C) A\sqrt{m/k} \quad D) Am/k \quad E) A^2m/k$$

Ans. a

25. A 0.200-kg mass attached to a spring whose spring constant is 500 N/m executes simple harmonic motion with amplitude 0.100 m. Its maximum speed is:

A) 25 m/s   *B) 5 m/s   C) 1 m/s   D) 15.8 m/s   E) 0.2 m/s

26. A simple harmonic oscillator consists of a mass and spring (m, k). It oscillates as shown in (i) with period T. If the spring is cut in half and used with the same mass m, as shown in (ii), the period will be:

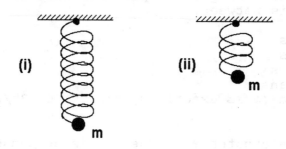

A) 2T   B) $\sqrt{2}T$ *C) $T/\sqrt{2}$ D) T   E) T/2

27. A particle moves in simple harmonic motion according to x = 2cos(50t), where x is in meters and t is in seconds. Its maximum velocity in m/s is:

A) 100 sin(50t)   D) 200
B) 100 cos(50t)   E) none of these
*C) 100

172

28. A 3-kg block, attached to a spring, executes simple harmonic motion according to $x = 2\cos(50t)$ where x is in meters and t is in seconds. The spring constant of the spring is:

A) 1 N/m
B) 100 N/m
C) 150 N/m

*D) 7500 N/m
E) none of these

29. Let U be the potential energy (with the zero at zero displacement) and K be the kinetic energy of a simple harmonic oscillator. A "bar" over a symbol denotes its average value over a cycle. Then:

A) $\bar{K} > \bar{U}$
B) $\bar{K} < \bar{U}$
*C) $\bar{K} = \bar{U}$

D) K = 0 when U = 0
E) K + U = 0

30. A 0.25-kg block oscillates on the end of the spring with a spring constant of 200 N/m. If the system has an energy of 6.0 J, then the amplitude of the oscillation is:

A) 0.06 m   B) 0.17 m   *C) 0.24 m   D) 4.9 m   E) 6.9 m

31. A 0.25-kg block oscillates on the end of the spring with a spring constant of 200 N/m. If the system has an energy of 6.0 J, then the maximum speed of the block is:

A) 0.06 m/s   B) 0.17 m/s   C) 0.24 m/s   D) 4.9 m/s   *E) 6.9 m/s

32. A 0.25-kg block oscillates on the end of the spring with a spring constant of 200 N/m. If the oscillation is started by elongating the spring 0.15 m and giving the block a speed of 3.0 m/s, then the maximum speed of the block is:

A) 0.13 m/s   B) 0.18 m/s   C) 3.7 m/s   *D) 5.2 m/s   E) 13 m/s

33. A 0.25-kg block oscillates on the end of the spring with a spring constant of 200 N/m. If the oscillation is started by elongating the spring 0.15 m and giving the block a speed of 3.0 m/s, then the amplitude of the oscillation is:

A) 0.13 m   *B) 0.18 m   C) 3.7 m   D) 5.2 m   E) 13 m

34. A mass on the end of a spring is set into oscillation by giving it an initial velocity while it is at its equilibrium position. In the first trial the initial velocity is v_0 and in the second it is $4v_0$. In the second trial:

   A) the amplitude is half as great and the maximum acceleration is twice as great
   B) the amplitude is twice as great and the maximum acceleration is half as great
  *C) both the amplitude and the maximum acceleration are twice as great
   D) both the amplitude and the maximum acceleration are four times as great
   E) the amplitude is four times as great and the maximum acceleration is twice as great

35. A block attached to a spring undergoes simple harmonic motion on a horizontal frictionless surface. Its total energy is 50 J. When the displacement is half the amplitude, the kinetic energy is:

   A) zero   B) 12.5 J   C) 25 J   *D) 37.5 J   E) 50 J

36. A mass-spring system is oscillating with amplitude A. The kinetic energy will equal the potential energy only when the displacement is

   A) zero   D) $\pm A/2$
   B) $\pm A/4$ E) anywhere between $-A$ and $+A$
  *C)
       $\pm A/\sqrt{2}$

37. If the length of a simple pendulum is doubled, its period will:

   A) halve   D) remain the same
  *B) double   E)
   C)   decrease by a factor of $\sqrt{2}$
       increase by a factor of $\sqrt{2}$

38. The period of a simple pendulum is 1 s on earth. When brought to a planet where g is one-tenth that on earth, its period becomes:

   A) 1s   B) $1/\sqrt{10}$s   C) 1/10s   D) $\sqrt{10}$s   E) 10s

Ans. d

39. The amplitude of oscillation of a simple pendulum is increased from 1° to 4°. Its maximum acceleration changes by a factor of:

A) 1/4   B) 1/2   C) 2   *D) 4   E) 16

40. A simple pendulum has a frequency of 3 Hz. To increase its frequency to 6 Hz:

A) increase its length by factor of 4
B) increase its length by factor of 2
C) decrease its length by factor of 2
*D) decrease its length by factor of 4
E) decrease its mass by factor of 4

41. A simple pendulum consists of a mass tied to a string and set in oscillation. As the pendulum swings the tension in the string is:

A) constant
B) a sinusoidal function of time
C) the square of a sinusoidal function of time
D) the reciprocal of a sinusoidal function of time
*E) none of the above

42. A simple pendulum has length L and period T. As it passes through its equilibrium position, the string is suddenly clamped at its mid-point. The period then becomes:

A) 2T   D) T/4
B) T   *E) none of these
C) T/2

43. A simple pendulum is suspended from the ceiling of an elevator. The elevator is accelerating upwards with acceleration a. The period of this pendulum, in terms of its length L, g and a is:

A) $2\pi\sqrt{L/g}$ B) $2\pi\sqrt{L/(g+a)}$ C) $2\pi\sqrt{L/(g-a)}$ D) $2\pi\sqrt{L/a}$ E) $(1/2\pi)\sqrt{g/L}$

Ans. b

175

44. The rotational inertia of a uniform thin rod about its end is $ML^2/3$, where M is the mass and L is the length. Such a rod is hung vertically from one end and set into small amplitude oscillation. If L = 1.0 m and M = 200 gram, this rod will have the same period as a simple pendulum of length:

A) 33 cm   B) 50 cm   *C) 67 cm   D) 100 cm   E) 150 cm

45. Two uniform spheres are pivoted on horizontal axes that are tangent to their surfaces. The one with the longer period of oscillation is the one with:

A) the larger mass   D) the smaller rotational inertia
B) the smaller mass   *E) the larger radius
C) the larger rotational inertia

46. Both the x and y coordinates of a point execute simple harmonic motion. The result might be a circular orbit if:

A) the amplitudes are the same but the frequencies are different
*B) the amplitudes and frequencies are both the same
C) the amplitudes and frequencies are both different
D) the phase constants are the same but the amplitudes are different
E) the amplitudes and the phase constants are both different

47. Both the x and y coordinates of a point execute simple harmonic motion. The frequencies are the same but the amplitudes are different. The resulting orbit might be:

*A) an ellipse   D) a hyperbola
B) a circle   E) none of the above
C) a parabola

48. For an oscillator subjected to a damping force proportional to its velocity:

A) the displacement is a sinusoidal function of time
B) the velocity is a sinusoidal function of time
C) the frequency is a decreasing function of time
D) the mechanical energy is constant
*E) none of the above is true

49. A sinusoidal force with a given amplitude is applied to an oscillator. To maintain the largest amplitude oscillation the frequency of the applied force should be:

  A) half the natural frequency of the oscillator
 *B) the same as the natural frequency of the oscillator
  C) twice the natural frequency of the oscillator
  D) unrelated to the natural frequency of the oscillator
  E) determined from the maximum speed desired

50. A sinusoidal force with a given amplitude is applied to an oscillator. At resonance the amplitude of the oscillation is limited by:

 *A) the damping force
  B) the initial amplitude
  C) the initial velocity

  D) the force of gravity
  E) none of the above

1. In the formula $F = Gm_1m_2/r^2$, the quantity G:

A) depends on the local value of g
B) is used only when the earth is one of the two masses
C) is greatest at the surface of the earth
*D) is a universal constant of nature
E) is related to the sun in the same way that g is related to the earth

2. The magnitude of the acceleration of a planet in orbit around the sun is proportional to:

A) the mass of the planet
*B) the mass of the sun
C) the distance between the planet and the sun
D) the reciprocal of the distance between the planet and the sun
E) the product of the mass of the planet and the mass of the sun

3. Suitable units for the gravitational constant G are:

A) $kg \cdot m/s^2$
B) m/s^2
C) $N \cdot s/m$

D) $kg \cdot m/s$
*E) $m^3/(kg \cdot s^2)$

4. The gravitational constant G has the derived units

A) $N \cdot m$ B) $N \cdot m/kg$ C) $N \cdot kg/m$ *D) $N \cdot m^2/kg^2$ E) $N \cdot kg^2/m^2$

5. The earth exerts a gravitational force on the moon, keeping it in its orbit. The reaction to this force, in the sense of Newton's third law, is:

A) the centripetal force on the moon
B) the nearly circular orbit of the moon
*C) the gravitational force exerted on the earth by the moon
D) the tides due to the moon
E) the apple hitting Newton on the head

6. Let F_1 be the magnitude of the gravitational force exerted on the sun by the earth and F_2 be the magnitude of the force exerted on the earth by the sun. Then:

A) F_1 is much greater than F_2
B) F_1 is slightly greater than F_2
*C) F_1 is equal to F_2

D) F_1 is slightly less than F_2
E) F_1 is much less than F_2

7. Let M denote the mass of the earth and let R denote its radius. The ratio g/G at the earth's surface is:

A) R^2/M *B) M/R^2 C) MR^2 D) M/R E) R/M

8. Mars has about 1/10 the mass of the earth and about 1/2 the diameter of the earth. The acceleration (in ft/s^2) of a falling body on Mars is about:

A) 32
B) 6.4
*C) 13

D) 16
E) none of these

9. The approximate value of g (in m/s^2) at an altitude above the earth equal to one earth diameter is:

A) 9.8   B) 4.9   C) 2.5   D) 1.9   *E) 1.1

10. A rocket ship is coasting toward a planet. Its captain wishes to know the value of g at the surface of the planet. This may be inferred by:

A) measuring the apparent weight of one of the crew
B) measuring the apparent weight of an object of known mass in the ship
C) measuring the diameter of the planet
D) measuring the density of the planet
*E) observing the ship's acceleration and correcting for the distance from the center of the planet

11. To measure the mass of a planet with the same radius as the earth, an astronaut drops an object from rest (relative to the planet) from an altitude of one radius above the surface. When the object hits its speed is 4 times what it would be if the same experiment were carried out for the earth. In units of earth masses, the mass of the planet is:

A) 2   B) 4   C) 8   *D) 16   E) 32

12. Suppose you have a pendulum clock which keeps correct time on earth. Without changing the clock, you take it to the moon (g_e = 9.8 m/s^2, g_m = 1.6 m/s^2). For every hour interval (on earth) the moon clock will record:

A) 9.8/1.6 h   B) 1h   C) $\sqrt{9.8/1.6}$ h   D) 1.6/9.8 h   E) $\sqrt{1.6/9.8}$ h

Ans. e

13. The mass of an object:

A) is slightly different at different locations on the earth
B) is a vector
*C) is independent of g
D) is the same for all objects of the same size and shape
E) can be measured directly and accurately on a spring scale

14. Which graph correctly shows the inertial mass m_i of an object as a function of its gravitational mass m_g?

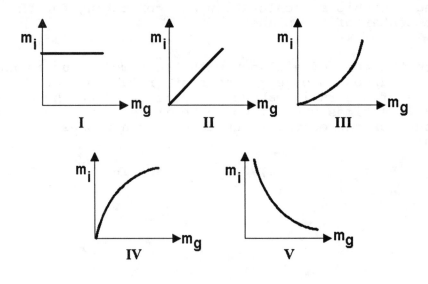

A) I.   *B) II.   C) III.   D) IV.   E) V.

15. An astronaut on the moon simultaneously drops a feather and a hammer. The fact that they land together shows that:

   A) no gravity forces act on a body in a vacuum
   B) g on the moon is less than g on the earth
  *C) in the absence of air resistance all bodies at a given location fall with the same acceleration
   D) the feather has a greater weight on the moon than on the earth
   E) G = 0 on the moon

16. The mass of a hypothetical planet is 1/100 that of the earth and its radius is 1/4 that of earth. If a person weighs 150 lb on earth, what would he weigh on this planet?

   A) 150 lb   B) 12 lb   C) 48 lb   D) 6 lb   *E) 24 lb

17. An object at the surface of the earth (at a distance R from the center of the earth) weighs 90 N. Its weight at a distance 3R from the center of the earth is:

  *A) 10 N   B) 30 N   C) 90 N   D) 270 N   E) 810 N

18. An object is raised from the surface of the earth to a height of two earth radii above the earth. Then:

   A) its mass increases and its weight remains constant
   B) both its mass and weight remain constant
  *C) its mass remains constant and its weight decreases
   D) both its mass and its weight decrease
   E) its mass remains constant and its weight increases

19. A spring scale, calibrated in newtons, is used to weigh sugar. If it were possible to weigh sugar at the following locations, where will the buyer get the most sugar to a newton?

   A) at the north pole   D) on the moon
   B) at the equator   E) on Jupiter
  *C) at the center of the earth

20. Where would the weight of an object be the least?

   A) 2000 miles above earth's surface
   B) at the north pole
   C) at the equator
  *D) at the center of the earth
   E) at the south pole

21. If the earth were to rotate only 100 times per year about its axis:

    A) airplanes flying W to E would make better time
    B) we would fly off the earth's surface
    *C) our weight would slightly increase
    D) the earth's atmosphere would float into outer space
    E) our weight would slightly decrease

22. An astronaut in an orbiting space-craft feels "weightless" because she:

    A) is beyond the range of gravity
    B) is pulled outwards by centrifugal force
    C) has no acceleration
    *D) has the same acceleration as the space-craft
    E) is outside the earth's atmosphere

23. Each of the four corners of a square with edge a is occupied by a point mass m. There is a fifth mass, also m, at the center of the square. To remove the mass the center to a point far away the work that must be done by an external agent is given by:

    A) $4Gm^2/a$
    B) $-4Gm^2/a$
    *C)
    $\quad 4\sqrt{2}Gm^2/a$

    D)
    $\quad -4\sqrt{2}Gm^2/a$
    E) $4Gm^2/a^2$

24. Two particles, each of mass m, are a distance d apart. To bring a third particle, also with mass m, from far away to the point midway between the two particles an external agent does work given by:

    A) $4Gm^2/d$
    *B) $-4Gm^2/d$
    C) $4Gm^2/d^2$

    D) $-4Gm^2/d^2$
    E) none of the above

25. The escape velocity at the surface of the earth is approximately 8 km/s. What is the escape velocity for a planet whose radius is 4 times and whose mass is 100 times that of earth?

    A) 1.6 km/s
    B) 8 km/s
    *C) 40 km/s

    D) 200 km/s
    E) none of the above

26. Neglecting air resistance, a 1.0 kg projectile has an escape velocity of about 5 miles per second at the surface of the earth. The corresponding escape velocity for a 2.0 kg projectile is:

    A) 10 mi/s
    B)
    $\quad 5\sqrt{2}$ mi/s
    *C) 5 mi/s

    D)
    $\quad 5/\sqrt{2}$ mi/s
    E) 2.5 mi/s

27. Neglecting air resistance, the escape speed from a certain planet of an empty space vehicle is 1.12×10^4 m/s. What is the corresponding escape speed for the fully loaded vehicle which has triple the mass of the empty one?

A) 3.73×10^3 m/s
*B) 9.98×10^4 m/s
C) 1.12×10^4 m/s

D) 1.40×10^{12} m/s
E) 3.36×10^4 m/s

28. An object is dropped from an altitude of one earth radius above the earth's surface. If M is the mass of the earth and R is its radius the speed of the object just before it hits the earth is given by:

A) $\sqrt{GM/R}$ B) $\sqrt{GM/2R}$ C) $\sqrt{2GM/R}$ D) $\sqrt{GM/R^2}$ E) $\sqrt{GM/2R^2}$

Ans. a

29. A projectile is fired straight upward from the earth's surface with a speed that is half the escape speed. If R is the radius of the earth, the highest altitude reached, measured from the surface, is:

A) R/4   *B) R/3   C) R/2   D) R   E) 2R

30. The mass density of a certain planet has spherical symmetry but varies in such a way that the mass inside every spherical surface with center at the center of the planet is proportional to the radius of the surface. If r is the distance from the center of the planet to a point mass inside the planet, the gravitational force on the mass is:

A) not dependent on r
B) proportional to r^2
C) proportional to r

*D) proportional to $1/r$
E) proportional to $1/r^2$

31. A spherical shell has inner radius R_1, outer radius R_2, and mass M, distributed uniformly throughout the shell. The magnitude of the gravitational force exerted on the shell by a point mass m a distance d from the center, inside the inner radius, is:

*A) 0

B) GMm/RD_1^2

C) GMm/d^2

D) $GMm/(R_2^2 - d^2)$

E) $GMm/(R_1 - d)^2$

32. A spherical shell has inner radius R_1, outer radius R_2, and mass M, distributed uniformly throughout the shell. The magnitude of the gravitational force exerted on the shell by a point mass m a distance d from the center, outside the outer radius, is:

A) 0

B) GMm/R_1^2

*C) GMm/d^2

D) $GMm/(R_2^2 - d^2)$

E) $GMm/(R_1 - d)^2$

33. An artificial satellite of the earth releases a bomb. Neglecting air resistance, the bomb strikes the earth at a point:

A) under the satellite at the instant of release
B) under the satellite at the instant of impact
C) ahead of the satellite at the instant of impact
D) behind the satellite at the instant of impact
*E) bomb never strikes earth

34. An astronaut finishes some work on the outside of his satellite, which is in circular orbit around the earth. He leaves his wrench outside the satellite. The wrench will:

A) fall directly down to the earth
B) continue in orbit at reduced speed
*C) continue in orbit with the satellite
D) fly off tangentially into space
E) spiral down to the earth

35. Consider the statement: "The earth moves in a stable orbit around the sun and is therefore in equilibrium". The statement is:

A) false, because no moving body can be in equilibrium
B) true, because the earth does not fall into or fly away from the sun
C) false, because the earth is rotating on its axis and no rotating body can be in equilibrium
*D) false, because the earth has a considerable acceleration
E) true, because if it were not in equilibrium then buildings and structures would not be stable

36. A planet travels in an elliptical orbit about a star X as shown. The magnitude of the acceleration of the planet is:

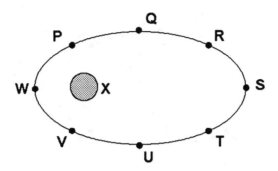

A) greatest at point Q
B) greatest at point S
C) greatest at point U

*D) greatest at point W
E) the same at all points

37. In planetary motion the line from the star to the planet sweeps out equal areas in equal times. This is a direct consequence of:

A) the conservation of energy
B) the conservation of momentum
*C) the conservation of angular momentum
D) the conservation of mass
E) none of the above

38. The speed of a comet in an elliptical orbit about the sun:

*A) decreases while it is receding from the sun
B) is constant
C) is greatest when farthest from the sun
D) varies sinusoidally with time
E) equals L/(mr), where L is its angular momentum and r is its distance from the sun

39. A planet travels in an elliptical orbit about a star as shown. At what pair of points is the speed of the planet the same?

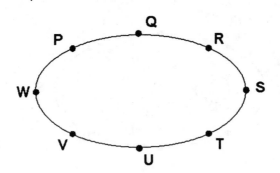

A) W and S
B) P and T
C) P and R

*D) Q and U
E) need to know where the star is

40. At perihelion a planet in another solar system is 175×10^6 km from its sun and is traveling at 40 km/s. At aphelion it is 250×10^6 km distant and is traveling at:

A) 20 km/s   *B) 28 km/s   C) 34 km/s   D) 40 km/s   E) 57 km/s

41. A planet is in circular orbit around the sun. Its distance from the sun is four times the average distance of the earth from the sun. The period of this planet, in earth years, is:

A) 4   *B) 8   C) 16   D) 64   E) 2.52

42. Two planets are orbiting a star in a distant galaxy. The first has a semimajor axis of 150×10^6 km, an eccentricity of 0.20, and a period of 1.0 earth years. The second has a semimajor axis of 250×10^6 km, an eccentricity of 0.30, and a period of:

A) 0.46 earth yr
B) 0.57 earth yr
C) 1.4 earth yr

D) 1.8 earth yr
*E) 2.2 earth yr

43. A small satellite is in elliptical orbit around the earth as shown.
    If L denotes angular momentum and K denotes kinetic energy:

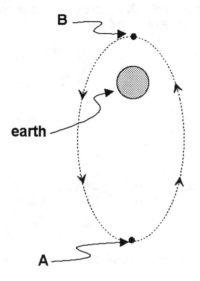

A) $L_B > L_A$ and $K_B > K_A$ D) $L_B = L_A$ and $K_B > K_A$
B) $L_B < L_A$ and $K_B = K_A$ *E) $L_B = L_A$ and $K_B = K_A$
C) $L_B > L_A$ and $K_B = K_A$

44. Assume that the earth is in circular orbit around the sun with
    kinetic energy K and potential energy U, taken to be zero for
    infinite separation. Then the relationship between K and U:

 A) is $K = U$
 B) is $K = -U$
 C) is $K = U/2$
*D) is $K = -U/2$
 E) depends on the radius of the orbit

45. An artificial satellite of the earth nears the end of its life due
    to air resistance. While still in orbit:

*A) it moves faster as the orbit lowers
 B) it moves slower as the orbit lowers
 C) it slowly spirals away from the earth
 D) it moves slower in the same orbit but with a decreasing period
 E) it moves faster in the same orbit but with an increasing period

46. A spaceship is returning to earth with its engine turned off. Consider only the gravitational field of the earth and let M be the mass of the earth, m be the mass of the spaceship, and R be the distance from the center of the earth. In moving from position 1 to position 2 the kinetic energy of the spaceship increases by:

A) GMm/R_2

B) GMm/R_2^2

C) $GMm(R_1 - R_2)/R_1^2$

*D) $GMm(R_1 - R_2)/R_1R_2$

E) $GMm(R_1 - R_2)/R_{12}^2$ 2R

47. Given the perihelion distance, aphelion distance, and speed at perihelion of a planet, which of the following CANNOT be calculated?

A) the mass of the star
*B) the mass of the planet
C) the speed of the planet at aphelion
D) the period of orbit
E) the semimajor axis of the orbit

48. The orbit of a certain a satellite has a semimajor axis of 1.5×10^7 m and an eccentricity of 0.20. Its perigee (minimum distance) and apogee (maximum distance) are respectively:

*A) 1.2×10^7 m, 1.8×10^7 m
B) 3.0×10^6 m, 1.2×10^7 m
C) 9.6×10^6 m, 1.0×10^7 m

D) 1.0×10^7 m, 1.2×10^7 m
E) 9.6×10^6 m, 1.8×10^7 m

49. A planet in another solar system orbits a star with a mass of 4.0×10^{30} kg. At one point in its orbit it is 250×10^6 km from the star and is moving at 35 km/s. Take the universal gravitational constant to be 6.67×10^{-11} $m^2/s^2 \cdot kg$ and calculate the semimajor axis of the planet's orbit. The result is:

A) 79×10^6 km
B) 160×10^6 km
*C) 240×10^6 km

D) 320×10^6 km
E) 590×10^6 km

50. A planet in another solar system orbits a star with a mass of 4.0×10^{30} kg. Its perihelion distance is 175×10^6 km and its semimajor axis is 250×10^6 km. Take the universal gravitational constant to be 6.67×10^{-11} $m^2/s^2 \cdot kg$ and calculate the speed of the planet at perihelion. The result is:

A) 21 km/s   *B) 45 km/s   C) 51 km/s   D) 64 km/s   E) 91 km/s

1. All fluids are:

A) gases
B) liquids
*C) gases or liquids

D) non-metallic
E) transparent

2. Gases may be distinguished from other forms of matter by their:

A) lack of color
B) small atomic weights
*C) inability to form free surfaces
D) ability to flow
E) ability to exert a buoyant force

3. 1 Pa is:

A) 1 N/m
B) 1 m/N
C) 1 kg/m $\cdot$s

*D) 1 kg/m $\cdot$s^2
E) 1 N/m $\cdot$s

4. Mercury is a convenient liquid to use in a barometer because:

A) it is a metal
B) it has a high boiling point
C) it expands little with temperature
*D) it has a high density
E) it looks silvery

5. To obtain the absolute pressure from the gauge pressure:

A) subtract atmospheric pressure
*B) add atmospheric pressure
C) subtract 273

D) add 273
E) convert to N/m^2

6. Barometers and open-tube manometers are two instruments that are used to measure pressure.

A) Both measure gauge pressure
B) Both measure absolute pressure
C) Barometers measure gauge pressure and manometers measure absolute pressure
*D) Barometers measure absolute pressure and manometers measure gauge pressure
E) Both measure an average of the absolute and gauge pressures

7. To measure moderately low pressures oil with a density of 8.5×10^2 kg/m^3 is used in place of mercury in a barometer. A pressure change of 1.0 Pa produces a change in the height of the oil column of about:

A) 1.2×10^{-2} m

B) 1.2×10^{-3} m

*C) 1.2×10^{-4} m

D) 1.2×10^{-5} m

E) 1.2×10^{-6} m

8. The pressure exerted on the ground by a man is greatest when:

A) he stands with both feet flat on the ground

B) he stands flat on one foot

*C) he stands on the toes of one foot

D) he lies down on the ground

E) all of the above yield the same pressure

9. In a stationary homogeneous liquid:

A) pressure is the same at all points

B) pressure depends on the direction

C) pressure is independent of any atmospheric pressure on the upper surface of the liquid

*D) pressure is the same at all points at the same level

E) none of the above

10. Which of the following five statements, concerning the upper surface pressure of a liquid, is FALSE?

A) it is independent of the surface area

B) it is the same for all points on that surface

C) it would not increase if the liquid depth were increased

*D) it would increase if the liquid density were increased

E) it would increase if the atmospheric pressure increased

11. Several cans of different sizes and shapes are all filled with the same liquid to the same depth. Then:

A) the weight of the liquid is the same for all cans

B) the force of the liquid on the bottom of each can is the same

C) the least pressure is at the bottom of the can with the largest bottom area

D) the greatest pressure is at the bottom of the can with the largest bottom area

*E) the pressure on the bottom of each can is the same

12. An airtight box, having a lid of area 12 in^2, is partially evacuated. Atmospheric pressure is 15 lb/in^2. A force of 108 lb is required to pull the lid off the box. The pressure in the box was:

*A) 6 lb/in^2
  B) 7.2 lb/in^2
  C) 3 lb/in^2

D) 9 lb.in^2
E) 15 lb/in^2

13. A closed hemispherical shell of radius R is filled with fluid at uniform pressure p. The net force of the fluid on the curved portion of the shell is given by:

  A) $2\pi R^2 p$
*B) $\pi R^2 p$
  C) $4\pi R^2 p$

D) $(4/3)\pi R^2 p$
E) $(4/3)\pi R^3 p$

14. The density of oil is 0.08 g/cm^3. The height h of the column of oil shown is:

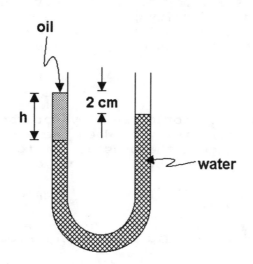

A) 2 cm   B) 4.6 cm   C) 8 cm   *D) 10 cm   E) 11.8 cm

15. A uniform U-tube is partially filled with water. Oil, of density 0.75 g/cm^3, is poured into the right arm until the water level in the left arm rises 3 cm. The length of the oil column is then:

  A) 2.25 cm
*B) 8 cm
  C) 6 cm
  D) 4 cm
  E) need to know the cross-sectional area of the U-tube

191

16. A long U-tube contains mercury (density = 14×10^3 kg/m^3). When 10 cm of water (density = 1.0×10^3 kg/m^3) is poured into the left arm, the mercury in the right arm rises above its original level by:

   *A) 0.36 cm   B) 0.72 cm   C) 14 cm   D) 35 cm   E) 70 cm

17. A bucket of water is pushed from left to right with increasing speed across a horizontal surface. Consider the pressure at two points at the same level in the water.

   A) It is the same
   *B) It is higher at the point on the left
   C) It is higher at the point on the right
   D) At first it is higher at the point on the left but as the bucket speeds up it is lower there
   E) At first it is higher at the point on the right but as the bucket speeds up it is lower there

18. A bucket resting on the floor of an elevator contains an incompressible fluid of density ρ. When the elevator has an upward acceleration a the pressure difference between two points in a fluid separated by a vertical distance Δh, is given by:

   A) ρaΔh   B) ρgΔh   *C) ρ(g+a)Δh   D) ρ(g−a)Δh   E) ρgaΔh

19. A bucket resting on the floor of an elevator contains an incompressible fluid of density ρ. When the elevator has a downward acceleration of magnitude a the pressure difference between two points in a fluid, separated by a vertical distance Δh, is given by:

   A) ρaΔh   B) ρgΔh   C) ρ(g+a)Δh   *D) ρ(g−a)Δh   E) ρgaΔh

20. "An object submerged in a fluid displaces its own volume of fluid." This is:

   A) Pascal's paradox   *D) true, but none of the above
   B) Archimedes' principle   E) false
   C) Pascal's principle

21. Two identical blocks of ice float in water as shown. Then:

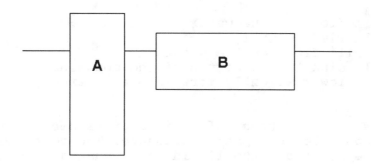

A) block A displaces a greater volume of water since the pressure acts on a smaller bottom area
B) block B displaces a greater volume of water since the pressure is less on its bottom
*C) the two blocks displace equal volumes of water since they have the same weight
D) the density of block A is less than that of block B
E) the density of block A is more than that of block B

22. A block of ice at 0°C is floating on the surface of ice water in a beaker. The surface of the water just comes to the top of the beaker. When the ice melts the water level will:

A) rise and overflow will occur
*B) remain the same
C) fall
D) depend on the initial ratio of water to ice
E) depend on the shape of the block of ice

23. A block of ice at 0°C containing a lead pellet is floating on the surface of ice water in a beaker. When the ice has melted the water level:

A) is higher
*B) is lower
C) is the same
D) depends on the initial ratio of water to ice
E) depends on the shape of the ice block

24. A pirate chest rests at the bottom of an ocean. If the water is still, the net force it exerts on the chest:

A) is upward
*B) is downward
C) is zero
D) depends on the mass of the chest
E) depends on the contents of the chest

25. A small steel ball floats in a half-full container of mercury. When water is added:

  A) the ball will float on the water
 *B) the ball will rise slightly
  C) the mercury will float on the water
  D) the ball will sink to the bottom of the container
  E) the ball will lower slightly more into the mercury

26. A cork floats on the surface of an incompressible liquid in a container exposed to atmospheric pressure. The container is then sealed and the air above the liquid is evacuated. The cork:

  A) sinks slightly
  B) rises slightly
 *C) floats at the same height
  D) bobs up and down about its old position
  E) behaves erratically

27. An object hangs from a spring balance. The balance indicates 30 N in air, 20 N when the object is submerged in water, and 24 N when the object is immersed in an unknown liquid. The density of the unknown liquid equals the density of water multiplied by:

  A) 10/4   *B) 6/10   C) 24/20   D) 4/10   E) 10/30

28. A fir wood board floats in fresh water with 60% of its volume under water. The density of the wood in g/cm^3 is:

  A) 0.4   D) less than 0.4
  B) 0.5   E) more than 0.6
 *C) 0.6

29. A boat floating in fresh water displaces 8000 lb of water. How many pounds of salt-water would it displace if it floats in salt-water of specific gravity 1.17?

  A) 7270   B) 8800   *C) 8000   D) 142   E) 117

30. A rock, which weighs 350 lb in air, weighs 226 lb when submerged in fresh water (62.4 lb/ft^3). The volume of the rock is:

 *A) 2 ft^3 B) 62.4 ft^3 C) 5.0 ft^3 D) 50 ft^3 E) 0.5 ft^3

31. A loaded ship passes from a lake (fresh water) to the ocean (salt water). Salt water is more dense than fresh water and as a result the ship will:

 *A) ride higher in the water
  B) settle lower in the water
  C) ride at the same level in the water
  D) experience an increase in buoyant force
  E) experience a decrease in buoyant force

32. A wooden raft (38.4 lb/ft^3) is 8 ft x 8 ft x 1 ft. What maximum load can it carry in sea water (64.0 lb/ft^3)?

  A) 4096 lb   *B) 1640 lb   C) 2460 lb   D) 3280 lb   E) 5100 lb

33. A tin can has a volume of 1000 cm^3 and a mass of 100 g. Approximately how many grams of lead shot can it carry without sinking in water?

 *A) 900   B) 100   C) 1000   D) 1100   E) 980

34. A block of wood weighs 37.5 lb and has a specific gravity of 0.60. To sink it in fresh water requires an additional downward force of:

  A) 12.5 lb   B) 15 lb   C) 22.5 lb   *D) 25 lb   E) 50 lb

35. A certain block of wood has a volume of 150 cm^3 and floats on water (density = 1.0x10^3 kg/m^3) with 25% of its volume submerged. The downward force that must be applied to hold it under water is about:

  A) 0.11 N   D) 1.5 N
  B) 0.37 N   E) 1.1x10^6 N
 *C) 1.1 N

36. A student standardizes the concentration of a salt-water solution by slowly adding salt until an egg will just float. The procedure is based on the assumption that:

  A) all eggs have the same volume
  B) all eggs have the same weight
 *C) all eggs have the same density
  D) all eggs have the same shape
  E) the salt tends to neutralize the cholesterol in the egg

37. A solid has a volume of 8 cm^3. When weighed on a spring scale calibrated in grams, the scale indicates 20 grams. What does the scale indicate if the object is weighed while immersed in a liquid of density 2 g/cm^3?

 *A) 4 g
  B) 10 g
  C) 12 g
  D) 16 g
  E) zero, since the object will float

38. A 210-gram object apparently loses 30 grams when suspended in a liquid of density 2.0 g/cm^3. The density of the object is:

  A) 7.0 g/cm^3 *D) 14 g/cm^3
  B) 3.5 g/cm^3 E) none of these
  C) 1.4 g/cm^3

39. A steel ax and an aluminum piston have the same apparent weight in water. When they are weighed in air:

  A) they weigh the same
  B) the ax is heavier
 *C) the piston is heavier
  D) both weigh less than they did in water
  E) depends on their shapes

40. The apparent weight of a steel sphere immersed in various liquids is measured using a spring scale. The greatest reading is obtained for that liquid:

 *A) having the smallest density
  B) having the largest density
  C) subject to the greatest atmospheric pressure
  D) having the greatest volume
  E) in which the sphere was submerged deepest

41. A 50-gram metal sinker appears (as measured using a spring scale) to have a mass of 45 grams when submerged in water. The specific gravity of the metal is:

  A) 6   B) 8   C) 9   *D) 10   E) 12

42. An object floats on the surface of a fluid. For purposes of calculating the torque on it, the buoyant force is taken to act at:

  A) the center of the bottom surface of the object
  B) the center of gravity of the object
 *C) the center of gravity of the fluid that the object replaced
  D) the geometric center of the object
  E) none of the above

43. A blast of wind tips a sailboat in the clockwise direction when viewed from the stern. When the wind ceases the boat rotates back toward the upright position if, when it is tilted, the center of buoyancy:

 A) is above the center of gravity
 B) is below the center of gravity
 C) is to the right of the center of gravity
*D) is to the left of the center of gravity
 E) coincides with the center of gravity

44. A cork floats in water in a bucket resting on the floor of an elevator. The elevator then accelerates upward. During the acceleration:

 A) the cork is immersed more
 B) the cork is immerse less
*C) the cork is immersed the same amount
 D) at first the cork is immersed less but as the elevator speeds up it is immersed more
 E) at first the cork is immersed more but as the elevator speeds up it is immersed less

45. Two balls have the same shape and size but one is denser than the other. If frictional forces are negligible when they are dropped in air, which has the greater acceleration?

*A) The heavier ball
 B) The lighter ball
 C) They have the same acceleration
 D) The heavier ball if atmospheric pressure is high, they lighter ball if it is low
 E) The lighter ball if atmospheric pressure is high, the heavier ball if it is low

46. The principle of fluid pressure which is used in hydraulic brakes or lifts is that:

 A) pressure is the same at all levels in a fluid
*B) increases of pressure are transmitted equally to all parts of a fluid
 C) the pressure at a point in a fluid is due to the weight of the fluid above it
 D) increases of pressure can only be transmitted through fluids
 E) the pressure at a given depth is proportional to the depth in the fluid

47. Which of the following statements about Pascal's principle is true?

   A) It is valid only for incompressible fluids
   B) It explains why light objects float
   C) It explains why the pressure is greater at the bottom of a lake than at the surface
   D) It is valid only for objects that are less dense than water
 *E) None of the above are true

48. The hydraulic automobile jack illustrates:

   A) Archimedes' principle   D) Newton's third law
 *B) Pascal's principle   E) Newton's second law
   C) Hooke's law

49. One piston in a hydraulic lift has an area that is twice the area of the other. When the pressure at the smaller piston is increased by Δp the pressure at the larger piston:

   A) increases by $2\Delta p$ D) increases by $4\Delta p$
   B) increases by $\Delta p/2$ E) does not change
 *C) increases by Δp

50. A hydraulic press has one piston of diameter 2 inches and the other piston of diameter 8 inches. If a 100-lb force is applied to the smaller piston, the force exerted on the larger piston will be:

   A) 6.25 lb   B) 25 lb   C) 100 lb   D) 400 lb   *E) 1600 lb

51. The two arms of a U-tube are not identical, one having twice the diameter of the other. A cork in the narrow arm requires a force of 16 N to remove it. The tube is filled with water and the wide arm is fitted with a piston. The minimum force that must be applied to the piston to push the cork out is:

   A) 4 N   B) 8 N   C) 16 N   D) 32 N   *E) 64 N

52. The diagram shows a U-tube having cross-sectional area A and partially filled with oil of density ρ. A solid cylinder, which fits the tube tightly but can slide without friction is placed in the right arm as shown. When the system reaches equilibrium, the position of the cylinder is as shown. The weight of the cylinder is:

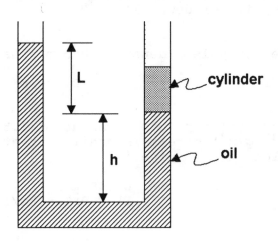

*A) ALρg
 B) L^3ρg
 C) Aρ(L + h)g

D) Aρ(L - h)g
E) none of these

53. A U-tube has dissimilar arms, one having twice the diameter of the other. It contains an incompressible fluid and is fitted with a sliding piston in each arm, with each piston in contact with the fluid. When the piston in the narrow arm is pushed down a distance d, the piston in the wide arm rises a distance:

A) d   B) 2d   C) d/2   D) 4d   *E) d/4

54. A U-tube has dissimilar arms, one having twice the diameter of the other. It contains an incompressible fluid and is fitted with a sliding piston in each arm, with each piston in contact with the fluid. When an applied force does work W in pushing the piston in the narrow arm down, the fluid does work _____ on the piston in the wide arm.

*A) W   B) 2W   C) W/2   D) 4W   E) W/4

55. A fluid is undergoing "incompressible" flow. This means that:

A) the pressure at a given point cannot change with time
B) the velocity at a given point cannot change with time
C) the velocity must be the same everywhere
D) the pressure must be the same everywhere
*E) the density cannot change with time or location

56. A fluid is undergoing steady flow. Therefore:

   A) the velocity of any given molecule of fluid does not change
   B) the pressure does not vary from point to point
  *C) the velocity at any given point does not vary with time
   D) the density does not vary from point to point
   E) the flow is not uphill or downhill

57. If p is a pressure and ρ is a density then p/ρ has units of:

   A) m^2 *B) m^2/s^2 C) N/m^2 D) kg/m^2 E) m^3/kg

58. One end of a cylindrical pipe has a radius of 1.5 cm. Water
    (density = 1.0×10^3 kg/m^3) streams steadily out at 7.0 m/s. The rate
    at which mass is leaving the pipe is:

   A) 2.5 kg/s   D) 48 kg/s
  *B) 4.9 kg/s   E) 7.0×10^3 kg/s
   C) 7.0 kg/s

59. One end of a cylindrical pipe has a radius of 1.5 cm. Water
    (density = 1.0×10^3 kg/m^3) streams steadily out at 7.0 m/s. The
    volume flow rate is:

  *A) 4.9×10^{-3} m^3/s D) 7.0 m^3/s
   B) 2.5 m^3/s E) 48 m^3/s
   C) 4.9 m^3/s

60. The equation of continuity for fluid flow can be derived from the
    conservation of:

   A) energy   D) volume
  *B) mass   E) pressure
   C) angular momentum

200

61. An incompressible liquid flows along the pipe as shown. The ratio of the speeds v_2/v_1 is:

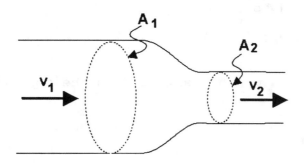

A) A_1 / A_2 B) A_2 / A_1 C) $\sqrt{A_1 / A_2}$ D) $\sqrt{A_2 / A_1}$ E) v_1 / v_2

Ans. a

62. Water flows through a cylindrical pipe of varying cross-section. The velocity is 3 ft/s at a point where the pipe diameter is one inch. At a point where the pipe diameter is three inches, the velocity is:

A) 9 ft/s
B) 3 ft/s
C) 1 ft/s

*D) 0.33 ft/s
E) 0.11 ft/s

63. A constriction in a pipe reduces its diameter from 4.0 cm to 2.0 cm. Where the pipe is wide the fluid velocity is 8.0 m/s. Where it is narrow the fluid velocity is:

A) 2.0 m/s   B) 4.0 m/s   C) 8.0 m/s   D) 16 m/s   *E) 32 m/s

64. Water flows from a 6-inch diameter pipe into an 8-inch diameter pipe. The speed in the 6-inch pipe is 16 ft/s. The speed in the 8-inch pipe is:

*A) 9 ft/s
B) 12 ft/s
C) 21.3 ft/s

D) 28.4 ft/s
E) 12 ft/s

65. A lawn sprinkler is made of a 1.0 cm diameter garden hose with one
    end closed and 25 holes, each with a diameter of 0.050 cm, cut near
    the closed end. If water flows at 2.0 m/s in the hose, the speed of
    the water leaving a hole is:

A) 2.0 m/s   *B) 32 m/s   C) 40 m/s   D) 600 m/s   E) 800 m/s

66. Bernoulli's equation can be derived from the conservation of:

*A) energy   D) volume
 B) mass   E) pressure
 C) angular momentum

67. Which of the following assumptions is NOT made in the derivation of
    Bernoulli's equation?

A) assume streamline flow   *D) neglect gravity
B) neglect viscosity   E) neglect turbulence
C) neglect friction

68. The quantity "y" appearing in Bernoulli's equation MUST be measured:

 A) upward from the center of the earth
 B) upward from the surface of the earth
 C) upward from the lowest point in the flow
 D) downward from the highest point in the flow
*E) upward from any convenient level

69. Water flows through a constriction in a horizontal pipe. As it
    enters the constriction, the water's:

*A) speed increases and pressure decreases
 B) speed increases and pressure remains constant
 C) speed increases and pressure increases
 D) speed decreases and pressure increases
 E) speed decreases and pressure decreases

70. A non-viscous incompressible liquid is flowing through a horizontal
    pipe of constant cross-section. Bernoulli's equation predicts that
    the drop in pressure along the pipe:

*A) is zero
 B) depends on the length of the pipe
 C) depends on the fluid velocity
 D) depends on the cross-sectional area of the pipe
 E) depends on the height of the pipe

71. A non-viscous incompressible fluid is pumped steadily into the narrow end of a long tapered pipe and emerges from the wide end. The pressure at the input is greater than at the output. A possible explanation is:

A) the fluid speed increases from input to output
B) the fluid speed is the same at the two ends
*C) the fluid is flowing uphill
D) the fluid is flowing downhill
E) the fluid is flowing horizontally

72. Water is pumped into one end of a long pipe at the rate of 10 gallons per minute. It emerges at the other end at 6 gallons per minute. A possible reason for this decrease in flow is:

A) the water is being pumped uphill
B) the water is being pumped downhill
C) the diameter of the pipe is not the same at the two ends
D) friction in the pipe
*E) a leak in the pipe

73. Consider a pipe containing a fluid, with the fluid being at rest. To apply Bernoulli's equation to this situation:

*A) set v equal to zero because there is no motion
B) set g equal to zero because there is no acceleration
C) set v and g both equal to zero
D) set p equal to the atmospheric pressure
E) cannot be done, Bernoulli's equation applies only to fluids in motion

74. Water (density = 1.0×10^3 kg/m^3) flows through a horizontal tapered pipe. At the wide end its speed is 4.0 m/s and at the narrow end it is 5.0 m/s. The difference in pressure between the two ends is:

A) 5.0×10^2 Pa, with the wide end at the higher pressure
B) 5.0×10^2 Pa, with the narrow end at the higher pressure
*C) 4.5×10^3 Pa, with the wide end at the higher pressure
D) 4.5×10^3 Pa, with the narrow end at the higher pressure
E) 5.0×10^4 Pa, with the wide end at the higher pressure

75. Water is streaming downward from a faucet opening with an area of 3.0×10^{-5} m^2. It leaves the faucet with a speed of 5.0 m/s. The cross sectional area of the stream 0.50 m below the faucet is:

A) 1.5×10^{-5} m^2
B) 2.0×10^{-5} m^2
*C) 2.5×10^{-5} m^2
D) 3.0×10^{-5} m^2
E) 3.5×10^{-5} m^2

76. A large water tank, open at the top, has a small hole in the bottom. When the water level is 30 m above the bottom of the tank, the speed of the water leaking from the hole:

A) is 2.5 m/s
*B) is 24 m/s
C) is 44 m/s
D) cannot be calculated unless the area of the hole is given
E) cannot be calculated unless the areas of the hole and tank are given

77. A large tank filled with water has two holes in the bottom, one with twice the radius of the other. In steady flow the speed of water leaving the larger hole is _____ the speed of the water leaving the smaller.

A) twice
B) four times
C) half

D) one fourth
*E) the same as

78. A non-viscous incompressible fluid is pumped steadily up a vertical pipe with uniform cross section. The difference in pressure between points at the top and bottom:

*A) is the same as it would be if the fluid were motionless
B) is greater at higher flow rates than at lower flow rates
C) is less at higher flow rates than at lower flow rates
D) does not depend on the density of the fluid
E) is zero

79. A water line enters a house 2.0 m below ground. A smaller diameter pipe carries water to a faucet 5.0 m above ground, on the second floor. Water flows at 2.0 m/s in the main line and at 7.0 m/s on the second floor. Take the density of water to be 1.0×10^3 kg/m^3. If the pressure in the main line is 2.0×10^5 Pa, then the pressure on the second floor is:

A) 5.3×10^4 Pa
*B) 1.1×10^5 Pa
C) 1.5×10^5 Pa

D) 2.5×10^5 Pa
E) 3.4×10^5 Pa

80. A person blows across the top of one arm of a U-tube partially filled with water. The water in that arm:

*A) rises slightly
B) drops slightly
C) remains at the same height
D) rises if the blowing is soft but drops if it is hard
E) rises if the blowing is hard but drops if it is soft

81. A Venturi meter is normally used to measure:

   A) absolute pressure
   B) gauge pressure
   C) mass flux

   *D) fluid speed
   E) distance

82. Which of the following must be considered in an analysis of a
    Venturi meter to find an expression for the fluid speed in terms of
    the difference in height of the columns in the U-tube?
       I.   variation of pressure with depth
       II. equation of continuity
       III. Bernoulli's equation

   A) I only
   B) II only
   C) III only

   D) II and III only
   *E) I, II and III only

83. Which of the following must be considered in an analysis of a Pitot
    tube to find an expression for the fluid speed in terms of the
    difference in height of the columns in the U-tube?
       I.   variation of pressure with depth
       II. equation of continuity
       III. Bernoulli's equation

   A) I only
   B) II only
   C) III only

   *D) I and III only
   E) I, II, and III

1. For a transverse wave on a string the string displacement is
   described by y(x,t) = f(x-at) where f is a given function and a is a
   positive constant. Which of the following does NOT necessarily
   follow from this statement?

   A) The shape of the string at time t = 0 is given by f(x).
   B) The shape of the waveform does not change as it moves along the
      string.
   C) The waveform moves in the positive x direction.
   D) The speed of the waveform is a.
   *E) The speed of the waveform is x/t.

2. A sinusoidal wave is traveling toward the right as shown. Which
   letter correctly labels the amplitude of the wave?

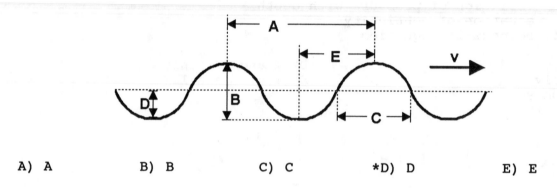

   A) A   B) B   C) C   *D) D   E) E

3. A sinusoidal wave is traveling toward the right as shown. Which
   letter correctly labels the wavelength of the wave?

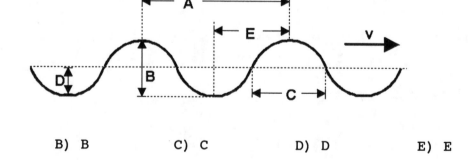

   *A) A   B) B   C) C   D) D   E) E

206

4. In the diagram below, the interval PQ represents:

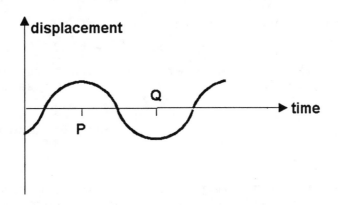

A) wavelength/2   *D) period/2
B) wavelength   E) period
C) 2 x amplitude

5. Let f be the frequency, v the speed, and T the period of a
   sinusoidal traveling wave. The correct relationship is:

*A) f = 1/T   D) f = v/T
 B) f = v + T   E) f = T/v
 C) f = vT

6. Let f be the frequency, v the speed, and T the period of a
   sinusoidal traveling wave. The angular frequency is given by:

A) 1/T   *B) 2π/T   C) vT   D) f/T   E) T/f

7. The displacement of a string is given by $y(x,t) = y_m \sin(kx + \omega t)$.
   The wavelength of the wave is:

A) 2πk/ω   B) k/ω   C) ωk   *D) 2π/k   E) k/2π

8. The displacement of a string is given by $y(x,t) = y_m \sin(kx + \omega t)$.
   The speed of the wave is:

A) 2πk/ω   *B) ω/k   C) ωk   D) 2π/k   E) k/2π

9. A wave is described by $y(x,t) = 0.1 \sin(3x + 10t)$, where x is in
   meters, y is in centimeters and t is in seconds. The wavelength is:

A) 6π m   B) 3π m   *C) 2π/3 m   D) π/3 m   E) 0.1 cm

10. A wave is described by y(x,t) = 0.1 sin(3x - 10t), where x is in
    meters, y is in centimeters and t is in seconds. The frequency is:

    A) 20π Hz   B) 10π Hz   C) 10/π Hz   *D) 5/π Hz   E) 20/π Hz

11. Water waves in the sea are observed to have a wavelength of 1000 ft
    and a frequency of 0.07 Hz. The velocity of these waves is:

    A) 0.0007 ft/s   D) 700 ft/s
    B) 7 ft/s   E) none of these
    *C) 70 ft/s

12. Sinusoidal water waves are generated in a large ripple tank. The
    waves travel at 20 cm/s and their adjacent crests are 5.0 cm apart.
    The time required for each new whole cycle to be generated is:

    A) 100 s   B) 4.0 s   C) 2.0 s   D) 0.5 s   *E) 0.25 s

13. A traveling sinusoidal wave is shown below. At which point is the
    motion 180° out of phase with the motion at point P?

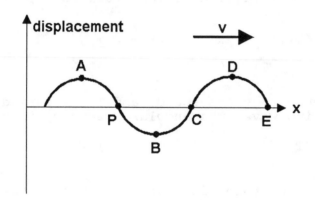

    A) A   B) B   *C) C   D) D   E) E

14. The displacement of a string carrying a traveling sinusoidal wave is
    given by y(x,t) = y_m sin(kx-ωt-Φ). At time t = 0 the point at x = 0
    has a displacement of 0 and is moving in the positive y direction.
    The phase constant Φ is:

    A) 45°   B) 90°   C) 135°   *D) 180°   E) 270°

15. The displacement of a string carrying a traveling sinusoidal wave is given by $y(x,t) = y_m\sin(kx-\omega t-\Phi)$. At time $t = 0$ the point at $x = 0$ has a velocity of 0 and a positive displacement. The phase constant Φ is:

A) 45°   B) 90°   C) 135°   D) 180°   *E) 270°

16. The displacement of a string carrying a traveling sinusoidal wave is given by $y(x,t) = y_m\sin(kx-\omega t-\Phi)$. At time $t = 0$ the point at $x = 0$ has velocity v_0 and displacement y_0. The phase constant Φ is given by $\tan\Phi =$:

A) $v_0/\omega y_0$ *B) $\omega y_0/v_0$ C) $\omega v_0/y_0$ D) $y_0/\omega v_0$ E) $\omega v_0 y_0$

17. A sinusoidal transverse wave is traveling on a string. Any point on the string:

A) moves in the same direction as the wave
B) moves in simple harmonic motion with a different frequency than that of the wave
*C) moves in simple harmonic motion with the same angular frequency as the wave
D) moves in uniform circular motion with a different angular speed than the wave
E) moves in uniform circular motion with the same angular speed as the wave

18. The transverse wave shown is traveling from left to right in a medium. The direction of the instantaneous velocity of the medium at point P is:

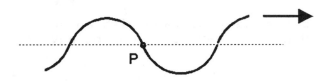

*A) ↑
B) ↓
C) →

D) ↗
E) no direction since v = 0

209

19. A wave traveling to the right on a stretched string is shown below. The direction of the instantaneous velocity of the point P on the string is:

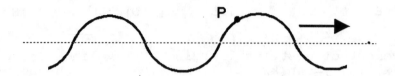

A) ↑
B) ↓
*C) →

D) ↗
E) no direction since v = 0

20. Any point on a string carrying a sinusoidal wave is moving with its maximum speed when:

A) the magnitude of its acceleration is a maximum
B) the magnitude of its displacement is a maximum
*C) the magnitude of its displacement is a minimum
D) the magnitude of its displacement is half the amplitude
E) the magnitude of its displacement is one fourth the amplitude

21. Suppose the maximum speed of a string carrying a sinusoidal wave is v_s. When the displacement of a point on the string is half its maximum, the speed of the point is:

A) $v_s/2$ B) $2v_s$ C) $v_s/4$ D) $3v_s/4$ *E) $\sqrt{3}v_s/2$

22. A string carries a sinusoidal wave with an amplitude of 2.0 cm and a frequency of 100 Hz. The maximum speed of any point on the string is:

A) 2.0 m/s
B) 4.0 m/s
C) 6.3 m/s
*D) 13 m/s
E) unknown (not enough information is given)

23. A transverse traveling sinusoidal wave on a string has a frequency of 100 Hz, a wavelength of 0.040 m and an amplitude of 2.0 mm. The maximum velocity in m/s of any point on the string is:

A) 0.2   *B) 1.3   C) 4   D) 15   E) 25

24. A transverse traveling sinusoidal wave on a string has a frequency of 100 Hz, a wavelength of 0.040 m and an amplitude of 2.0 mm. The maximum acceleration in m/s^2 of any point on the string is:

A) 0   B) 130   *C) 395   D) 1500   E) 2500

25. The speed of a sinusoidal wave on a string depends on:

A) the frequency of the wave   *D) the tension in the string
B) the wavelength of the wave   E) the amplitude of the wave
C) the length of the string

26. The time required for a small pulse to travel from A to B on a stretched cord shown is NOT altered by changing:

A) the linear density of the cord
B) the length between A and B
*C) the shape of the pulse
D) the tension in the cord
E) none of the above (changes in all alter the time)

27. For a given medium, the frequency of a wave is:

A) independent of wavelength
B) proportional to wavelength
*C) inversely proportional to wavelength
D) proportional to the amplitude
E) inversely proportional to the amplitude

28. The tension in a string with a linear density of 0.0010 kg/m is 0.40 N. A 100 Hz sinusoidal wave on this string has a wavelength of:

A) 0.05 cm   *B) 2.0 cm   C) 5.0 cm   D) 500 cm   E) 2000 cm

29. When a 100 Hz vibrator is used to generate a sinusoidal wave on a certain string the wavelength is 10 cm. When the tension in the string is doubled the generator produces a wave with a frequency and wavelength of:

A) 200 Hz and 20 cm   *D) 100 Hz and 14 cm
B) 141 Hz and 10 cm   E) 50 Hz and 14 cm
C) 100 Hz and 20 cm

30. A source of frequency f sends waves of wavelength traveling with speed v in some medium. If the frequency is changed from f to 2f, then the new wavelength and new speed are (respectively):

A) 2λ, v   *B) λ/2, v   C) λ, 2v   D) λ, v/2   E) λ/2, 2v

31. A long string is constructed by joining the ends of 2 shorter strings. The tension in the strings is the same but string I has 4 times the linear density of string II. When a sinusoidal wave passes from string I to string II:

  A) the frequency decreases by a factor of 4
  B) the frequency decreases by a factor of 2
  C) the wavelength decreases by a factor of 4
 *D) the wavelength decreases by a factor of 2
  E) the wavelength increases by a factor of 2

32. Three strings are made of the same material. String 1 has length L and tension T, string 2 has length 2L and tension 2T, and string 3 has length 3L and tension 3T. A pulse is started at one end of each string. If the pulses start at the same time, the order in which they reach the other end is:

 *A) 123
  B) 321
  C) 231

  D) 312
  E) they all take the same time

33. A long string is constructed by joining the ends of 2 shorter strings. The tension in the strings is the same but string I has 4 times the linear density of string II. When a sinusoidal wave passes from string I to string II:

  A) the frequency decreases by a factor of 4
  B) the frequency decreases by a factor of 2
  C) the wave speed decreases by a factor of 4
 *D) the wave speed decreases by a factor of 2
  E) the wave speed increases by a factor of 2

34. Two identical but separate strings, with the same tension, carry sinusoidal waves with the same amplitude. Wave A has a frequency that is twice that of wave B and transmits energy at a rate that is _____ that of wave B.

  A) half
  B) twice
  C) one fourth

 *D) four times
  E) eight times

35. Two identical but separate strings, with the same tension, carry sinusoidal waves with the same frequency. Wave A has an amplitude that is twice that of wave B and transmits energy at a rate that is _____ that of wave B.

  A) half
  B) twice
  C) one fourth

 *D) four times
  E) eight times

36. A sinusoidal wave is generated by moving the end of a string up and down periodically. The generator must supply the greatest power when the end of the string:

   A) has its greatest acceleration
   B) has its greatest displacement
   C) has half its greatest displacement
   D) has one fourth its greatest displacement
  *E) has its least displacement

37. A sinusoidal wave is generated by moving the end of a string up and down periodically. The generator does not supply any power when the end of the string

   A) has its least acceleration
  *B) has its greatest displacement
   C) has half its greatest displacement
   D) has one fourth its greatest displacement
   E) has its least displacement

38. The sum of two sinusoidal traveling waves is a sinusoidal traveling wave only if:

   A) their amplitudes are the same and they travel in the same direction
   B) their amplitudes are the same and they travel in opposite directions
  *C) their frequencies are the same and they travel in the same direction
   D) their frequencies are the same and they travel in opposite directions
   E) their frequencies are the same and their amplitudes are the same

39. Constructive interference between two sinusoidal waves of the same frequency occurs only if they:

   A) travel in opposite directions and are in phase
   B) travel in opposite directions and are 180° out of phase
  *C) travel in the same direction and are in phase
   D) travel in the same direction and are 180° out of phase
   E) travel in the same direction and are 90° out of phase

40. Total destructive interference between two sinusoidal waves of the same frequency and amplitude occurs only if they:

   A) travel in opposite directions and are in phase
   B) travel in opposite directions and are 180° out of phase
   C) travel in the same direction and are in phase
  *D) travel in the same direction and are 180° out of phase
   E) travel in the same direction and are 90° out of phase

41. Two sinusoidal waves travel in the same direction and have the same frequency. Their amplitudes are y_{1m} and y_{2m}. The smallest possible amplitude of the resultant wave is:

A) $y_{1m} + y_{2m}$ and occurs when they are 180° out of phase
*B) $|y_{1m} - y_{2m}|$ and occurs when they are 180° out of phase
C) $y_{1m} + y_{2m}$ and occurs when they are in phase
D) $|y_{1m} - y_{2m}|$ and occurs when they are in phase
E) $|y_{1m} - y_{2m}|$ and occurs when they are 90° out of phase

42. Two sinusoidal waves have the same angular frequency, the same amplitude y_m, and travel in the same direction in the same medium. If they differ in phase by 50°, the amplitude of the resultant wave is given by

A) $y_m \cos 50°$
B) $2y_m \cos 50°$
C) $y_m \cos 25°$

*D) $2y_m \cos 25°$
E) $2y_m \cos 100°$

43. Two separated sources emit sinusoidal traveling waves that have the same wavelength λ and are in phase at their respective sources. One travels a distance ℓ_1 to get to the observation point while the other travels a distance ℓ_2. The amplitude is a minimum at the observation point if $\ell_1 - \ell_2$ is:

*A) an odd multiple of $\lambda/2$
B) an odd multiple of $\lambda/4$
C) a multiple of λ

D) an odd multiple of $\pi/2$
E) a multiple of π

44. Two separated sources emit sinusoidal traveling waves that have the same wavelength λ and are in phase at their respective sources. One travels a distance ℓ_1 to get to the observation point while the other travels a distance ℓ_2. The amplitude is a maximum at the observation point if $\ell_1 - \ell_2$ is:

A) an odd multiple of $\lambda/2$
B) an odd multiple of $\lambda/4$
*C) a multiple of λ

D) an odd multiple of $\pi/2$
E) a multiple of π

45. Two sources, S_1 and S_2, each emit waves of wavelength λ in the same medium. The phase difference between the two waves, at the point P shown, is $(2\pi/\lambda)(\ell_2 - \ell_1) + \in$. The quantity $\in$ is:

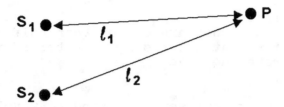

A) the distance S_1S_2
B) the angle S_1PS_2
C) $\pi/2$
*D) the phase difference between the two sources
E) zero for transverse waves, π for longitudinal waves

46. A wave on a stretched string is reflected from a fixed end P of the string. The phase difference, at P, between the incident and reflected waves is:

A) zero
*B) π rad
C) $\pi/2$ rad
D) depends on the velocity of the wave
E) depends on the frequency of the wave

47. The sinusoidal wave $y(x,t) = y_m\sin(kx - \omega t)$ is incident on the fixed end of a string at $x = L$. The reflected wave is given by:

A) $y_m\sin(kx + \omega t)$
B) $-y_m\sin(kx + \omega t)$
C) $y_m\sin(kx + \omega t - kL)$
*D) $y_m\sin(kx + \omega t - 2kL)$
E) $-y_m\sin(kx + \omega t + 2kL)$

48. A wave on a string is reflected from a fixed end. The reflected wave:

A) is in phase with the original wave at the end
*B) is 180° out of phase with the original wave at the end
C) has a larger amplitude than the original wave
D) has a larger speed than the original wave
E) cannot be transverse

49. A standing wave:

  *A) can be constructed from two similar waves traveling in opposite
      directions
   B) must be transverse
   C) must be longitudinal
   D) has motionless points that are closer than half a wavelength
   E) has a wave velocity that differs by a factor of two from what it
      would be for a traveling wave

50. Which of the following represents a standing wave?

   A) y = 6sin(3x + 2t) - 6cos(3x + 2t)
  *B) y = 6cos(3x - 2t) + 6cos(2t - 3x)
   C) y = 6cos(3x - 2t) - 6sin(2t - 3x)
   D) y = 6sin(3x - 2t) - 6cos(2t + 3x)
   E) y = 6sin(3x) + 6cos(2t)

51. Two traveling waves:
$$y_1 = A \sin[k(x - vt)]$$
    and
$$y_2 = A \sin[k(x + vt)]$$
    are superposed on the same string. The distance between the adjacent
    nodes is:

   A) vt/π B) $vt/2\pi$ C) $\pi/2k$ *D) π/k E) $2\pi/k$

52. If λ is the wavelength of the each of the component sinusoidal
    traveling waves that form a standing wave, the distance between
    adjacent nodes in the standing wave is:

   A) $\lambda/4$ *B) $\lambda/2$ C) $3\lambda/4$ D) λ E) 2λ

53. A standing wave pattern is established in a string as shown. The
    wavelength of one of the component traveling waves is:

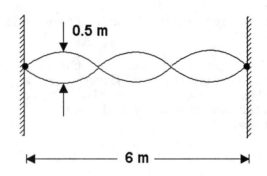

   A) 0.25 m   B) 0.5 m   C) 1 m   D) 2 m   *E) 4 m

216

54. Standing waves are produced by the interference of two traveling sinusoidal waves, each of frequency 100 Hz. The distance from the 2nd node to the 5th node is 60 cm. The wavelength of each of the two original waves is:

A) 50 cm   *B) 40 cm   C) 30 cm   D) 20 cm   E) 15 cm

55. A string of length 100 cm is held fixed at both ends. This string CANNOT be made to vibrate with a wavelength of:

*A) 400 cm   B) 200 cm   C) 100 cm   D) 66.7 cm   E) 50 cm

56. A string of length L is clamped at each end. It CANNOT vibrate with a wavelength equal to:

A) L   B) 2L   C) L/2   D) 2L/3   *E) 4L

57. Two sinusoidal waves, each of wavelength 5 m and amplitude 10 cm, travel in opposite directions on a 20 m stretched string which is clamped at each end. Excluding the nodes at the ends of the string, how many nodes appear in the resulting standing wave?

A) 3   B) 4   C) 5   *D) 7   E) 8

58. A string, clamped at its ends, vibrates in three segments. The string is 100 cm long. The wavelength is:

A) 33.3 cm   D) 300 cm
*B) 66.7 cm   E) need to know the frequency
C) 150 cm

59. A stretched string, clamped at its ends, vibrates in its fundamental frequency. To double the fundamental frequency, one can change the string tension by a factor of:

A) 2   *B) 4   C) $\sqrt{2}$ D) 1/2   E) $1/\sqrt{2}$

60. When a string is vibrating in a standing wave pattern _____ power is transmitted across an antinode than across a node.

A) more
B) less
*C) the same (zero)
D) the same (non-zero)
E) sometimes more, sometimes less, and sometimes the same

61. A 40-cm long string, with one end clamped and the other free to move transversely, is vibrating in its fundamental standing wave mode. The wavelength of the constituent traveling waves is:

A) 10 cm   B) 20 cm   C) 40 cm   D) 80 cm   *E) 160 cm

62. A 30-cm long string, with one end clamped and the other free to move transversely, is vibrating in its second harmonic. The wavelength of the constituent traveling waves is:

A) 10 cm   B) 30 cm   *C) 40 cm   D) 60 cm   E) 120 cm

63. A 40-cm long string, with one end clamped and the other free to move transversely, is vibrating in its fundamental standing wave mode. If the wave speed is 320 cm/s the frequency is:

A) 32 Hz   B) 16 Hz   C) 8 Hz   D) 4 Hz   *E) 2 Hz

64. A 30-cm long string, with one end clamped and the other free to move transversely, is vibrating in its fundamental standing wave mode. If the wave speed is 240 cm/s the frequency is:

A) 24 Hz   B) 8 Hz   *C) 6 Hz   D) 3 Hz   E) 2 Hz

1. The speed of a sound wave is determined by:

A) its amplitude
B) its intensity
C) its pitch
D) number of overtones present
*E) the transmitting medium

2. Take the speed of sound to be 340 m/s. A thunder clap is heard about 3 s after the lightning is seen. The source of both light and sound is:

A) moving overhead faster than the speed of sound
B) emitting a much higher frequency than is heard
C) emitting a much lower frequency than is heard
*D) about 1000 m away
E) much more than 1000 m away

3. A sound wave has a wavelength of 3.0 m. The distance from a compression center to the adjacent rarefaction center is:

A) 0.75 m
*B) 1.5 m
C) 3.0 m
D) need to know wave speed
E) need to know frequency

4. A fire whistle emits a tone of 170 Hz. Take the speed of sound in air to be 340 m/s. The wavelength of this sound is about:

A) 0.5 m   B) 1.0 m   *C) 2.0 m   D) 3.0 m   E) 340 m

5. During a time interval of exactly one period of vibration of a tuning fork, the emitted sound travels a distance:

A) equal to the length of the tuning fork
B) equal to twice the length of the tuning fork
C) of about 330 m
D) which decreases with time
*E) of one wavelength in air

6. You are listening to an "A" note played on a violin string. Let the subscript "s" refer to the violin string and "a" refer to the air. Then:

*A) $f_s = f_a$ but $\lambda_s \neq \lambda_a$
 B) $f_s = f_a$ and $\lambda_s = \lambda_a$
 C) $\lambda_s = \lambda_a$ but $f_s \neq f_a$
 D) $\lambda_s \neq \lambda_a$ and $f_s \neq f_a$
 E) linear density of string = volume density of air

7. "Beats" in sound refer to:

 A) interference of two waves of the same frequency
*B) combination of two waves of slightly different frequency
 C) reversal of phase of reflected wave relative to incident wave
 D) two media having slightly different sound velocities
 E) effect of relative motion of source and observer

8. To produce beats it is necessary to use two waves:

 A) traveling in opposite directions
*B) of slightly different frequencies
 C) of equal wavelengths
 D) of equal amplitudes
 E) whose ratio of frequencies is an integer

9. In order for two sound waves to produce audible beats, it is essential that the two waves have:

 A) the same amplitude   D) slightly different amplitudes
 B) the same frequency   *E) slightly different frequencies
 C) the same number of overtones

10. The largest number of beats per second will be heard from which pair of tuning forks?

 A) 200 and 201 Hz   *D) 763 and 774 Hz
 B) 256 and 260 Hz   E) 8420 and 8422 Hz
 C) 534 and 540 Hz

11. Two stationary tuning forks (350 and 352 Hz) are struck simultaneously. The resulting sound is observed to:

*A) beat with a frequency of 2 beats/s
 B) beat with a frequency of 351 beats/s
 C) be loud but not beat
 D) be Doppler shifted by 2 Hz
 E) have a frequency of 702 Hz

12. When listening to tuning forks of frequency 256 Hz and 259 Hz, one hears the following number of beats per second:

A) 0.67   B) 1.5   C) 257.5   D) 515   *E) 3

13. Two identical tuning forks vibrate at 256 Hz. One of them is then loaded with a drop of wax, after which 6 beats per second are heard. The period of the loaded tuning fork is:

A) 0.006 s   D) 0.003 s
B) 0.005 s   E) none of these
*C) 0.004 s

14. Which of the following properties of a sound wave determine its "pitch"?

A) amplitude
B) distance form source to detector
*C) frequency
D) phase
E) speed

15. Two notes are an "octave" apart. The ratio of their frequencies is:

A) 8   B) 10   C) $\sqrt{8}$ *D) 2   E) $\sqrt{2}$

16. Consider two imaginary spherical surfaces of different radius, both centered on a point sound source emitting spherical waves. The power transmitted across the larger sphere is _____ the power transmitted across the smaller and the intensity at a point on the larger sphere is _____ the intensity at a point on the smaller.

A) greater than, the same as   *D) the same as, less than
B) greater than, greater than   E) the same as, the same as
C) greater than, less than

17. If the power output of a sound source emitting spherical waves is 100 W, the sound intensity 5.0 m from the source is:

*A) 0.32 W/m^2 B) 1.6 W/m^2 C) 4.0 W/m^2 D) 20 W/m^2 E) 100 W/m^2

18. The standard reference sound level is about:

*A) the threshold of human hearing at 1000 Hz
B) the threshold of pain for human hearing at 1000 Hz
C) the level of sound produced when the 1 kg standard mass is dropped 1 m onto a concrete floor
D) the level of normal conversation
E) the level of sound emitted by a standard 60 Hz tuning fork

19. The intensity of sound wave A is 100 times that of sound wave B. Relative to wave B the sound level of wave A is:

A) -2 db   B) +2 db   C) +10 db   *D) +20 db   E) +100 db

20. The intensity of a certain sound wave is 6 microwatts/cm^2. If its intensity is raised by 10 decibels, the new intensity (in microwatts/cm^2) is:

*A) 60   B) 6.6   C) 6.06   D) 600   E) 12

21. If the sound level is increased by 10 db the intensity increases by a factor of:

A) 2   B) 5   *C) 10   D) 20   E) 100

22. A spherical sound wave is emitted by a point source. Relative to the sound level 1 m from the source, the sound level 5 m from the source is about:

A) 0 db   B) +7 db   C) -7 db   D) +14 db   *E) -14 db

23. To raise the pitch of a certain piano string, the piano tuner:

A) loosens the string
*B) tightens the string
C) shortens the string from the string
D) lengthens the string
E) removes some mass

24. A piano wire has length L and mass M. If its fundamental frequency is f, its tension is:

A) 2Lf/m   B) 4MLf   C) 2Mf^2/L   D) 4f^{2}L^3/M   *E) 4LMf^2

25. If the length of a piano wire (of given density) is increased by 5%, what approximate change in tension is necessary to keep its fundamental frequency unchanged?

A) decrease of 10%   *D) increase of 10%
B) decrease of 5%   E) increase of 20%
C) increase of 5%

26. A piano wire has a length of 81 cm and a mass of 2.0 gram. If its fundamental frequency is to be 394 Hz, it must be stretched by a tension of:

A) 650 N
B) 831 N
C) 990 N

*D) 1001 N
E) none of these

27. A stretched wire of length 1.0 m is clamped at both ends. It is plucked at its center as shown. The three longest wavelengths in the wire are (in meters):

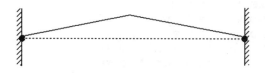

A) 4, 2, 1
B) 2, 1, 0.5
*C) 2, 0.67, 0.4

D) 1, 0.5, 0.33
E) 1, 0.67, 0.5

28. A column of argon is open at one end and closed at the other. The shortest such column which will resonate with a 200 Hz tuning fork is 42.5 cm. The speed of sound in argon must be:

A) 85.0 m/s   B) 170 m/s   *C) 340 m/s   D) 470 m/s   E) 940 m/s

29. A tuning fork produces sound waves of wavelength λ in air. This sound is used to cause resonance in an air column, closed at one end. The length of this column CANNOT be:

A) $\lambda/4$ *B) $2\lambda/4$ C) $3\lambda/4$ D) $5\lambda/4$ E) $7\lambda/4$

30. A 1024 Hz tuning fork is used to obtain a series of resonance levels in a gas column. The length of the column changes by 20 cm from resonance to resonance. From this data, the speed of sound in this gas is:

A) 20 cm/s
B) 51.2 cm/s
C) 102.4 cm/s

D) 204.8 m/s
*E) 409.6 m/s

31. A vibrating tuning fork is held over a water column. As the water level is allowed to fall, a loud sound is heard for water levels separated by 17 cm. If the speed of sound in air is 340 m/s, the frequency of the tuning fork is:

   A) 500 Hz
  *B) 1000 Hz
   C) 2000 Hz

   D) 5780 Hz
   E) 578,000 Hz

32. An open organ pipe is operating at one of its resonant frequencies. The open and closed ends are respectively:

   A) pressure node, pressure node
  *B) pressure node, displacement node
   C) displacement antinode, pressure node
   D) displacement node, displacement node
   E) pressure antinode, pressure antinode

33. An organ pipe has length L. Its fundamental frequency is proportional to:

   A) L   *B) 1/L   C) $1/L^2$ D) L^2 E) $\sqrt{L}$

34. Five organ pipes are described below. Which one has the highest frequency fundamental?

  *A) an 8 ft open pipe
   B) a 10 ft open pipe
   C) a 5 ft closed pipe
   D) a 9 ft closed pipe
   E) a pipe in which the displacement nodes are 16 ft apart

35. If the speed of sound is 340 m/s, the shortest closed pipe which resonates at 218 Hz is:

   A) 23 cm   B) 17 cm   *C) 39 cm   D) 78 cm   E) 1.56 cm

36. The lowest tone produced by a certain organ comes from a 16 ft closed pipe. If the speed of sound is 1120 ft/s, the frequency of this tone is approximately:

  *A) 17.5 Hz   B) 35 Hz   C) 44 Hz   D) 52 Hz   E) 26 Hz

37. The speed of sound in air is 340 m/s. The shortest air column, closed at one end, which will respond to a 512 Hz tuning fork is approximately:

   A) 4.2 cm   B) 9.4 cm   *C) 17 cm   D) 33 cm   E) 66 cm

224

38. If the speed of sound is 340 m/s, the two lowest frequencies of an 0.5 m organ pipe, closed at one end, are approximately:

A) 170 and 340 Hz
*B) 170 and 510 Hz
C) 340 and 680 Hz

D) 340 and 1020 Hz
E) 57 and 170 Hz

39. Organ pipe X (open at both ends) is twice as long as organ pipe Y (open at one end) as shown. The ratio of their fundamental frequencies $f_X : f_Y$ is:

*A) 1:1   B) 1:2   C) 2:1   D) 1:4   E) 4:1

40. A 200 cm open organ pipe is in resonance with a sound wave of wavelength 200 cm. The pipe is operating in its:

A) fundamental frequency
*B) first overtone
C) second overtone

D) third overtone
E) fourth overtone

41. An open organ pipe is 2.8 ft long. Assuming that the speed of sound is 1120 ft/s, the frequency of the third harmonic of this pipe is:

A) 200 Hz
B) 300 Hz
C) 400 Hz

*D) 600 Hz
E) none of these

42. The "A" on a trumpet and a clarinet have the same pitch, but the two are clearly distinguishable. Which property is most important in enabling one to distinguish between these two instruments?

A) intensity
B) fundamental frequency
C) displacement amplitude

D) pressure amplitude
*E) harmonic content

43. The valves of a trumpet and the slide of a trombone are for the purpose of:

A) playing short (staccato) notes
B) tuning the instruments
C) changing the harmonic content
*D) changing the length of the air column
E) producing gradations in loudness

44. Two small identical speakers are connected (in phase) to the same source. The speakers are 3 m apart and at ear level. An observer stands at X, 4 m in front of one speaker as shown. The sound he hears will be least intense if the wavelength is:

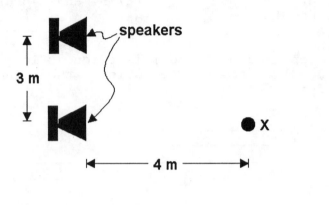

A) 1 m   *B) 2 m   C) 3 m   D) 4 m   E) 5 m

45. Two small identical speakers are connected (in phase) to the same source. The speakers are 3 m apart and at ear level. An observer stands at X, 4 m in front of one speaker as shown. The sound she hears will be most intense if the wavelength is:

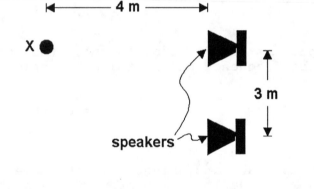

A) 5 m   B) 4 m   C) 3 m   D) 2 m   *E) 1 m

46. The rise in pitch of an approaching siren is an apparent increase in its:

A) speed   D) wavelength
B) amplitude   E) number of overtones
*C) frequency

47. A stationary source generates 5.0 Hz water waves whose speed is 2.0 m/s. A boat is approaching the source at 10 m/s. The frequency of these waves, as observed by a person in the boat, is:

A) 5.0 Hz   B) 15 Hz   C) 20 Hz   D) 25 Hz   *E) 30 Hz

48. A source S generates circular outgoing waves on a lake. The wave speed is 5.0 m/s and the crest-to-crest distance is 2.0 m. A person in a motor boat heads directly toward S at 3.0 m/s. To this person, the frequency of these waves is:

A) 1.0 Hz   B) 1.5 Hz   C) 2.0 Hz   *D) 4.0 Hz   E) 8.0 Hz

49. A source emits a sound wave of frequency f. If it were possible for a man to travel toward the source at the speed of sound, he would observe the emitted sound to have a frequency of:

A) zero   B) f/2   C) 2f/3   *D) 2f   E) infinity

50. A source emits sound with a frequency of 1000 Hz. Both it and an observer are moving in the same direction with the same speed, 100 m/s. If the speed of sound is 340 m/s, the observer hears sound with a frequency of:

A) 294 Hz   B) 545 Hz   *C) 1000 Hz   D) 1830 Hz   E) 3400 Hz

51. A source emits sound with a frequency of 1000 Hz. Both it and an observer are moving toward each other, each with a speed of 100 m/s. If the speed of sound is 340 m/s, the observer hears sound with a frequency of:

A) 294 Hz   B) 545 Hz   C) 1000 Hz   *D) 1830 Hz   E) 3400 Hz

52. A source emits sound with a frequency of 1000 Hz. It is moving at 20 m/s toward a reflecting wall. If the speed of sound is 340 m/s an observer at rest directly behind the source hears a beat frequency of:

A) 11 Hz   B) 86 Hz   C) 97 Hz   D) 118 Hz   *E) 183 Hz

53. In each of the following two situations a source emits sound with a frequency of 1000 Hz. In situation I the source is moving at 100 m/s toward an observer at rest. In situation II the observer is moving at 100 m/s toward the source, which is stationary. The speed of sound is 340 m/s. The frequencies heard by the observers in the two situations are:

*A) I: 1417 Hz; II: 1294 Hz   D) I: 773 Hz; II: 706 Hz
 B) I: 1417 Hz; II: 1417 Hz   E) I: 773 Hz; II: 773 Hz
 C) I: 1294 Hz; II: 1294 Hz

54. A plane produces a sonic boom only when:

   A) it breaks the sound barrier
   B) it emits sound waves of high frequency
   C) it flys at high altitudes
   D) it flys on a curved path
  *E) it flys faster than the speed of sound

55. If the speed of sound is 340 m/s a plane flying at 400 m/s creates a conical shock wave with an apex half angle of:

   A) 0 (no shock wave)   D) 50°
   B) 32°   *E) 58°
   C) 40°

56. The speed of sound is 340 m/s. A plane flys horizontally at an altitude of 10,000 m and a speed of 400 m/s. When an observer on the ground hears the sonic boom the horizontal distance from the point on its path directly above the observer to the plane is:

   A) 5800 m   *B) 6200 m   C) 8400 m   D) 12,000 m   E) 16,000 m

1. If two objects are in thermal equilibrium with each other

A) they cannot be moving
B) they cannot be undergoing an elastic collision
C) they cannot have different pressures
*D) they cannot be at different temperatures
E) they cannot be falling in the earth's gravitational field

2. When two gases separated by a diathermal wall are in thermal equilibrium with each other:

A) only their pressure must be the same
B) only their volumes must be the same
C) they must have the same number of particles
D) they must have the same pressure and the same volume
*E) only their temperatures must be the same

3. A balloon is filled with cold air and placed in a warm room. It is NOT in thermal equilibrium with the air of the room until

A) it rises to the ceiling   D) it starts to contract
B) it sinks to the floor   E) none of the above
*C) it stops expanding

4. Suppose object C is in thermal equilibrium with object A and with object B. The zeroth law of thermodynamics states:

A) that C will always be in thermal equilibrium with both A and B
B) that C must transfer energy to both A and B
*C) that A is in thermal equilibrium with B
D) that A cannot be in thermal equilibrium with B
E) nothing about the relationship between A and B

5. The zeroth law of thermodynamics allows us to define

A) work   D) thermal equilibrium
B) pressure   E) internal energy
*C) temperature

6. If the zeroth law of thermodynamics were not valid, which of the following could not be considered a property of an object?

A) pressure   D) momentum
B) center of mass energy   *E) temperature
C) internal energy

7. The international standard thermometer is kept:

A) near Washington, D.C. D) near Rome, Italy
B) near Paris, France *E) nowhere (there is none)
C) near the north pole

8. In constructing a thermometer it is NECESSARY to use a substance that:

A) expands with rising temperature
B) expands linearly with rising temperature
C) will not freeze
D) will not boil
*E) undergoes some change when heated or cooled

9. The "triple point" is that point for which the temperature and pressure are such that:

A) only solid and liquid are in equilibrium
B) only liquid and vapor are in equilibrium
C) only solid and vapor are in equilibrium
*D) solid, liquid and vapor are all in equilibrium
E) the temperature, pressure and density are all numerically equal

10. Constant-volume gas thermometers using different gases all indicate nearly the same temperature when in contact with the same object if:

A) the volumes are all extremely large
B) the volumes are all the same
C) the pressures are all extremely large
D) the pressures are the same
*E) the particle concentrations are all extremely small

11. A constant-volume gas thermometer is used to measure the temperature of an object. When the thermometer is in contact with water at its triple point (273.16 K) the pressure in the thermometer is 8.500×10^4 Pa. When it is in contact with the object the pressure is 9.650×10^4 Pa. The temperature of the object is:

A) 37.0 K   B) 241 K   *C) 310 K   D) 314 K   E) 2020 K

12. When a certain constant volume gas thermometer is in thermal contact with water at its triple point (273.16 K) the pressure is 6.30×10^4 Pa. For this thermometer a kelvin corresponds to a change in pressure of about:

A) 4.34×10^2 Pa   D) 2.31×10^3 Pa
*B) 2.31×10^2 Pa   E) 1.72×10^7 Pa
C) 1.72×10^3 Pa

230

13. The lowest temperature that can be measured by a constant-volume gas
    thermometer is about:

A) 0 K   *B) 1 K   C) 20 K   D) 50 K   E) 100 K

14. The Celsius and Fahrenheit temperature systems agree in the:

   A) size of their degree
  *B) manner in which their fixed points are determined
   C) location of their zero points
   D) location of their -20° points
   E) temperature reading they give for liquid nitrogen

15. There is a temperature at which the reading on the Kelvin scale is
    numerically:

   A) equal to that on the Celsius scale
   B) lower than that on the Celsius scale
  *C) equal to that on the Fahrenheit scale
   D) less than zero
   E) none of the above

16. Fahrenheit and Kelvin scales agree at a reading of:

   A) -40   B) 0   C) 273   D) 301   *E) 574

17. Which one of the following statements is true?

   A) temperatures differing by 25° on the Fahrenheit scale must differ by
      45° on the Celsius scale
   B) 40 K corresponds to -40°C
  *C) temperatures which differ by 10° on the Celsius scale must differ by
      18° on the Fahrenheit scale
   D) water at 90°C is warmer than water at 202°F
   E) 0°F corresponds to -32°C

18. A Kelvin thermometer and a Fahrenheit thermometer both give the same
    reading for a certain sample. The corresponding Celsius temperature
    is:

A) 574°C   B) 232°C   *C) 301°C   D) 614°C   E) 276°C

19. Room temperature is about 20 degrees on the:

   A) Kelvin scale   D) absolute scale
  *B) Celsius scale   E) C major scale
   C) Fahrenheit scale

20. A thermometer indicates 98.6°C. It may be:

A) outdoors on a cold day
B) in a comfortable room
*C) in a cup of hot tea
D) in a normal person's mouth
E) in liquid air

21. The two metallic strips that constitute some thermostats must differ in:

A) length
B) thickness
C) mass
D) rate at which they conduct heat
*E) coefficient of linear expansion

22. Thin strips of iron and zinc are riveted together to form a bimetallic strip which bends when heated. The iron is on the inside of the bend because:

A) it has a higher coefficient of linear expansion
*B) it has a lower coefficient of linear expansion
C) it has a higher specific heat
D) it has a lower specific heat
E) it conducts heat better

23. It is more difficult to measure the coefficient of expansion of a liquid than a solid because:

A) no relation exists between linear and volume expansion coefficients
B) a liquid tends to evaporate
C) a liquid expands too much when heated
D) a liquid expands too little when heated
*E) the containing vessel also expands

24. A surveyor's 100 ft steel tape is correct at 68°F. On a hot day the tape has expanded to 100.02 ft. On that day, the tape indicates a distance of 46.57 ft between two points. The true distance between these points is:

A) 46.59 ft   B) 46.58 ft   C) 46.57 ft   *D) 46.56 ft   E) 46.55 ft

25. The figure shows a rectangular brass plate at 0°C in which there is cut a rectangular hole of dimensions indicated. If the temperature of the plate is raised to 150°C:

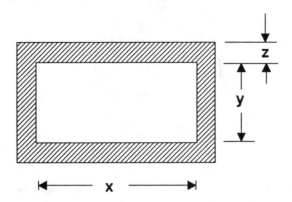

   A) x will increase and y will decrease
   B) both x and y will decrease
   C) x will decrease and y will increase
  *D) both x and y will increase
   E) depends on the dimension z

26. The Stanford linear accelerator contains hundreds of brass disks tightly fitted into a steel tube (see figure). The coefficient of linear expansion of the brass is 2.00×10^{-5} per C°. The system was assembled by cooling the disks in dry ice (-57°C) to enable them to just slide into the close-fitting tube. If the diameter of a disk is 80.00 mm at 43°C, what is its diameter (mm) in the dry ice?

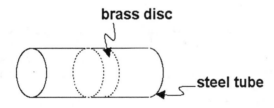

brass disc

steel tube

   A) 78.40   *D) 79.84
   B) 79.68   E) none of these
   C) 80.16

27. When the temperature of a copper penny is increased by 100 C°, its diameter increases by 0.17%. The area of one of its faces increases by:

   A) 0.17%   *B) 0.34%   C) 0.51%   D) 0.13%   E) 0.27%

28. An annular ring of aluminum is cut from an aluminum sheet as shown.
    When this ring is heated:

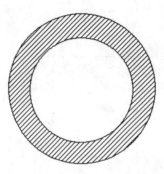

A) the aluminum expands outward and the hole remains the same in size
B) the hole decreases in diameter
C) the area of the hole expands the same percent as any area of the
   aluminum
*D) the area of the hole expands a greater percent than any area of the
   aluminum
E) linear expansion forces the shape of the hole to be slightly
   elliptical

29. Possible units for the coefficient of volume expansion are:

A) $mm/C°$ B) $mm^3/C°$ C) $(C°)^3$ D) $1/(C°)^3$ *E) $1/C°$

30. The mercury column in an ordinary medical thermometer doubles in
    length when its temperature changes from 95°F to 105°F. Choose the
    correct statement:

A) the coefficient of volume expansion of mercury is 0.1 per F°
B) the coefficient of volume expansion of mercury is 0.3 per F°
C) the coefficient of volume expansion of mercury is (0.1/3) per F°
D) the vacuum above the column helps to "pull up" the mercury this
   large amount
*E) none of the above is true

31. The coefficient of linear expansion of iron is 10^{-5} per C°. The
    volume of an iron cube, 5 cm on edge, will increase by what amount
    if it is heated from 10°C to 60°C?

A) 0.00375 cm^3 D) 0.00125 cm^3
*B) 0.1875 cm^3 E) 0.0625 cm^3
C) 0.0225 cm^3

32. The coefficient of linear expansion of steel is 11×10^{-6} per C°. A steel ball has a volume of 100 cm^3 (exactly) at 0°C. When heated to 100°C, its volume becomes:

*A) 100.33 cm^3
B) 100.0011 cm^3
C) 100.0033 cm^3
D) 100.000011 cm^3
E) none of these

33. The coefficient of expansion of a certain steel is 0.000012 per C°. The coefficient of volume expansion, in (C°)$^{-1}$, is:

A) $(0.000012)^3$
B) $(4\pi/3)(0.000012)^3$
*C) 3 x 0.000012
D) 0.000012
E) depends on the shape of the volume to which it will be applied

34. A common model of a solid assumes the atoms to be point masses which execute simple harmonic motion about their average location. The coefficient of linear expansion of such a model is:

*A) zero
B) small and positive
C) small and negative
D) infinite
E) varies in sign according to the phase of the SHM

35. Metal pipes, used to carry water, sometimes burst in the winter because:

A) metal contracts more than water
B) outside of the pipe contracts more than the inside
C) metal becomes brittle when cold
D) ice expands when it melts
*E) water expands when it freezes

36. A gram of distilled water at 4°C:

A) will increase slightly in weight when heated to 6°C
B) will decrease slightly in weight when heated to 6°C
C) will increase slightly in volume when heated to 6°C
*D) will decrease slightly in volume when heated to 6°C
E) will not change in either volume or weight

235

1. Heat is:

*A) energy transferred by virtue of a temperature difference
 B) energy transferred by macroscopic work
 C) energy content of an object
 D) a temperature difference
 E) a property objects have by virtue of their temperatures

2. Heat has the same units as:

 A) temperature
*B) work
 C) energy/time
 D) heat capacity
 E) energy/volume

3. A calorie is about:

 A) 0.24 J   B) 8.3 J   C) 250 J   *D) 4.2 J   E) 4200 J

4. The heat capacity of an object is:

*A) the amount of heat energy to raise its temperature by 1°C
 B) the amount of heat energy to change its state without changing its temperature
 C) the amount of heat energy per kilogram to raise its temperature by 1°C
 D) the ratio of its specific heat to that of water
 E) the change in its temperature caused by adding 1 J of heat

5. The specific heat of an object is:

 A) the amount of heat energy to change the state of one gram of the substance
 B) the amount of heat energy per unit mass emitted by oxidizing the substance
 C) the amount of heat energy per unit mass to raise the substance from its freezing to its boiling point
*D) the amount of heat energy per unit mass to raise the temperature of the substance by 1 °C
 E) the temperature of the object divided by its mass

6. Two different samples have the same mass and temperature. Equal quantities of heat are absorbed by each. Their final temperatures may be different because the samples have different:

A) thermal conductivities
B) coefficients of expansion
C) densities
D) volumes
*E) heat capacities

7. For constant volume processes the heat capacity of gas A is greater than the heat capacity of gas B. We conclude that when they both absorb the same heat at constant volume:

A) the temperature of A increases more than the temperature of B
*B) the temperature of B increases more than the temperature of A
C) the internal energy of A increases more than the internal energy of B
D) the internal energy of B increases more than the internal energy of A
E) A does more positive work than B

8. The heat capacity at constant volume and the heat capacity at constant pressure have different values because:

A) heat increases the internal energy at constant volume but not at constant pressure
B) heat increases the internal energy at constant pressure but not at constant volume
C) the system does work at constant volume but not at constant pressure
*D) the system does work at constant pressure but not at constant volume
E) the system does more work at constant volume than at constant pressure

9. Textbooks frequently mention the two specific heats C_p and C_v but never mention C_T. This is because:

A) $C_T = 0$ for all materials
*B) C_T is infinite for all materials
C) C_T can be obtained from the other two specific heats by simply adding or subtracting R
D) the implied process is impossible since one cannot add heat at a constant temperature
E) one needs only two specific heats to describe all processes

10. A cube of aluminum is 1.0 ft on edge. Aluminum has a density 2.7 times that of water and a specific heat 0.217 times that of water. The heat needed to raise the temperature of the cube from 70°F to 80°F is approximately:

*A) 370 BTU   B) 11.5 BTU   C) 778 BTU   D) 550 BTU   E) 5.85 BTU

11. A cube of aluminum is 20 cm on edge. Aluminum has a density 2.7 times that of water and a specific heat 0.217 times that of water. The heat in calories needed to raise the temperature of the cube from 20°C to 30°C is about:

A) 27   B) 37   C) 47   D) 27000   *E) 47000

12. The molar heat capacity of a solid is 3R at a high temperature and:

A) increases as the temperature increases
B) increases as the temperature decreases
*C) decreases as the temperature decreases
D) increases as the temperature increases but remains constant as the temperature decreases
E) does not depend on the temperature

13. A insulated container, filled with water, contains a thermometer and a paddle wheel. The paddle wheel can be rotated by an external source. This apparatus can be used to determine:

A) specific heat of water
B) relation between $(1/2)mv^2$ and absolute temperature
C) thermal conductivity of water
D) efficiency of changing work into heat
*E) mechanical equivalent of heat

14. Take the mechanical equivalent of heat as 4 J/cal. A 10-gram bullet moving at 2000 m/s plunges into 1 kg of paraffin wax (specific heat 0.7 cal/g · °C). The wax was initially at 20°C. Assuming that all the bullet's energy heats the wax, its final temperature (°C) is:

A) 20.14   B) 23.5   C) 20.006   *D) 27.1   E) 30.23

15. The heat given off by 300 grams of an alloy as it cools through 50°C raises the temperature of 300 grams of water from 30°C to 40°C. The specific heat of the alloy (in cal/g · °C) is:

A) 0.015   B) 0.10   C) 0.15   *D) 0.20   E) 0.50

16. The specific heat of lead is 0.030 cal/g · °C. 300 grams of lead shot at 100°C is mixed with 100 grams of water at 70°C in an insulated container. The final temperature of the mixture is:

A) 100°C   B) 85.5°C   C) 79.5°C   D) 74.5°C   *E) 72.5°C

17. Object A, with heat capacity C_A and initially at temperature T_A, is placed in thermal contact with object B, with heat capacity C_B and initially at temperature T_B. The combination is thermally isolated. If the heat capacities are independent of the temperature and no phase changes occur, the final temperature of both objects is:

A) $(C_A T_A - C_B T_B)/(C_A + C_B)$
*B) $(C_A T_A + C_B T_B)/(C_A + C_B)$
C) $(C_A T_A - C_B T_B)/(C_A - C_B)$

D) $(C_A - C_B)|T_A - T_B|$
E) $(C_A + C_B)|T_A - T_B|$

18. The heat capacity of object B is twice that of object A. Initially A is at 300 K and B is at 450 K. They are placed in thermal contact and the combination is isolated. The final temperature of both objects is:

A) 200 K   B) 300 K   *C) 400 K   D) 450 K   E) 600 K

19. A heat of transformation of a substance is:

A) the heat absorbed during a phase transformation
*B) the heat per unit mass absorbed during a phase transformation
C) the same as the heat capacity
D) the same as the specific heat
E) the same as the molar specific heat

20. The heat of fusion of water is 333 kJ/kg. This means 333 kJ of heat are required to:

A) raise the temperature of 1 kg of water by 1 K
B) turn 1 kg of water to steam
C) raise the temperature of 1 kg of ice by 1 K
*D) melt 1 kg of ice
E) increase the internal energy of 1 kg of water by 1 kJ

21. Solid A, with mass M, is at its melting point T_A. It is placed in thermal contact with solid B, with heat capacity C_B and initially at temperature T_B ($T_B > T_A$). The combination is thermally isolated. A has latent heat of fusion L and when it has melted has heat capacity C_A. If A completely melts the final temperature of both A and B is:

A) $(C_A T_A + C_B T_B - ML)/(C_A + C_B)$
*B) $(C_A T_A - C_B T_B + ML)/(C_A + C_B)$
C) $(C_A T_A - C_B T_B - ML)/(C_A + C_B)$

D) $(C_A T_A + C_B T_B + ML)/(C_A - C_B)$
E) $(C_A T_A + C_B T_B + ML)/(C_A - C_B)$

22. During the time that latent heat is involved in a change of state:

*A) the temperature does not change
B) the substance always expands
C) a chemical reaction takes place
D) molecular activity remains constant
E) kinetic energy changes into potential energy

23. The formation of ice from water is accompanied by:

 *A) absorption of heat   D) an evolution of heat
  B) temperature increase   E) temperature decrease
  C) decrease in volume

24. How many calories are required to change one gram of 0°C ice to
    100°C steam?

  A) 100   B) 540   C) 620   *D) 720   E) 90

25. Ten grams of ice at -20°C is to be changed to steam at 130°C. The
    specific heat of both ice and steam is 0.5 cal/g ·°C. The heat of
    fusion is 80 cal/g and the heat of vaporization is 540 cal/g. The
    entire process requires:

  A) 750 cal   B) 1250 cal   C) 6950 cal   *D) 7450 cal   E) 7700 cal

26. Steam (at 1 atm and 100°C) enters a radiator and leaves as water (at
    1 atm and 80°C). Take the heat of vaporization to be 540 cal/g. Of
    the total heat given off, what percent arises from the cooling of
    the water?

  A) 100   B) 54   C) 26   D) 14   *E) 3.6

27. A certain humidifier operates by raising water to the boiling point
    and then evaporating it. Every minute 30 grams of water at 20°C are
    added to replace the 30 grams which are evaporated. The heat of
    fusion of water is 80 cal/g and the heat of vaporization is 540
    cal/g. How many calories per minute does this humidifier require?

  A) 4800   *B) 18,600   C) 16,200   D) 24,600   E) 2400

28. A metal sample of mass M requires a power input P to just remain
    molten. When the heater is turned off, the metal solidifies in a
    time T. The specific latent heat of fusion of this metal is:

  A) P/MT   B) T/PM   C) PM/T   D) PMT   *E) PT/M

29. Fifty grams of ice at 0°C is placed in a thermos bottle containing
    one hundred grams of water at 6°C. How many grams of ice will melt?

 *A) 7.5   B) 2.0   C) 8.3   D) 17   E) 50

240

30. According to the first law of thermodynamics, applied to a gas, the increase in the internal energy during any process:

  A) equals the heat input minus the work done on the gas
 *B) equals the heat input plus the work done on the gas
  C) equals the work done on the gas minus the heat input
  D) is independent of the heat input
  E) is independent of the work done on the gas

31. During an adiabatic process an object does 100 J of work and its temperature decreases by 5 K. During another process it does 25 J of work and its temperature decreases by 5 K. Its heat capacity for the second process is:

  A) 20 J/K   B) 0.05 K/J   C) 5 J/K   *D) 15 J/K   E) 0.07 K/J

32. A system undergoes an adiabatic process in which its internal energy increases by 20 J. Which entry (a,b,c,d,e) in the table below is correct?

	heat	work
*A)	none	20 J on system
B)	none	20 J by system
C)	20 J removed	none
D)	20 J added	none
E)	40 J added	20 J by system

33. In an adiabatic process:

  A) the heat absorbed equals the work done by the system on its environment
  B) the heat absorbed equals the work done by the environment on the system
  C) the heat absorbed equals the change in internal energy
 *D) the work done by the environment on the system equals the change in internal energy
  E) the work done by the system on its environment equals to the change in internal energy

34. Suppose a certain gas has a molar heat capacity at constant volume of C_v and a molar heat capacity at constant pressure of C_p. Both are independent of the temperature. If the temperature of n moles is increased by ΔT at constant pressure, the work done by the gas is:

  A) $nC_v\Delta T$
  B) $nC_p\Delta T$
  C) $n(C_v + C_p)\Delta T$

  D) $n(C_v - C_p)\Delta T$
 *E) $n(C_p - C_v)\Delta T$

35. One mole of a gas with a constant volume molar heat capacity of 20 J/mol ·K and a constant pressure molar heat capacity of 28 J/mol ·K undergoes a process during which it absorbs 150 J of heat and does 80 J of work on its environment. Its change in temperature is:

A) 2.5 K   *B) 3.5 K   C) 4.0 K   D) 5.4 K   E) 7.5 K

36. In a certain process a gas ends in its original thermodynamic state. Of the following, which is possible as the net result of the process?

   A) it is adiabatic and the gas does 50 J of work
   B) the gas does no work but absorbs 50 J of heat
   C) the gas does no work but rejects 50 J of heat
   D) the gas rejects 50 J of heat and does 50 J of work
  *E) the gas absorbs 50 J of heat and does 50 J of work

37. Of the following which might NOT vanish over one cycle of a cyclic process?

   A) ΔE_{int} B) Δp *C) W   D) ΔV E) ΔT

38. Of the following which might NOT vanish over one cycle of a cyclic process?

   A) W-Q   B) Δp *C) Q   D) ΔV E) ΔT

39. A slab of material has area A, thickness L and thermal conductivity k. One of its surfaces (P) is maintained at temperature T_1 and the other surface (Q) is maintained at a lower temperature T_2. The rate of heat flow from P to Q is:

   A) $kA(T_1 - T_2)/L^2$ D) $LA(T_1 - T_2)/k$
   B) $k(T_1 - T_2)/(LA)$ *E) $kA(T_1 - T_2)/L$
   C) $kL(T_1 - T_2)/A$

40. Units of thermal conductivity are:

   A) cal ·cm/(s ·°C)   D) °C/(cal ·cm ·s)
   B) cm ·s ·°C/cal   E) cal ·s/(cm ·°C)
  *C) cal/(cm ·s ·°C)

41. The rate of heat flow through a slab does NOT depend upon the:

   A) temperature difference between opposite faces of the slab
   B) thermal conductivity of the slab
   C) slab thickness
   D) cross-sectional area of the slab
  *E) specific heat of the slab

42. The rate of heat flow through a slab is H. If the slab thickness is doubled, its cross-sectional area is halved, and the temperature difference across it is doubled, then the rate of heat flow becomes:

A) 2H   *B) H/2   C) H   D) H/8   E) 8H

43. Inside a room at a uniform comfortable temperature, metallic objects generally feel cooler to the touch than wooden objects do. This is because:

   A) a given mass of wood contains more heat than the same mass of metal
  *B) metal conducts heat better than wood
   C) heat tends to flow from metal to wood
   D) the equilibrium temperature of metal in the room is lower than that of wood
   E) the human body, being organic, resembles wood more closely than it resembles metal

44. On a very cold day, a child puts his tongue against a fence post. It is much more likely that his tongue will stick to a steel post than to a wooden post. This is because:

   A) steel has a higher specific heat
   B) steel is a better radiator of heat
   C) steel has a higher specific gravity
  *D) steel is a better heat conductor
   E) steel is a highly magnetic material

45. An iron stove, used for heating a room by radiation, is more efficient if:

   A) its inner surface is highly polished
   B) its inner surface is covered with aluminum paint
   C) its outer surface is covered with aluminum paint
  *D) its outer surface is rough and black
   E) its outer surface is highly polished

46. To help keep buildings cool in the summer, dark colored window shades have been replaced by light colored shades. This is because light colored shades:

   A) are more pleasing to the eye
   B) absorb more sunlight
  *C) reflect more sunlight
   D) transmit more sunlight
   E) have a lower thermal conductivity

47. Which of the following statements pertaining to a vacuum flask
    (thermos) is NOT correct?

  A) silvering reduces radiation loss
  B) vacuum reduces conduction loss
  C) vacuum reduces convection loss
 *D) vacuum reduces radiation loss
  E) glass walls reduce conduction loss

48. A thermos bottle works well because:

  A) its glass walls are thin
  B) silvering reduces convection
  C) vacuum reduces heat radiation
  D) silver coating is a poor heat conductor
 *E) none of the above

1. Evidence that a gas consists mostly of empty space is the fact that:

*A) the density of a gas becomes much greater when it is liquefied
 B) gases exert pressure on the walls of their containers
 C) gases are transparent
 D) heating a gas increases the molecular motion
 E) nature abhors a vacuum

2. Air enters a hot-air furnace at 7°C and leaves at 77°C. If the pressure does not change each entering cubic foot of air expands to:

A) 0.8 ft^3 *B) 1.25 ft^3 C) 1.91 ft^3 D) 7 ft^3 E) 11 ft^3

3. 273 cm^3 of an ideal gas is at 0°C. It is heated at constant pressure to 10°C. It will now occupy:

A) 263 cm^3 B) 273 cm^3 *C) 283 cm^3 D) 278 cm^3 E) 293 cm^3

4. Two identical rooms in a house are connected by an open doorway. The temperatures in the two rooms are maintained at different values. Which room contains more air?

A) the room with higher temperature
*B) the room with lower temperature
 C) the room with higher pressure
 D) neither because both have the same pressure
 E) neither because both have the same volume

5. It is known that 28 grams of a certain ideal gas occupy 22.4 liters at standard conditions (0°C, 1 atm). The volume occupied by 42 grams of this gas at standard conditions is:

A) 14.9   D) 42
B) 22.4   E) more data is needed
*C) 33.6

6. An automobile tire is pumped up to a gauge pressure of 30 lb/in^2 when the temperature is 27°C. What is its gauge pressure after the car has been running on a hot day so that the tire temperature is 77°C? Assume that the volume remains fixed and take atmospheric pressure to be 15 lb/in^2.

A) 35 lb/in^2 D) 113.3 lb/in^2
B) 85.5 lb/in^2 E) 52.5 lb/in^2
*C) 37.5 lb/in^2

7. A sample of an ideal gas is compressed by a piston from 10 ft^3 to 5 ft^3 and simultaneously cooled from 273°C to 0°C. As a result there is:

A) an increase in pressure
B) a decrease in pressure
C) a decrease in density
D) no change in volume
*E) an increase in density

8. A 2 m^3 weather balloon is loosely filled with helium at 1 atm (76 cm Hg) and at 27°C. At an elevation of 20,000 ft, the atmospheric pressure is down to 38 cm Hg and the helium has expanded, being under no constraint from the confining bag. If the temperature at this elevation is -48°C, the gas volume (in m^3) is:

*A) 3   B) 4   C) 2   D) 2.5   E) 5.3

9. Oxygen (molar mass = 32 g) occupies a volume of 12 liters when its temperature is 20°C and its pressure is 1 atm. Using R = 0.082 liter ·atm/mole ·K, calculate the number of grams of oxygen:

A) 6.4   B) 10.7   *C) 16   D) 32   E) 64

10. An ideal gas occupies 12 liters at 20°C and 1 atm (76 cm Hg). Its temperature is now raised to 100°C and its pressure increased to 215 cm Hg. The new volume is:

A) 0.2
*B) 5.4
C) 13.6
D) 20.8
E) none of these

11. Use R = 8.2x10^{-5} m^3 ·atm/mole ·K and N_A = 6.02x10^{-23} mole^{-1}. The approximate number of air molecules in a 1 m^3 volume at room temperature and atmospheric pressure is:

A) 10^{15} B) 10^{20} *C) 10^{25} D) 10^{30} E) 10^{46}

12. An air bubble doubles in volume as it rises from the bottom of a lake (62.5 lb/ft^3). Ignoring any temperature changes, the depth of the lake is:

A) 68 ft   B) 30 in   C) 16 ft   *D) 34 ft   E) 3.24 ft

13. An isothermal process for an ideal gas is represented on a pV diagram by:

A) a horizontal line
B) a vertical line
C) a portion of an ellipse
D) a portion of a parabola
*E) a hyperbola

246

14. During slow adiabatic expansion of a gas:

A) the pressure remains constant   *D) no heat enters or leaves
B) heat is added   E) the temperature is constant
C) work is done on the gas

15. An adiabatic process for an ideal gas is represented on a pV diagram by:

A) a horizontal line   D) a circle
B) a vertical line   *E) none of these
C) a hyperbola

16. A real gas undergoes a process which can be represented as a curve on a pV diagram. The work done by the gas during this process is:

A) pV   *D) $\int p dV$
B) $p(V2 - V1)$ E) Vdp
C) $(p2 - p1)V$

17. A real gas is changed slowly from state #1 to state #2. During this process no work is done on or by the gas. This process must be:

A) isothermal
B) adiabatic
*C) isovolumic
D) isobaric
E) a closed cycle with point #1 coinciding with point #2

18. A given mass of gas is enclosed in a suitable container so that it may be maintained at constant volume. Under these conditions, there can be no change is what property of the gas?

A) pressure   D) internal energy
*B) density   E) temperature
C) molecular kinetic energy

19. A quantity of an ideal gas is compressed to half its initial volume. The process may be adiabatic, isothermal or isobaric. The greatest amount of work is required if the process is:

*A) adiabatic
B) isothermal
C) isobaric
D) adiabatic or isothermal (both require the same work; isobaric requires less)
E) isothermal or isobaric (both require the same work, adiabatic requires less)

20. During a reversible adiabatic expansion of an ideal gas, which of the following is NOT true?

A) pV^γ = constant

B) $pV = nRT$

C) $TV^{\gamma-1}$ = constant

D) $W = -\int p dV$

*E) pV = constant

21. In order that a single process be both isothermal and isobaric:

A) one must use an ideal gas

B) such a process is impossible

*C) a change of phase is essential

D) one may use any real gas such as N_2

E) one must use a solid

22. Over 1 cycle of a cyclic process in which a system does net work on its environment:

A) the change in the pressure of the system cannot be zero

B) the change in the volume of the system cannot be zero

C) the change in the temperature of the system cannot be zero

D) the change in the internal energy of the system cannot be zero

*E) none of the above

23. Evidence that molecules of a gas are in constant motion is:

A) winds exert pressure

*B) two gases interdiffuse quickly

C) warm air rises

D) heat is needed to vaporize a liquid

E) gases are easily compressed

24. According to the kinetic theory of gases, the pressure of a gas is due to:

A) change of kinetic energy of molecules as they strike the wall

*B) change of momentum of molecules as the strike the wall

C) average kinetic energy of the molecules

D) force of repulsion between the molecules

E) rms speed of the molecules

25. The force exerted on the walls of a vessel by a contained gas is due to:

A) repulsive force between gas molecules

B) slight loss in average speed of a gas molecule after collision with wall

*C) change in momentum of a gas molecule due to collision with wall

D) elastic collisions between gas molecules

E) inelastic collisions between gas molecules

26. A gas is confined to a cylindrical container of radius 1 cm and length 1 m. The pressure exerted on an end face, compared with the pressure exerted on the long curved face, is:

  A) smaller because its area is smaller
  B) smaller because most molecules cannot traverse the length of the cylinder without undergoing collisions
  C) larger because the face is flat
  D) larger because the molecules have a greater distance in which to accelerate before they strike the face
 *E) none of these

27. Air is pumped into a bicycle tire at constant temperature. The pressure increases because:

 *A) more molecules strike the tire wall per second
  B) the molecules are larger
  C) the molecules are farther apart
  D) each molecule is moving faster
  E) each molecule has more kinetic energy

28. The temperature of a gas is most closely related to:

 *A) the kinetic energy of translation of its molecules
  B) its total molecular kinetic energy
  C) the sizes of its molecules
  D) the potential energy of its molecules
  E) the total energy of its molecules

29. The temperature of low pressure hydrogen is reduced from 100°C to 20°C. The rms speed of its molecules decreases by approximately:

  A) 80%   B) 89%   C) 46%   D) 21%   *E) 11%

30. The mass of an oxygen molecule is 16 times that of a hydrogen molecule. At room temperature, the ratio of the rms speed of an oxygen molecule to that of a hydrogen molecule is:

  A) 16   B) 4   C) 1   *D) 1/4   E) 1/16

31. The rms speed of an oxygen molecule at 0°C is 460 m/s. If the molar mass of oxygen is 32 g and of helium is 4 g, then the rms speed of a helium molecule at 0°C is:

  A) 230 m/s   B) 326 m/s   C) 650 m/s   D) 920 m/s   *E) 1300 m/s

32. A sample of oxygen gas (molar mass 32 g) is at four times the absolute temperature of a sample of hydrogen gas (molar mass 2 g). The ratio of the rms speed of the oxygen molecules to that of the hydrogen is:

A) 1/4   *B) 1/2   C) $1/\sqrt{2}$ D) 1   E) $\sqrt{2}$

33. If the molecules in a tank of hydrogen have the same rms speed as the molecules in a tank of oxygen, we may be sure that:

A) the pressures are the same
B) the hydrogen is at the higher temperature
C) the hydrogen is at the greater pressure
D) the temperatures are the same
*E) the oxygen is at the higher temperature

34. The "Principle of Equipartition of Energy" states that the internal energy of a gas is shared equally:

A) among the molecules
B) between kinetic and potential energy
*C) among the relevant degrees of freedom
D) between translational and vibrational kinetic energy
E) between temperature and pressure

35. The number of degrees of freedom of a rigid diatomic molecule is:

A) 2   B) 3   C) 4   *D) 5   E) 6

36. The number of degrees of freedom of a triatomic molecule is:

A) 1   B) 3   C) 6   D) 8   *E) 9

37. Five molecules have speeds of 2.8, 3.2, 5.8, 7.3, and 7.4 m/s. Their root-mean-square speed is closest to:

A) 5.3 m/s   *B) 5.7 m/s   C) 7.3 m/s   D) 28 m/s   E) 32 m/s

38. The speeds of 25 molecules are distributed as follows: 5 in the range from 2 to 3 m/s, 10 in the range from 3 to 4 m/s, 5 in the range from 4 to 5 m/s, 3 in the range from 5 to 6 m/s, 1 in the range from 6 to 7 m/s, and 1 in the range from 7 to 8 m/s. Their average speed is about:

A) 2 m/s   B) 3 m/s   *C) 4 m/s   D) 5 m/s   E) 6 m/s

39. In a system of N gas molecules, the individual speeds are v_1, $v_2, \ldots, v_N$. The rms speed of these molecules is:

A) $\frac{1}{N}\sqrt{(v_1 + v_2 + \ldots + v_N)^2}$ C) $\sqrt{(v_1^2 + v_2^2 + \ldots + v_N^2)/N}$

B) $\frac{1}{N}\sqrt{v_1^2 + v_2^2 + \ldots v_N^2}$ D) $\sqrt{[(v_1 + v_2 + \ldots + v_N)/N]^2}$

E) $\sqrt{(v_1 + v_2 + \ldots + v_N)^2/N}$

Ans. c

40. A system consists of N gas molecules each of mass m. Their rms speed is v_{rms}. Their total translational kinetic energy is:

A) $(1/2)m(Nv_{rms})^2$

B) $(1/2)Nmv_{rms}^2$

C) $(1/2)N(mv_{rms})^2$

*D) $N[(1/2)mv_{rms}]^2$

E) $(1/2)mv_{rms}^2$

41. The internal energy of an ideal gas depends on:

*A) the temperature only
B) the pressure only
C) the volume only
D) the temperature and pressure only
E) temperature, pressure, and volume

42. An ideal gas of N monatomic molecules is in thermal equilibrium with an ideal gas of the same number of diatomic molecules. The ratio of the internal energies E_{dia}/E_{mon} is:

A) 1/2   B) 3/5   C) 1   *D) 5/3   E) 2

43. Two ideal gases, each consisting of N monatomic molecules, are in thermal equilibrium with each other. A molecule of the first gas has mass m and a molecule of the second has mass 4m. The ratio of the internal energies E_{4m}/E_m is:

A) 1/4   B) 1/2   *C) 1   D) 2   E) 4

44. Three gases, one consisting of monatomic molecules, the second consisting of diatomic molecules, and the third consisting of polyatomic molecules, are in thermal equilibrium with each other. All have the same number of molecules. The gases with the least and greatest internal energy are respectively:

  A) polyatomic, monatomic   D) polyatomic, diatomic
 *B) monatomic, polyatomic   E) monatomic, diatomic
  C) diatomic, monatomic

45. An ideal gas of N diatomic molecules has temperature T. If the number of molecules is doubled without changing the temperature, the internal energy increases by:

A) 0   B) 1/2NkT   C) 3/2NkT   *D) 5/2NkT   E) 3NkT

46. Both the pressure and volume of an ideal gas of diatomic molecules are doubled. The ratio of the new internal energy to the old is:

A) 1/4   B) 1/2   C) 1   D) 2   *E) 4

47. The pressure of an ideal gas of diatomic molecules is doubled by halving the volume. The ratio of the new internal energy to the old is:

A) 1/4   B) 1/2   *C) 1   D) 2   E) 4

48. When work W is done on an ideal gas of N diatomic molecules in thermal isolation the temperature increases by:

A) W/2Nk   B) W/3Nk   C) 2W/3Nk   *D) 2W/5Nk   E) W/Nk

49. When work W is done on an ideal gas of diatomic molecules in thermal isolation the increase in the total <u>rotational</u> energy of the molecules is:

A) 0   B) W/3   C) 2W/3   *D) 2W/5   E) W

50. When work W is done on an ideal gas of diatomic molecules in thermal isolation the increase in the total translational kinetic energy of the molecules is:

A) 0   B) 2W/3   C) 2W/5   *D) 3W/5   E) W

51. The pressure of an ideal gas is doubled in an isothermal process. The root-mean-square speed of the molecules:

*A) does not change
 B) increases by a factor of $\sqrt{2}$
 C) decreases by a factor of $1/\sqrt{2}$
 D) increases by a factor of 2
 E) decreases by a factor of 1/2

52. The Maxwellian speed distribution provides a direct explanation of:

A) thermal expansion
B) the ideal gas law
C) heat
*D) evaporation
E) boiling

53. For a gas at thermal equilibrium the average speed $\bar{v}$, the most probable speed v_p, and the root-mean-square speed v_{rms} are in the order:

A) $v_p < v_{rms} < \bar{v}$
B) $v_{rms} < v_p < \bar{v}$
C) $\bar{v} < v_{rms} < v_p$
*D) $v_p < \bar{v} < v_{rms}$
E) $\bar{v} < v_p < v_{rms}$

54. The average speed of air molecules at room temperature is about:

A) zero
B) 500 m/s (supersonic airplane)
C) 2 m/s (walking speed)
*D) 3×10^8 m/s (speed of light)
E) 30 m/s (fast car)

55. According to the Maxwellian speed distribution, the quantity v_{rms} is:

A) the most probable speed
B) that speed such that half the molecules are moving faster than v_{rms} and the other half are moving slower
C) the average speed of the molecules
D) the square root of the square of the average speed
*E) none of the above

56. According to the Maxwellian speed distribution, as the temperature increases the number of molecules with speeds within a small interval near the most probable speed:

A) increases
*B) decreases
C) increases at high temperatures and decreases at low
D) decreases at high temperatures and increases at low
E) stays the same

57. According to the Maxwellian speed distribution, as the temperature increases the most probable speed:

*A) increases
 B) decreases
 C) increases at high temperatures and decreases at low
 D) decreases at high temperatures and increases at low
 E) stays the same

58. According to the Maxwellian speed distribution, as the temperature increases the average speed:

*A) increases
 B) decreases
 C) increases at high temperatures and decreases at low
 D) decreases at high temperatures and increases at low
 E) stays the same

59. As the pressure in an ideal gas is increased isothermally the average molecular speed:

 A) increases
 B) decreases
 C) increases at high temperature, decreases at low
 D) decreases at high temperature, increases at low
*E) stays the same

60. As the volume of an ideal gas is increased at constant pressure the average molecular speed:

*A) increases
 B) decreases
 C) increases at high temperature, decreases at low
 D) decreases at high temperature, increases at low
 E) stays the same

61. Two ideal monatomic gases are in thermal equilibrium with each other. Gas A is composed of molecules with mass m while gas B is composed of molecules with mass 4m. The ratio of the average molecular speeds $\bar{v}_A/\bar{v}_B$ is:

A) 1/4   B) 1/2   C) 1   *D) 2   E) 4

62. Ideal monatomic gas A is composed of molecules with mass m while ideal monatomic gas B is composed of molecules with mass 4m. The average molecular speeds are the same if the ratio of the temperatures T_A/T_B is:

*A) 1/4   B) 1/2   C) 1   D) 2   E) 4

63. Two monatomic ideal gases are in thermal equilibrium with each other. Gas A is composed of molecules with mass m while gas B is composed of molecules with mass 4m. The ratio of the average molecular kinetic energy $\bar{K}_A/\bar{K}_B$ is:

A) 1/4   B) 1/2   *C) 1   D) 2   E) 4

64. Ideal monatomic gas A is composed of molecules with mass m while ideal monatomic gas B is composed of molecules with mass 4m. The average molecular energies are the same if the ratio of the temperatures T_A/T_B is:

A) 1/4   B) 1/2   *C) 1   D) 2   E) 4

65. Which of the following changes when the pressure of an ideal gas is changed isothermally?

*A) mean free path
 B) root-mean-square molecular speed
 C) internal energy
 D) most probable kinetic energy
 E) average speed

66. When an ideal gas undergoes a quasi-static isothermal expansion:

*A) the work done by the gas is the same as the heat absorbed
 B) the work done by the environment is the same as the heat absorbed
 C) the increase in internal energy is the same as the heat absorbed
 D) the increase in internal energy is the same as the work done by the gas
 E) the increase in internal energy is the same as the work done by the environment

67. The pressure of an ideal gas is doubled during a process in which the heat given up by the gas equals the work done on the gas. As a result, the volume is:

A) doubled
*B) halved
 C) unchanged
 D) need more information to answer
 E) nonsense, the process is impossible

68. The heat absorbed by an ideal gas for an isothermal process equals:

*A) the work done by the gas
 B) the work done on the gas
 C) the change in the internal energy of the gas
 D) the negative of the change in internal energy of the gas
 E) zero since the process is isothermal

69. An ideal gas has molar specific heat C_p at constant pressure. When the temperature of n moles is increased by ΔT the increase in the internal energy is:

A) $nC_p\Delta T$
B) $n(C_p + R)\Delta T$
*C) $n(C_p - R)\Delta T$

D) $n(2C_p + R)\Delta T$
E) $n(2C_p - R)\Delta T$

70. The temperature of n moles of an ideal monatomic gas is increased by ΔT at constant pressure. The heat absorbed, work done by the environment, and change in internal energy are given by:

A) $Q = 5/2nR\Delta T$, $\Delta U = 0$, $W = -nR\Delta T$
B) $Q = 3/2nR\Delta T$, $\Delta U = 5/2nR\Delta T$, $W = -3/2nR\Delta T$
C) $Q = 5/2nR\Delta T$, $\Delta U = 5/2nR\Delta T$, $W = 0$
D) $Q = 3/2nR\Delta T$, $\Delta U = 0$, $W = -3/2nR\Delta T$
*E) $Q = 5/2nR\Delta T$, $\Delta U = 3/2nR\Delta T$, $W = -nR\Delta T$

71. The temperature of n moles of an ideal monatomic gas is increased by ΔT at constant volume. The heat absorbed, work done by the environment, and change in internal energy are given by:

A) $Q = 5/2nR\Delta T$, $\Delta U = 0$, $W = 0$
*B) $Q = 3/2nR\Delta T$, $\Delta U = 3/2nR\Delta T$, $W = 0$
C) $Q = 3/2nR\Delta T$, $\Delta U = 1/2nR\Delta T$, $W = -nR\Delta T$
D) $Q = 5/2nR\Delta T$, $\Delta U = 3/2nR\Delta T$, $W = -nR\Delta T$
E) $Q = 3/2nR\Delta T$, $\Delta U = 0$, $W = -3/2nR\Delta T$

72. The heat capacity at constant volume of an ideal gas depends on:

A) the temperature
B) the pressure
C) the volume

*D) the number of molecules
E) none of the above

73. The specific heat at constant volume of an ideal gas depends on:

A) the temperature
B) the pressure
C) the volume

D) the number of molecules
*E) none of the above

74. The difference between the molar specific heat at constant pressure and the molar specific heat at constant volume for an ideal gas is:

A) the Boltzmann constant k
*B) the universal gas constant R
C) the Avogadro number N_A

D) kT
E) RT

256

75. An ideal monatomic gas has a molar specific heat at constant volume, C_v, of:

A) R   *B) 3R/2   C) 5R/2   D) 7R/2   E) 9R/2

76. The specific heat, C_v, of a monatomic gas at low pressure is proportional to T^w where the exponent w is:

A) -1   *B) 0   C) 1   D) 1/2   E) 2

77. An ideal diatomic gas has a molar specific heat at constant pressure, C_p, of:

A) R   B) 3R/2   C) 5R/2   *D) 7R/2   E) 9R/2

78. The specific heat of a diatomic gas is greater than the specific heat of a monatomic gas because:

A) the diatomic gas does more positive work when heat is absorbed
B) the monatomic gas does more positive work when heat is absorbed
*C) the energy absorbed by the diatomic gas is split among more degrees of freedom
D) the pressure is greater in the diatomic gas
E) a monatomic gas cannot hold as much heat

79. The ratio of the specific heat of a gas at constant volume to its specific heat at constant pressure is:

A) 1   D) has units of pressure/volume
*B) less than 1   E) has units of volume/pressure
C) more than 1

80. The ratio of the specific heat of an ideal gas at constant volume to its specific heat at constant pressure is:

A) R
B) 1/R
C) dependent on the temperature
D) dependent on the pressure
*E) different for monatomic, diatomic, and polyatomic gases

81. Consider the ratios of the heat capacities $\gamma = C_p/C_v$ for the three types of ideal gases: monatomic, diatomic, and polyatomic.

*A) γ is the greatest for monatomic gases
B) γ is the greatest for polyatomic gases
C) γ is the same only for diatomic and polyatomic gases
D) γ is the same only for monatomic and diatomic gases
E) γ is the same for all three

82. TV$^\gamma$ is constant for an ideal gas undergoing an adiabatic process, where γ is the ratio of heat capacities C_p/C_v. This is a direct consequence of:

  A) the zeroth law of thermodynamics alone
  B) the zeroth law and the ideal gas equation of state
  C) the first law of thermodynamics alone
  D) the ideal gas equation of state alone
  *E) the first law and the equation of state

83. Monatomic, diatomic, and polyatomic ideal gases each undergo adiabatic quasi-static expansions from the same initial volume to the same final volume. The magnitude of the work done by the environment on the gas:

  *A) is greatest for the polyatomic gas
  B) is greatest for the diatomic gas
  C) is greatest for the monatomic gas
  D) is the same only for the diatomic and polyatomic gases
  E) is the same for all three gases

84. The mean free path of a gas molecule is:

  A) the shortest dimension of the containing vessel
  B) the cube root of the volume of the containing vessel
  C) approximately the diameter of a molecule
  D) average distance between adjacent molecules
  *E) average distance a molecule travels between intermolecular collisions

85. The mean free path of molecules in a gas is:

  A) the average distance they travel before escaping
  *B) the average distance they travel between collisions
  C) the greatest distance they travel between collisions
  D) the shortest distance they travel between collisions
  E) the average distance they travel before splitting apart

86. The mean free path of air molecules near the surface of the earth is about:

  A) 10^{-9} m   *B) 10^{-7} m   C) 10^{-5} m   D) 10^{-3} m   E) 10^{-1} m

87. The mean free path of air molecules at room temperature and atmospheric pressure is about:

  A) 10^{-3} m   B) 10^{-5} m   *C) 10^{-7} m   D) 10^{-9} m   E) 10^{-11} m

88. The mean free path of molecules in a gas is proportional to:

   A) the molecular cross sectional area
  *B) the reciprocal of the molecular cross sectional area
   C) the root-mean-square molecular speed
   D) the square of the average molecular speed
   E) the molar mass

89. The mean free path of molecules in a gas is proportional to:

   A) the molecular diameter
   B) the reciprocal of the molecular diameter
   C) the molecular concentration
  *D) the reciprocal of the molecular concentration
   E) the average molecular speed

90. In a certain gas the molecules are 5.0×10^{-9} m apart on average, have a mean free path of 5.0×10^{-6} m, and have an average speed of 500 m/s. The rate at which a molecule suffers collisions is about:

   A) $10x^{-11}$ s^{-1} *D) 10^8 s^{-1}
   B) 10^{-8} s^{-1} E) 10^{11} s^{-1}
   C) 1 s^{-1}

91. If the temperature T of an ideal gas is increased at constant pressure the mean free path:

   A) decreases in proportion to $1/T$ D) increases in proportion to T^2
   B) decreases in proportion to $1/T^2$ E) does not change
  *C) increases in proportion to T

92. A certain ideal gas has a temperature 300 K and a pressure 5.0×10^4 Pa. The molecules have a mean free path of 4.0×10^{-7} m. If the temperature is raised to 350 K and the pressure is reduced to 1.0×10^4 Pa the mean free path is then:

   A) 6.9×10^{-8} m   D) 1.7×10^{-6} m
   B) 9.3×10^{-8} m   *E) 2.3×10^{-6} m
   C) 3.3×10^{-7} m

1. In a reversible process the system:

*A) is always close to equilibrium states
 B) is close to equilibrium states only at the beginning and end
 C) might never be close to any equilibrium state
 D) is close to equilibrium states throughout, except at the beginning and end
 E) is none of the above

2. A quasi-static process is NOT reversible if:

 A) the temperature changes   *D) friction is present
 B) heat is absorbed or emitted   E) the pressure changes
 C) work is done on the system

3. According to the second law of thermodynamics:

*A) heat cannot be completely converted to work
 B) work cannot be completely converted to heat
 C) for all cyclic processes we have dQ/T < 0
 D) the reason all heat engine efficiencies are less than 100% is friction, which is unavoidable

4. Consider the following processes.
   I.   Heat flows from a hot object to a colder object
   II.   Work is done on a system and an equivalent amount of heat is rejected by the system
   III. Heat is absorbed by a system and an equivalent amount of work is done by the system
   Which are never found to occur?

 A) only I   D) only II and III
 B) only II   E) I, II and III
*C) only III

260

5. An inventor suggests that a house might be heated by using a refrigerator to draw heat from the earth and reject heat into the house. He claims that the heat supplied to the house can exceed the work required to run the refrigerator. This:

A) is impossible by first law
B) is impossible by second law
C) would only work if the earth and the house were at the same temperature
D) is impossible since heat flows from the (hot) house to the (cold) earth
*E) is possible

6. In a thermally insulated kitchen, an ordinary refrigerator is turned on and its door is left open. The temperature of the room:

A) remains constant by first law
*B) increases by first law
C) decreases by first law

D) remains constant by second law
E) increases by second law

7. A heat engine:

A) converts heat input to an equivalent amount of work
B) converts work to an equivalent amount of heat
*C) takes heat in, does work, and rejects heat
D) uses positive work done on the system to transfer heat from a low temperature reservoir to a high temperature reservoir
E) uses positive work done on the system to transfer heat from a high temperature reservoir to a low temperature reservoir

8. A heat engine absorbs heat of magnitude $|Q_H|$ from a high temperature reservoir, does work of magnitude $|W|$, and rejects heat of magnitude $|Q_L|$ to a low temperature reservoir. Its efficiency is:

A) $|Q_H|/|W|$
B) $|Q_L|/|W|$
C) $|Q_H|/|Q_L|$

*D) $|W|/|Q_H|$
E) $|W|/|Q_L|$

9. A certain heat engine draws 500 cal/s from a water bath at 27°C and rejects 400 cal/s to a reservoir at a lower temperature. The efficiency of this engine is:

A) 80%   B) 75%   C) 55%   D) 25%   *E) 20%

10. A heat engine that in each cycle does positive work and rejects heat, with no heat input, would violate:

  A) the zeroth law of thermodynamics
 *B) the first law of thermodynamics
  C) the second law of thermodynamics
  D) the third law of thermodynamics
  E) Newton's second law

11. A cyclical process that transfers heat from a high temperature reservoir to a low temperature reservoir with no other change would violate:

  A) the zeroth law of thermodynamics
  B) the first law of thermodynamics
  C) the second law of thermodynamics
  D) the third law of thermodynamics
 *E) none of the above

12. On a warm day a pool of water rejects heat to the air and freezes. This is a direct violation of:

  A) the zeroth law of thermodynamics
  B) the first law of thermodynamics
 *C) the second law of thermodynamics
  D) the third law of thermodynamics
  E) none of the above

13. A heat engine in each cycle absorbs heat of magnitude $|Q_H|$ from a high temperature reservoir, does work of magnitude $|W|$, and then absorbs heat of magnitude $|Q_L|$ from a low temperature reservoir. If $|W| = |Q_H| + |Q_L|$ this engine violates:

  A) the zeroth law of thermodynamics
  B) the first law of thermodynamics
 *C) the second law of thermodynamics
  D) the third law of thermodynamics
  E) none of the above

14. A heat engine in each cycle absorbs heat from a reservoir and does an equivalent amount of work, with no other changes. This engine violates:

  A) the zeroth law of thermodynamics
  B) the first law of thermodynamics
 *C) the second law of thermodynamics
  D) the third law of thermodynamics
  E) none of the above

15. A Carnot cycle:

 *A) is bounded by two isotherms and two adiabats
  B) is a rectangle on a p-V graph
  C) is any four sided process on a p-V graph
  D) only exists for an ideal gas
  E) has an efficiency equal to the enclosed area on a p-V diagram

16. By the second law of thermodynamics:

  A) all heat engines have the same efficiency
  B) all reversible heat engines have the same efficiency
  C) the efficiency of any heat engine is independent of its working
     substance
 *D) the efficiency of a Carnot engine depends only on the temperatures
     of the two reservoirs
  E) all Carnot engines theoretically have 100% efficiency

17. A Carnot cycle heat engine operates between 227°C and 127°C. Its
    efficiency is:

 *A) 20%   B) 25%   C) 44%   D) 79%   E) 100%

18. A reversible heat engine operates between a hot reservoir at
    absolute temperature T_1 and a cold reservoir at absolute temperature
    T_2. Its efficiency is:

  A) T_1/T_2 B) T_2/T_1 C) $1 - T_1/T_2$ *D) $1 - T_2/T_1$ E) 100%

19. A heat engine operates between a high temperature reservoir at T_H
    and a low temperature reservoir at T_L. Its efficiency is given by
    $1 - T_L/T_H$:

  A) only if the working substance is an ideal gas
 *B) only if the engine is reversible
  C) only if the engine is quasi-static
  D) only if the engine operates on a Carnot cycle
  E) no matter what characteristics the engine has

20. The maximum theoretical efficiency of a heat engine operating
    between reservoirs at the steam point and at room temperature is
    about:

  A) 10%   *B) 20%   C) 50%   D) 80%   E) 99%

21. A heat engine operates between 200°C and 20°C. Its maximum possible
    efficiency is:

  A) 90%   B) 100%   *C) 38%   D) 72%   E) 24%

263

22. A reversible heat engine and an irreversible heat engine both operate between the same high temperature and low temperature reservoirs. They absorb the same heat from the high temperature reservoir. The irreversible engine:

A) does more work
*B) rejects more heat to the low temperature reservoir
C) has the greater efficiency
D) has the same efficiency as the reversible engine
E) cannot absorb the same heat from the high temperature reservoir without violating the second law

23. A perfectly reversible heat pump supplies heat to a building to maintain its temperature at 27°C. The cold reservoir is a river at 7°C. If work is supplied to the pump at the rate of 1 kW, at what rate does the pump supply heat to the building?

*A) 15 kW   B) 3.85 kW   C) 1.35 kW   D) 1.07 kW   E) 1.02 kW

24. A heat engine operates between 200 K and 100 K. In each cycle it takes 100 J from the hot reservoir, loses 25 J to the cold reservoir, and does 75 J of work. This heat engine violates:

A) both the first and second laws of thermodynamics
B) the first law but not the second law of thermodynamics
*C) the second law but not the first law of thermodynamics
D) neither the first law nor the second law of thermodynamics
E) cannot answer without knowing the mechanical equivalent of heat

25. A refrigerator absorbs heat of magnitude $|Q_L|$ from a low temperature reservoir and rejects heat of magnitude $|Q_H|$ to a high temperature reservoir. Work W is done on the working substance. The coefficient of performance is given by:

*A) $|Q_L|/W$ D) $W/|Q_L|$
B) $|Q_H|/W$ E) $W/|Q_H|$
C) $(|Q_L| + |Q_H|)/W$

26. A reversible refrigerator operates between a low temperature reservoir at T_L and a high temperature reservoir at T_H. Its coefficient of performance is given by:

A) $(T_H - T_L)/T_L$ D) $T_H/(T_H - T_L)$
*B) $T_L/(T_H - T_L)$ E) $T_H(T_H + T_L)$
C) $(T_H - T_L)/T_H$

27. The thermodynamic temperature of an object can be found by running a reversible heat engine between a reservoir at that temperature and one at the temperature of the triple point of water T_{tr}. If $|Q|$ is the magnitude of the heat exchanged at the temperature of the object and $|Q_{tr}|$ is the magnitude of the heat exchanged at the triple point of water then the temperature of the object is:

A) $(|Q_{tr}|/|Q|)T_{tr}$
B) $(|Q_{tr}| - |Q|)T_{tr}$
C) $T_{tr}/(|Q_{tr}| - |Q|)$

*D) $(|Q|/|Q_{tr}|)T_{tr}$
E) $T_{tr} + |Q_{tr}|/|Q|$

28. The difference in entropy $\Delta S = S_B - S_A$ for two states A and B of a system can computed as the integral $\int dQ/T$ provided:

A) A and B are on the same adiabat
B) A and B have the same temperature
*C) a reversible path is used for the integral
D) the work done on the system is first computed
E) the heat absorbed by the system is first computed

29. Entropy units are:

A) J
*B) J/K
C) J^{-1}

D) liter ·atm
E) cal/mol

30. Which of the following is NOT a state variable?

*A) work
B) internal energy
C) entropy

D) temperature
E) pressure

31. The change in entropy is zero for:

*A) reversible adiabatic processes
B) reversible isothermal processes
C) reversible processes during which no work is done
D) reversible isobaric processes
E) all adiabatic processes

32. Which process leads to $\Delta S = 0$?

A) non-cyclic isobaric
B) non-cyclic isovolumic
C) non-cyclic isothermal

*D) any closed cycle
E) none of these

33. An ideal gas, consisting of n moles, undergoes a reversible isothermal process during which the volume changes from V_i to V_f. The change in entropy of the thermal reservoir in contact with the gas is given by:

   A) $nR(V_f - V_i)$
   B) $nR\ln(V_f - V_i)$
   *C) $nR\ln(V_i/V_f)$
   D) $nR\ln(V_f/V_i)$
   E) none of the above (entropy can't be calculated for an irreversible process)

34. One mole of an ideal gas expands slowly and isothermally at temperature T until its volume is doubled. The change of entropy of this gas for this process is:

   *A) $R\ln 2$ B) $(\ln 2)/T$ C) zero   D) $RT\ln 2$ E) $2R$

35. An ideal gas expands into a vacuum in a rigid vessel. As a result there is:

   *A) a change in entropy   D) a decrease of internal energy
   B) an increase of pressure   E) a change in phase
   C) a change in temperature

36. An ideal gas, consisting of n moles, undergoes an irreversible process in which the temperature has the same value at the beginning and end. If the volume changes from V_i to V_f, the change in entropy is given by:

   A) $nR(V_f - V_i)$
   B) $nR\ln(V_f - V_i)$
   C) $nR\ln(V_i/V_f)$
   *D) $nR\ln(V_f/V_i)$
   E) none of the above (entropy can't be calculated for an irreversible process)

37. Consider all possible isothermal contractions of an ideal gas. The change in entropy of the gas:

   A) is zero for all of them
   B) does not decrease for any of them
   C) does not increase for any of them
   D) increases for all of them
   *E) decreases for all of them

38. The temperature of n moles of a gas is increased from T_i to T_f at constant pressure. If the molar specific heat at constant pressure is C_p and is independent of temperature, then change in the entropy of the gas is:

*A) $nC_p \ln(T_f/T_i)$
 B) $nC_p \ln(T_i/T_f)$
 C) $nC_p \ln(T_f - T_i)$

D) $nC_p \ln(1 - T_i/T_f)$
E) $nC_p(T_f - T_i)$

39. Consider the following processes: The temperature of two identical gases are increased from the same initial temperature to the same final temperature. Reversible processes are used. For gas A the process is carried out at constant volume while for gas B it is carried out at constant pressure. The change in entropy:

 A) is the same for A and B
 B) is greater for A
*C) is greater for B
 D) is greater for A only if the initial temperature is low
 E) is greater for A only if the initial temperature is high

40. A hot object and a cold object are placed in thermal contact and the combination is isolated. They transfer energy until they reach a common temperature. The change ΔS_h in the entropy of the hot object, the change ΔS_c in the entropy of the cold object, and the change ΔS_{total} in the entropy of the combination are:

 A) $\Delta S_h > 0$, $\Delta S_c > 0$, $\Delta S_{total} > 0$
*B) $\Delta S_h < 0$, $\Delta S_c > 0$, $\Delta S_{total} > 0$
 C) $\Delta S_h < 0$, $\Delta S_c > 0$, $\Delta S_{total} < 0$

D) $\Delta S_h > 0$, $\Delta S_c < 0$, $\Delta S_{total} > 0$
E) $\Delta S_h > 0$, $\Delta S_c < 0$, $\Delta S_{total} < 0$

41. After one complete cycle of a reversible heat engine, which of the following quantities is NOT zero?

 A) S   B) p   C) U   *D) W   E) T

42. Let S_I denote the change in entropy of a sample for an irreversible process from state A to state B. Let S_R denote the change in entropy of the same sample for a reversible process from state A to state B. Then:

 A) $S_I > S_R$ *B) $S_I = S_R$ C) $S_I < S_R$ D) $S_I = 0$ E) $S_R = 0$

43. For all adiabatic processes:

 A) the entropy does not change
 B) the entropy increases
 C) the entropy decreases

D) the entropy does not increase
*E) the entropy does not decrease

267

44. For all reversible processes involving a system and its environment:

  A) the entropy of the system does not change
  B) the entropy of the system increases
 *C) the total entropy of the system and its environment does not change
  D) the total entropy of the system and its environment increases
  E) none of the above

45. For all irreversible processes involving a system and its environment:

  A) the entropy of the system does not change
  B) the entropy of the system increases
  C) the total entropy of the system and its environment does not change
 *D) the total entropy of the system and its environment increases
  E) none of the above

1. A coulomb is the same as:

A) ampere/second
B) (1/2)ampere $\cdot$second^2
C) ampere/meter^2

*D) ampere $\cdot$second
E) newton $\cdot$meter^2

2. A kiloampere $\cdot$hour is a unit of:

A) current
B) charge per time
C) power

*D) charge
E) energy

3. The magnitude of the charge on an electron is approximately:

A) 10^{23} C   B) 10^{-23} C   C) 10^{19} C   *D) 10^{-19} C   E) 10^9 C

4. The total negative charge on the electrons in 1 mol of helium (atomic number 2, atomic mass 4) is:

A) 4.8×10^4 C
B) 9.6×10^4 C
*C) 1.9×10^5 C

D) 3.8×10^5 C
E) 7.7×10^5 C

5. The total negative charge on the electrons in 1 kg of helium (atomic number 2, atomic mass 4) is:

A) 48 C
B) 2.4×10^4 C
*C) 4.8×10^4 C

D) 9.6×10^5 C
E) 1.9×10^5 C

6. A wire contains a steady current of 2 A. The charge that passes a cross section in 2 s is:

A) 3.2×10^{-19} C
B) 6.4×10^{-19} C
C) 1 C

D) 2 C
*E) 4 C

7. A wire contains a steady current of 2 A. The number of electrons that pass a cross section in 2 s is:

A) 2   B) 4   C) 6.3×10^{18} D) 1.3×10^{19} *E) 2.5×10^{19}

8. The charge on a glass rod which has been rubbed with silk is called positive:

*A) by arbitrary convention
 B) so that the proton charge will be positive
 C) to conform to the conventions adopted for G and m in Newton's law of gravitation
 D) because like charges repel
 E) because glass is an insulator

9. To make an uncharged object have a negative charge we must:

 A) add some atoms
 B) remove some atoms
*C) add some electrons
 D) remove some electrons
 E) write down a negative sign

10. To make an uncharged object have a positive charge:

 A) remove some neutrons
 B) add some neutrons
 C) add some electrons
*D) remove some electrons
 E) heat it to cause a change of phase

11. When a hard rubber rod is given a negative charge by rubbing it with wool:

 A) positive charges are transferred from rod to wool
 B) negative charges are transferred from rod to wool
 C) positive charges are transferred from wool to rod
*D) negative charges are transferred from wool to rod
 E) negative charges are created and stored on the rod

12. An electrical insulator is a material:

 A) containing no electrons
*B) through which electrons do not flow easily
 C) which has more electrons than protons on its surface
 D) cannot be a pure chemical element
 E) must be a crystal

13. A conductor is distinguished from an insulator with the same number of atoms by the number of:

 A) nearly free atoms
 B) electrons
*C) nearly free electrons
 D) protons
 E) molecules

14. A neutral metal ball is suspended by a string. A positively charged insulating rod is placed near the ball, which is observed to be attracted to the rod. This is because:

    A) the ball becomes positively charged by induction
    B) the ball becomes negatively charged by induction
    C) the number of electrons in the ball is more than the number in the rod
    D) the string is not a perfect insulator
  *E) there is a rearrangement of the electrons in the ball

15. A positively charged insulating rod is brought close to an object that is suspended by a string. If the object is attracted toward the rod we can conclude:

    A) the object is positively charged
    B) the object is negatively charged
    C) the object is an insulator
    D) the object is a conductor
  *E) none of the above

16. A positively charged insulating rod is brought close to an object that is suspended by a string. If the object is repelled away from the rod we can conclude:

  *A) the object is positively charged
    B) the object is negatively charged
    C) the object is an insulator
    D) the object is a conductor
    E) none of the above

17. Two uncharged metal spheres, L and M, are in contact. A negatively charged rod is brought close to L, but not touching it, as shown. The two spheres are slightly separated and the rod is then withdrawn. As a result:

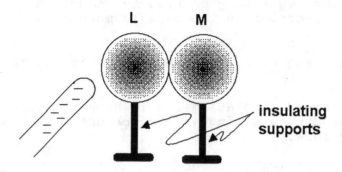

A) both spheres are neutral
B) both spheres are positive
C) both spheres are negative
D) L is negative and M is positive
*E) L is positive and M is negative

18. A positively charged metal sphere A is brought into contact with an uncharged metal sphere B. As a result:

*A) both spheres are positively charged
B) A is positively charged and B is neutral
C) A is positively charged and B is negatively charged
D) A is neutral and B is positively charged
E) A is neutral and B is negatively charged

19. The leaves of a positively charged electroscope diverge more when an object is brought near the knob of the electroscope. The object must be:

A) a conductor   D) negatively charged
B) an insulator   E) uncharged
*C) positively charged

20. A negatively charged rubber rod is brought near the knob of a positively charged electroscope. The result is that:

A) electroscope leaves will move farther apart
B) the rod will lose its charge
*C) electroscope leaves will tend to collapse
D) electroscope will become discharged
E) nothing noticeable will happen

272

21. An electroscope is charged by induction using a glass rod (which has been made positive by rubbing it with silk). The electroscope leaves:

*A) gain electrons
 B) gain protons
 C) lose electrons
 D) lose protons
 E) gain an equal number of protons and electrons

22. Consider the following procedural steps:
    (1) ground the electroscope
    (2) remove the ground from the electroscope
    (3) touch a charged rod to the electroscope
    (4) bring a charged rod near, but not touching, the electroscope
    (5) remove the charged rod
   To charge an electroscope by induction, use the sequence:

 A) 1 4 5 2   *B) 4 1 2 5   C) 3 1 2 5   D) 4 1 5 2   E) 3 5

23. A charged insulator can be discharged by passing it just above a flame. This is because the flame:

 A) warms it
 B) dries it
 C) contains carbon dioxide
*D) contains ions
 E) contains more rapidly moving atoms

24. A small object has charge Q. Charge q is removed from it and placed on a second small object. The two objects are placed 1 m apart. For the force that each object exerts on the other to be a maximum q should be:

 A) 2Q   B) Q   *C) Q/2   D) Q/4   E) 0

25. Two small charged objects repel each other with a force F when separated by a distance d. If the charge on each object is reduced to one-fourth of its original value and the distance between them is reduced to d/2, the force becomes:

 A) F/16   B) F/8   *C) F/4   D) F/2   E) F

26. Two identical conducting spheres, A and B, carry equal charge. They are separated by a distance much larger than their diameters. A third identical conducting sphere, C, is uncharged. Sphere C is first touched to A, then to B, and finally removed. As a result, the electrostatic force between A and B, which was originally F, becomes:

 A) F/2   B) F/4   *C) 3F/8   D) F/16   E) 0

273

27. Two particles, X and Y, are 4 m apart. X has a charge of 2Q and Y has a charge of Q. The ratio of the magnitude of the electrostatic force on X to that on Y is:

A) 4:1   B) 2:1   *C) 1:1   D) 1:2   E) 1:4

28. The units of $1/4\pi\epsilon_o$ are:

A) N^2/C^2
B) $N \cdot m/C$
C) $N^2 \cdot m^2/C^2$

*D) $N \cdot m^2/C^2$
E) m^2/C^2

29. A 5.0-coulomb charge is 10 m from a -2.0-coulomb charge. The electrostatic force is on the positive charge is:

*A) 9.0×10^8 N toward the negative charge
B) 9.0×10^8 N away from the negative charge
C) 9.0×10^9 N toward the negative charge
D) 9.0×10^9 N away from the negative charge
E) none of these

30. Two identical charges, 2.0 m apart, exert forces of magnitude 4.0 N on each other. The value of each charge is:

A) 1.8×10^{-9} C
B) 2.1×10^{-5} C
*C) 4.2×10^{-5} C

D) 1.9×10^5 C
E) 3.8×10^5 C

31. Two particles have charges Q and -Q (equal magnitude and opposite sign). For a net force of zero to be exerted on a third charge it must be placed:

A) midway between Q and -Q
B) on the perpendicular bisector of the line joining Q and -Q
C) on the line joining Q and -Q, to the side of Q opposite -Q
D) on the line joining Q and -Q, to the side of -Q opposite Q
*E) at none of these places (there is no place)

32. Charges q_1 and q_2 are on the x axis, with q_1 at x = a and q_2 at x = 2a. For the net force on a another charge at the origin to be zero q_1 and q_2 must be related by q_2 =:

A) $2q_1$ B) $4q_1$ C) $-2q_1$ *D) $-4q_1$ E) $-q_1/4$

274

33. Two particles A and B have identical charge Q. For a net force of zero to be exerted on a third charge it must be placed:

*A) midway between A and B
 B) on the perpendicular bisector of the line joining A and B but away from the line
 C) on the line joining A and B, not between the particles
 D) on the line joining A and B, closer to one of them than the other
 E) at none of these places (there is no place)

34. A 2-μC charge is placed at the origin, an identical charge is placed 2 m from the origin on the x axis, and a third identical charge is placed 2 m from the origin on the y axis. The magnitude of the force on the charge at the origin is:

 A) 9.0×10^{-3} N
 B) 6.4×10^{-3} N
*C) 1.3×10^{-2} N
 D) 1.8×10^{-2} N
 E) 3.6×10^{-2} N

35. Charges Q, -Q, and q are placed at the vertices of an equilateral triangle as shown. The total force exerted on the charge q is:

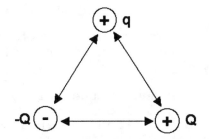

 A) toward charge Q
 B) toward charge -Q
 C) away from charge Q
 D) at right angles to the line joining Q and -Q
*E) parallel to the line joining Q and -Q

36. A charge Q is spread uniformly along the circumference of a circle of radius R. A point charge q is placed at the center of this circle. The total force exerted on q can be calculated by Coulomb's law:

 A) just use R for the distance
 B) just use 2R for the distance
 C) just use 2πR for the distance
*D) result of the calculation is zero
 E) none of the above

37. Charge Q is on the y axis a distance a from the origin and charge q is on the x axis a distance d from the origin. The value of d for which the x component of the force on q is the greatest is:

A) 0   B) a   C) $\sqrt{2}a$ D) a/2   *E) $a/\sqrt{2}$

38. In the Rutherford model of the hydrogen atom, a proton (mass M, charge Q) is the nucleus and an electron (mass m, charge q) moves around the proton in a circle of radius r. Let k denote the Coulomb force constant $(1/4\pi\epsilon_0)$ and G the universal gravitational constant. The ratio of the electrostatic force to the gravitational force between electron and proton is:

A) $kQq/GMmr^2$ B) GQq/kMm   C) kMm/GQq   D) GMm/kQq   *E) kQq/GMm

39. A particle with a charge of 5×10^{-6} C and a mass of 20 g moves uniformly with a speed of 7 m/s in a circular orbit around a stationary particle with a charge of -5×10^{-6} C. The radius of the orbit is:

A) 0   *B) 0.23 m   C) 0.62 m   D) 1.6   E) 4.4 m

40. Charge is distributed uniformly on the surface of a spherical balloon (an insulator) with a point charge q inside. The electrical force on q is greatest when:

A) it is near the inside surface of the balloon
B) it is at the center of the balloon
C) it is halfway between the balloon center and the inside surface
D) it is anywhere inside (the force is same everywhere and is not zero)
*E) it is anywhere inside (the force is zero everywhere)

41. Charge is distributed on the surface of a spherical conducting shell with a point charge q inside. If polarization effects are negligible the electrical force on q is greatest when:

*A) it is near the inside surface of the balloon
B) it is at the center of the balloon
C) it is halfway between the balloon center and the inside surface
D) it is anywhere inside (the force is same everywhere and is not zero)
E) it is anywhere inside (the force is zero everywhere)

1. An electric field is most directly related to:

 A) the momentum of a test charge
 B) the kinetic energy of a test charge
 C) the potential energy of a test charge
*D) the force acting on a test charge
 E) the charge carried by a test charge

2. As used in the definition of electric field intensity, a "test charge":

 A) has zero charge
 B) has charge of magnitude 1 C
 C) has charge of magnitude 1.6×10^{-19} C
 D) must be an electron
*E) none of the above

3. Experimenter A uses a test charge q_o and experimenter B uses a test charge $2q_o$ to measure an electric field produced by stationary charges. A finds a field that is:

*A) the same as the field found by B
 B) greater than the field found by B
 C) less than the field found by B
 D) either greater or less than the field found by B, depending on the masses of the test charges
 E) either greater or less than the field found by B, depending on the accelerations of the test charges

4. The units of the electric field are:

 A) N $\cdot C^2$ B) C/N   C) N   *D) N/C   E) C/m^2

5. The units of the electric field are:

*A) J/(C $\cdot$m)   D) J/m
 B) J/C   E) none of these
 C) J $\cdot$C

6. Electric field lines:

 A) are trajectories of a test charge
 B) are vectors in the direction of the electric field
 C) form closed loops
 D) cross each other in the region between two point charges
*E) are none of the above

7. Two spheres, one with radius R and the other with radius 2R,
   surround an isolated point charge. The ratio of the number of field
   lines through the larger sphere to the number through the smaller
   is:

*A) 1   B) 2   C) 4   D) 1/2   E) 1/4

8. A certain physics textbook shows a region of space in which two
   electric field lines cross each other. We conclude that:

 A) at least two point charges are present
 B) an electrical conductor is present
 C) an insulator is present
 D) the field points in two directions at the same place
*E) the author made a mistake

9. Choose the correct statement concerning electric field lines:

 A) field lines may cross
*B) field lines are close together where the field is large
 C) field lines point away from negative charge
 D) a point charge released from rest moves along a field line
 E) none of these are correct

10. The diagram shows the electric field lines due to two charged parallel metal plates. We conclude that:

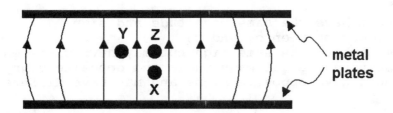

A) the upper plate is positive and the lower plate is negative
*B) a positive charge at X would experience the same force if it were placed at Y
C) a positive charge at X experiences a greater force than if it were placed at Z
D) a positive charge at X experiences less force than if it were placed at Z
E) a negative charge at X could have its weight balanced by the electrical force

11. Letting k denote $1/4\pi\epsilon_o$, the magnitude of the electric field due to a point charge q at a distance r from this charge is:

A) kq/r B) kr/q C) kq/r^3 *D) kq/r^2 E) kq^2/r^2

12. The electric field at a distance of 10 cm from an isolated point charge of 2×10^{-9} C is:

A) 1.8 N/C   *D) 1800 N/C
B) 180 N/C   E) none of these
C) 18 N/C

13. An isolated point charge produces an electric field with magnitude E at a point 2 m away. A point at which the field magnitude is E/4 is:

A) 1 m away   *D) 4 m away
B) 0.5 m away   E) 8 m away
C) 2 m away

14. An isolated point charge produces an electric field with magnitude E at a point 2 m away. At a point 1 m from the charge the magnitude of the field is:

A) E   B) 2E   *C) 4E   D) E/2   E) E/4

15. Two point charges, q_1 and q_2, are placed a distance r apart. The electric field is zero at a point P between the charges on the line segment connecting them. We conclude that:

  A) q_1 and q_2 must have the same magnitude and sign
  B) P must be midway between q_1 and q_2
*C) q_1 and q_2 must have the same sign but may have different magnitudes
  D) q_1 and q_2 must have equal magnitudes and opposite signs
  E) q_1 and q_2 must have opposite signs and may have different magnitudes

16. A positive charge Q is at point A and a negative charge -Q is at point B. The electric field at point P on the perpendicular bisector of AB as shown is:

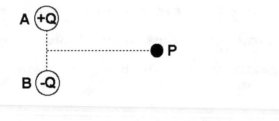

A) ↑   *B) ↓   C) →   D) ←   E) zero

17. A positive charge Q is at point A and another positive charge Q is at point B. The electric field at point P on the perpendicular bisector of AB as shown is:

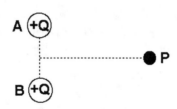

A) ↑   B) ↓   *C) →   D) ←   E) zero

18. The diagram shows the electric field lines in a region of space containing two small charged spheres (Y and Z). Then:

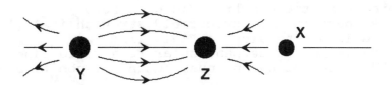

A) Y is negative and Z is positive
B) the magnitude of the electric field is the same everywhere
C) the electric field is strongest midway between Y and Z
*D) a small negatively charged body placed at X would be pushed to the right
E) Y and Z must have the same sign

19. Two point charges, $+8 \times 10^{-9}$ C and -2×10^{-9} C are separated by 4 m. The electric field intensity (in N/C) midway between them is:

A) 9×10^9 B) 13,500   C) 135,000   D) 36×10^{-9} *E) 22.5

20. Point charges are located at two vertices of an equilateral triangle and the electric field is zero at the third vertex. We conclude:

A) the two charges have opposite signs and the same magnitude
B) the two charges have opposite signs and different magnitudes
C) the two charges are identical
D) the two charges have the same sign but different magnitudes
*E) at least one other charge is present

21. Identical point charges are located at two vertices of an equilateral triangle. A third charge is placed so the electric field at the third vertex is zero. The third charge must:

*A) be on the perpendicular bisector of the line joining the first two charges
B) be on the line joining the first two charges
C) be identical to the first two charges
D) have the same magnitude as the first two charges but may have a different sign
E) be at the center of the triangle

22. The electric field due to a uniform distribution of charge on a spherical shell is zero:

A) everywhere
B) nowhere
C) only at the center of the shell
*D) only inside the shell
E) only outside the shell

23. A point charge is placed in an electric field which varies with location. No force is exerted on this charge:

  *A) at locations where the electric field is zero
   B) at locations where the electric field strength is $1/(1.6 \times 10^{-19})$ N/C
   C) if the charge is moving along a field line
   D) if the charge is moving perpendicular to a field line
   E) if the field is caused by an equal amount of positive and negative charge

24. The magnitude of the force on a 0.02 C point charge due to an electric field of 4000 N/C is:

   A) 80 N   *B) 8×10^{-5} N   C) 8×10^{-3} N   D) 0.08 N   E) 2×10^{11} N

25. A 200-N/C electric field is in the positive x direction. The force on an electron in this field is:

   A) 2.9×10^{13} m/s^2, in the positive x direction
  *B) 2.9×10^{13} m/s^2, in the negative x direction
   C) 3.2×10^{-17} m/s^2, in the positive x direction
   D) 3.2×10^{-17} m/s^2, in the negative x direction
   E) 0

26. An electron traveling north enters a region where the electric field is uniform and points north. The electron:

   A) speeds up
  *B) slows down
   C) veers east
   D) veers west
   E) continues with the same speed in the same direction

27. An electron traveling north enters a region where the electric field is uniform and points west. The electron:

   A) speeds up
   B) slows down
  *C) veers east
   D) veers west
   E) continues with the same speed in the same direction

28. Two point charges are arranged as shown. Where could a third charge +1 C be placed so that the net electrostatic force on it is zero?

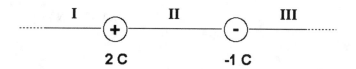

A) I only
B) I and II only
*C) lII only
D) I and III only
E) II only

29. An electric dipole consists of $+6\times10^{-6}$ C at the origin and -6×10^{-6} C on the x axis at $x = 3\times10^{-3}$ m. Its dipole moment is:

A) 1.8×10^{-8} C ·m, in the positive x direction
*B) 1.8×10^{-8} C ·m, in the negative x direction
C) 0, because the net charge is 0
D) 1.8×10^{-8} C ·m, perpendicular to the x-axis
E) none of the above

30. The force exerted by a uniform electric field on a dipole is:

A) parallel to the dipole moment
B) perpendicular to the dipole moment
C) parallel to the electric field
D) perpendicular to the electric field
*E) none of the above

31. An electric field exerts a torque on a dipole only if:

A) the field is parallel to the dipole moment
*B) the field is not parallel to the dipole moment
C) the field is perpendicular to the dipole moment
D) the field is not perpendicular to the dipole moment
E) the field is uniform

32. The torque exerted by an electric field on a dipole is:

A) parallel to the field and perpendicular to the dipole moment
B) parallel to both the field and dipole moment
*C) perpendicular to both the field and dipole moment
D) parallel to the dipole moment and perpendicular to the field
E) not related to the directions of the field and dipole moment

33. A uniform electric field of 300 N/C makes an angle of 25° with the dipole moment of an electric dipole. If the moment has a magnitude of 2×10^{-9} C·m the torque exerted by the field has a magnitude of:

A) 6.7×10^{-12} N·m
*B) 2.5×10^{-7} N·m
C) 5.4×10^{-7} N·m

D) 6.0×10^{-7} N·m
E) 2.8×10^{-7} N·m

34. When the dipole moment of a dipole in a uniform electric field rotates to become more nearly aligned with the field:

A) the field does positive work and the potential energy increases
*B) the field does positive work and the potential energy decreases
C) the field does negative work and the potential energy increases
D) the field does negative work and the potential energy decreases
E) the field does no work

35. The dipole moment of a dipole in a 300-N/C electric field is initially perpendicular to the field, but it rotates so it is in the same direction as the field. If the moment has a magnitude of 2×10^{-9} C·m the work done by the field is:

A) -12×10^{-7} J
B) -6×10^{-7} J
C) 0

*D) 6×10^{-7} J
E) 12×10^{-7} J

36. The purpose of the famous "oil drop" experiment was to determine:

A) the mass of an electron
*B) the charge of an electron
C) the ratio of charge to mass for an electron
D) the sign of the charge on an electron
E) viscosity

37. A charged oil drop with a mass of 2×10^{-4} kg is held suspended by a downward electric field of 300 N/C. The charge on the drop is:

A) $+1.5 \times 10^{-6}$ C
B) -1.5×10^{-6} C
C) $+6.5 \times 10^{-6}$ C

*D) -6.5×10^{-6} C
E) 0

1. A total charge of 6.3×10^{-8} C is distributed uniformly throughout a 2.7-cm radius sphere. The volume charge density is:

A) 3.7×10^{-7} C/m^3
B) 6.9×10^{-6} C/m^3
C) 6.9×10^{-6} C/m^2
D) 2.5×10^{-4} C/m^3
*E) 7.6×10^{-4} C/m^3

2. A total charge of 6.3×10^{-8} C is placed on a 2.7-cm radius isolated conducting sphere. The area charge density is:

A) 3.7×10^{-7} C/m^2
*B) 6.9×10^{-6} C/m^2
C) 2.5×10^{-4} C/m^3
D) 7.6×10^{-4} C/m^2
E) 7.6×10^{-4} C/m^3

3. A spherical shell has an inner radius of 3.7 cm and an outer radius of 4.5 cm. If charge is distributed uniformly throughout the shell with a volume density of 6.1×10^{-4} C/m^3 the total charge is:

*A) 1.0×10^{-7} C
B) 1.3×10^{-7} C
C) 2.0×10^{-7} C
D) 2.3×10^{-7} C
E) 4.0×10^{-7} C

4. A cylinder has a radius of 2.1 cm and a length of 8.8 cm. Total charge 6.1×10^{-7} C is distributed uniformly throughout. The volume charge density is:

A) 5.3×10^{-5} C/m^3
B) 5.3×10^{-5} C/m^2
C) 8.5×10^{-4} C/m^3
*D) 5.0×10^{-3} C/m^3
E) 6.3×10^{-2} C/m^3

5. When a piece of paper is held with one face perpendicular to a uniform electric field the flux through it is 25 N $\cdot$m^2/C. When the paper is turned 25° with respect to the field the flux through it is

A) 0
B) 12 N $\cdot$m^2/C
C) 21 N $\cdot$m^2/C
*D) 23 N $\cdot$m^2/C
E) 25 N $\cdot$m^2/C

6. The flux of the electric field $24\hat{\imath} + 30\hat{\jmath} + 16\hat{k}$ N/C through a 2.0 m^2 portion of the yz plane is:

A) 32 N $\cdot$m^2/C
B) 34 N $\cdot$m^2/C
C) 42 N $\cdot$m^2/C
*D) 48 N $\cdot$m^2/C
E) 60 N $\cdot$m^2/C

7. Consider Gauss's law: $\oint \mathbf{E} \cdot d\mathbf{A} = q/\epsilon_0$. Which of the following is true?

 A) $\mathbf{E}$ must be the electric field due to the enclosed charge
 B) If $q = 0$ then $\mathbf{E} = 0$ everywhere on the Gaussian surface
*C) If the charge inside consists of an electric dipole, then the integral is zero
 D) $\mathbf{E}$ is everywhere parallel to $d\mathbf{A}$ along the surface
 E) If a charge is placed outside the surface, then it cannot affect $\mathbf{E}$ on the surface

8. A point charge is placed at the center of a spherical Gaussian surface. The flux ϕ_E is changed:

 A) if the sphere is replaced by a cube of the same volume
 B) if the sphere is replaced by a cube of one-tenth the volume
 C) if the point charge is moved off center (but still inside the original sphere)
*D) if the point charge is moved to just outside the sphere
 E) if a second point charge is placed just outside the sphere

9. Choose the INCORRECT statement:

 A) Gauss' law can be derived from Coulomb's law
 B) Gauss' law states that the net number of lines crossing any closed surface in an outward direction is proportional to the net charge enclosed within the surface
 C) Coulomb's law can be derived from Gauss' law and symmetry
 D) Gauss' law applies to a closed surface of any shape
*E) According to Gauss' law, if a closed surface encloses no charge, then the electric field must vanish everywhere on the surface

10. The outer surface of the cardboard center of a paper towel roll:

 A) is a possible Gaussian surface
 B) cannot be a Gaussian surface because it encloses no charge
 C) cannot be a Gaussian surface since it is an insulator
*D) isn't a closed surface
 E) none of the above

11. A physics instructor in an anteroom charges an electrostatic generator to 25 μC, then carries it into the lecture hall. The net electric flux in $N \cdot m^2/C$ through the lecture hall walls is:

 A) 0
 B) 25×10^{-6}
 C) 2.2×10^5
*D) 2.8×10^6
 E) can't tell unless the lecture hall dimensions are given

12. A 5.0-μC point charge is placed at the center of a cube. The electric flux in N·m^2/C through one side of the cube is:

  A) 0   *B) 7.1x10^4 C) 9.4x10^4 D) 1.4x10^5 E) 5.6x10^5

13. A conducting sphere of radius 0.01 m has a charge of 1.0x10^{-9} C deposited on it. The magnitude of the electric field in N/C just outside the surface of the sphere is:

  A) zero   B) 450   *C) 900   D) 4500   E) 90,000

14. A round wastepaper basket with a 0.15-m radius opening is in a uniform electric field of 300 N/C, perpendicular to the opening. The total flux through the sides and bottom, in N·m^2/C, is:

  A) 0
  B) 4.2
 *C) 21
  D) 280
  E) can't tell without knowing the areas of the sides and bottom

15. 10 C of charge are placed on a spherical conducting shell. A -3 C-point charge is placed at the center of the cavity. The net charge in coulombs on the inner surface of the shell is:

  A) -7   B) -3   C) 0   *D) +3   E) +7

16. 10 C of charge are placed on a spherical conducting shell. A -3 C-point charge is placed at the center of the cavity. The net charge in coulombs on the outer surface of the shell is:

  A) -7   B) -3   C) 0   D) +3   *E) +7

17. A 30-N/C uniform electric field points perpendicularly toward the left face of a large neutral conducting sheet. The area charge density on the left and right faces, respectively, are:

 *A) -2.7x10^{-9} C/m^2; +2.7x10^{-9} C/m^2 D) +5.3x10^{-9} C/m^2; -5.3x10^{-9} C/m^2
  B) +2.7x10^{-9} C/m^2; -2.7x10^{-9} C/m^2 E) 0; 0
  C) -5.3x10^{-9} C/m^2; +5.3x10^{-9} C/m^2

18. A solid insulating sphere of radius R contains a uniform volume distribution of positive charge. Which of the graphs below correctly gives the magnitude E of the electric field as a function of r?

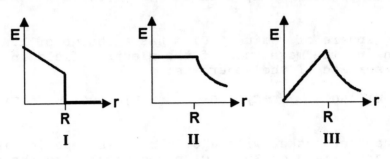

I   II   III

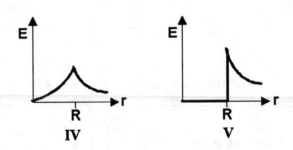

IV   V

A) I.   B) II.   *C) III.   D) IV.   E) V.

19. Which of the following graphs represents the magnitude of the electric field as a function of the distance from the center of a solid charged conducting sphere of radius R?

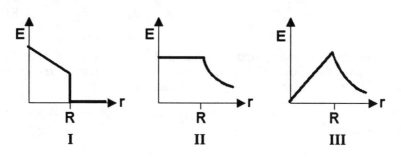

I   II   III

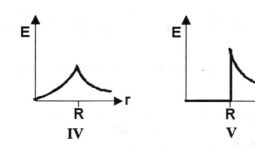

IV   V

A) I.   B) II.   C) III.   D) IV.   *E) V.

20. Charge Q is distributed uniformly throughout an insulating sphere of radius R. The magnitude of the electric field at a point R/2 from the center is:

A) $Q/4\pi\epsilon_o R^2$
B) $Q/\pi\epsilon_o R^2$
C) $3Q/4\pi\epsilon_o R^2$

*D) $Q/8\pi\epsilon_o R^2$ $= \frac{1}{4\pi\epsilon_o} \frac{1}{2} \frac{Q}{R^2}$
E) none of these

21. Positive charge Q is distributed uniformly throughout an insulating sphere of radius R, centered at the origin. A positive point charge Q is placed at x = 2R on the x axis. The magnitude of the electric field at x = R/2 on the x axis is:

A) $Q/4\pi\epsilon_o R^2$
B) $Q/8\pi\epsilon_o R^2$
*C) $Q/72\pi\epsilon_o/R^2$

D) $17Q/72\pi\epsilon_o R^2$
E) none of these

22. Charge Q is distributed uniformly throughout a spherical insulating shell. The net electric flux in N $\cdot$m^2/C through the inner surface of the shell is:

*A) 0   B) Q/ϵ_o C) $2Q/\epsilon_o$ D) $Q/4\pi\epsilon_o$ E) $Q/2\pi\epsilon_o$

23. Charge Q is distributed uniformly throughout a spherical insulating shell. The net electric flux in N $\cdot$m^2/C through the outer surface of the shell is:

A) 0   *B) Q/$\in_0$ C) 2Q/$\in_0$ D) Q/4$\in_0$ E) Q/2$\pi\in_0$

24. A 3.5-cm radius hemisphere contains a total charge of 6.6x10^{-7} C. The flux through the rounded portion of the surface is 9.8x10^4 N $\cdot$m^2/C. The flux through the flat base is:

A) 0
B) +2.3x10^4 N $\cdot$m^2/C
*C) -2.3÷10^4 N $\cdot$m^2/C
D) -9.8x10^4 N $\cdot$m^2/C
E) +9.8x10^4 N $\cdot$m^2/C

25. Charge is distributed uniformly along a long straight wire. The electric field 2 cm from the wire is 20 N/C. The electric field 4 cm from the wire is:

A) 120 N/C   B) 80 N/C   C) 40 N/C   *D) 10 N/C   E) 5 N/C

26. Charge is distributed uniformly on the surface of a large flat plate. The electric field 2 cm from the plate is 30 N/C. The electric field 4 cm from the plate is:

A) 120 N/C   B) 80 N/C   *C) 30 N/C   D) 15 N/C   E) 7.5 N/C

27. Positive charge Q is placed on a conducting spherical shell with inner radius R_1 and outer radius R_2. A point charge q is placed at the center of the cavity. The magnitude of the electric field at a point in the cavity, a distance r from the center, is:

A) $Q/4\pi\in_0 R_1^2$

B) $Q/4\pi\in_0 (R_1^2 - r^2)$

*C) $a/4\pi\in_0 r^2$
D) $(q + Q)/4\pi\in_0 r^2$
E) $(q + Q)/4\pi\in_0 (R_1^2 - r^2)$

28. Positive charge Q is placed on a conducting spherical shell with inner radius R_1 and outer radius R_2. A point charge q ia placed at the center of the cavity. The magnitude of the electric field at a point outside the shell, a distance r from the center, is:

A) $Q/4\pi\in_0 R_1^2$

B) $Q/4\pi\in_0 (R_1^2 - r^2)$

C) $a/4\pi\in_0 r^2$
*D) $(q + Q)/4\pi\in_0 r^2$
E) $(q + Q)/4\pi\in_0 (R_1^2 - r^2)$

29. Positive charge Q is placed on a conducting spherical shell with inner radius R_1 and outer radius R_2. A point charge q is placed at the center of the cavity. The magnitude of the electric field produced by the charge on the inner surface at a point in the interior of the conductor is:

A) 0   B) $Q/4\pi\epsilon_0 R_1^2$ C) $Q/4\pi\epsilon_0 R_2^2$ *D) $q/4\pi\epsilon_0 r^2$ E) $Q/4\pi\epsilon_0 r^2$

30. A positive point charge Q is placed outside a large neutral conducting sheet. At any point in the interior of the sheet the electric field produced by charges on the surface is directed:

A) toward the surface
B) away from the surface
*C) toward Q
D) away from Q
E) none of the above

31. A hollow conductor is positively charged. A small uncharged metal ball is lowered by a silk thread through a small opening in the top of the conductor and allowed to touch its inner surface. After the ball is removed, it will have:

A) a positive charge
B) a negative charge
*C) no appreciable charge
D) a charge whose sign depends on what part of the inner surface it touched
E) a charge whose sign depends on where the small hole is located in the conductor

1. A 5.5×10^{-6} C charge is 3.5 cm from a -2.3×10^{-8} C charge. The potential energy of this two-charge system, relative to the potential energy at infinite separation, is:

A) 3.2×10^{-4} J
*B) -3.2×10^{-4} J
C) 9.3×10^{-3} J
D) -9.3×10^{-3} J
E) zero

2. A 5.5×10^{-8} C charge is fixed at the origin. A -2.3×10^{-8} C charge is moved from x = 3.5 cm on the x axis to y = 4.3 cm on the y axis. The change in potential energy is:

A) 3.1×10^{-3} J
B) -3.1×10^{-3} J
*C) 6.0×10^{-5} J
D) -6.0×10^{-5} J
E) zero

3. A 5.5×10^{-8} C charge is fixed at the origin. A -2.3×10^{-8} C charge is moved from x = 3.5 cm on the x axis to y = 3.5 cm on the y axis. The change in potential energy is:

A) 3.2×10^{-4} J
B) -3.2×10^{-4} J
C) 9.3×10^{-3} J
D) -9.3×10^{-3} J
*E) zero

4. Three charges lie on the x axis: 1×10^{-8} C at x = 1 cm, 2×10^{-8} C at x = 2 cm, and 3×10^{-8} C at x = 3 cm. The potential energy of this arrangement, relative to the potential energy for infinite separation, is:

A) 7.9×10^{-2} J
*B) 8.5×10^{-4} J
C) 1.7×10^{-3} J
D) 0.16 J
E) zero

5. Two identical charges q are placed on the x axis, one at the origin and the other at x = 5 cm. A third charge -q is placed on the x axis so the potential energy of the three-charge system is the same as the potential energy at infinite separation. Its x coordinate is:

*A) 13 cm   B) 2.5 cm   C) 7.5 cm   D) 10 cm   E) -5 cm

6. Choose the correct statement:

A) A proton tends to go from a region of low potential to a region of high potential
B) The potential of a negatively charged conductor must be negative
C) If $E = 0$ at a point P then V must be zero at P
D) If $V = 0$ at a point P then E must be zero at P
*E) None of the above are correct

7. If 500 J of work are required to carry a 40 C charge from one point to another, the potential difference between these two points is:

*A) 12.5 V
 B) 20,000 V
 C) 0.08 V

D) depends on the path
E) none of these

8. The potential difference between two points is 100 volts. If 2 C is transported from one of these points to the other, the magnitude of the work done is:

*A) 200 J   B) 100 J   C) 50 J   D) 100 V   E) 2 J

9. During a lightning discharge, 30 C of charge move through a potential difference of 1.0×10^8 V in 2.0×10^{-2} s. The energy released by this lightning bolt is:

A) 1.5×10^{11} J
*B) 3.0×10^9 J
 C) 6.0×10^7 J

D) 3.3×10^6 J
E) 1500 J

293

10. Points R and T are each a distance d from each of two equal and
    opposite charges as shown. If $k = 1/4\pi\epsilon_o$, the work required to move
    a negative charge q from R to T is:

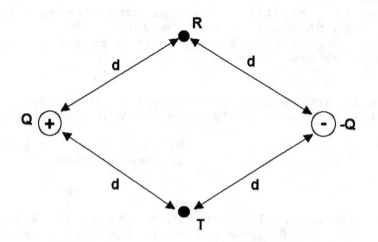

*A) zero   D)
 B) kqQ/d^2 kqQ/($\sqrt{2}$d)
 C) kqQ/d   E) kQq/(2d)

11. Points R and T are each a distance d from each of two equal positive
    charges as shown. If $k = 1/4\pi\epsilon_o$, the work required to move a test
    charge q from R to T is:

*A) zero   D)
 B) kQq/d^2 kQq/($\sqrt{2}$d)
 C) kQq/d   E) kQq/(2d)

12. The two charges Q are fixed at the vertices of an equilateral triangle with sides of length a. If $k = 1/4\pi\epsilon_0$, the work required to move q from the other vertex to the center of the line joining the fixed charges is:

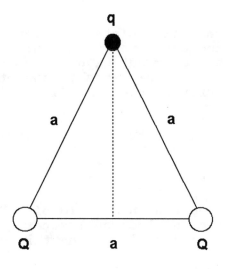

A) zero   B) kQq/a C) kQq/a^2 *D) $2kQq/a$ E) $\sqrt{2}kQq/a$

13. A particle (mass m, charge -q) is projected with speed v_0 into the region between two parallel plates as shown. The potential difference between the two plates is V and their separation is d. The change in kinetic energy of the particle as it traverses this region is:

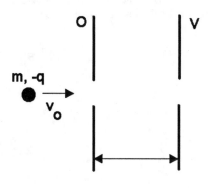

A) $-qV/d$

B) $2qV/mv_0^2$

*C) qV

D) $mv_0^2/2$

E) none of these

14. An electron is accelerated from rest through a potential difference V. Its final speed is proportional to:

A) V   B) V^2 *C) $\sqrt{V}$ D) 1/V   E) $1/\sqrt{V}$

15. Two large parallel conducting plates are separated by a distance d, placed in a vacuum, and connected to a source of potential difference V. A "doubly charged" oxygen ion starts from rest on the surface of one plate and accelerates to the other. If e denotes the magnitude of the electron charge, the final kinetic energy of this ion is:

A) eV/2   B) eV/d   C) eVd   D) Vd/e   *E) 2eV

16. An "electron volt" is the:

A) force acting on an electron in a field of 1 N/C
B) force required to move an electron 1 meter
*C) energy gained by an electron in moving through a potential difference of 1 volt
D) energy needed to move an electron through 1 meter in any electric field
E) work done when 1 coulomb of charge is moved through a potential difference of 1 volt

17. An electron has charge -e and mass m_e. A proton has charge e and mass $1840m_e$. A "proton volt" is equal to:

A) 1 eV   B) 1840 eV   C) (1/1840) eV   D) $\sqrt{1840}$ eV   E) $1/(\sqrt{1840})$ eV

Ans. a

18. Two conducting spheres, one having twice the diameter of the other, are separated by a distance large compared to their diameters. The smaller sphere (1) has charge q and the larger sphere (2) is uncharged. If the spheres are connected by a long thin wire:

*A) 1 and 2 have the same potential
 B) 2 has twice the potential as 1
 C) 2 has half the potential as 1
 D) 1 and 2 have the same charge
 E) all of the charge is dissipated

19. Two conducting spheres are far apart. The smaller sphere carries a total charge of $6x10^{-8}$ C. The larger sphere has a radius that is twice that of the smaller and is neutral. After the two spheres are connected by a conducting wire, the charges on the smaller and larger spheres, respectively, are:

 A) $4x10^{-8}$ C and $2x10^{-8}$ C
*B) $2x10^{-8}$ C and $4x10^{-8}$ C
 C) $-6x10^{-8}$ C and $12x10^{-8}$ C

 D) $6x10^{-8}$ C and 0
 E) $3x10^{-8}$ C and $3x10^{-8}$ C

20. A 5-cm radius conducting sphere is charged until the electric field just outside its surface is 2000 V/m. The electric potential of the sphere, relative to the potential far away, is:

 A) 0   B) 5 V   *C) 100 V   D) $4x10^4$ V   E) $8x10^5$ V

21. A 5-cm radius conducting sphere has a charge density of $2x10^{-6}$ C/m^2 on its surface. Its electric potential, relative to the potential far away, is:

*A) $1.1x10^4$ V
 B) $2.2x10^4$ V
 C) $2.3x10^5$ V

 D) $3.6x10^5$ V
 E) $7.2x10^6$ V

22. A hollow metal sphere is charged to a potential V. The potential at its center is:

*A) V   B) 0   C) -V   D) 2V   E) πV

23. Positive charge is distributed uniformly throughout a non-conducting sphere. The highest electric potential occurs:

   *A) at the center
    B) at the surface
    C) halfway between the center and surface
    D) just outside the surface
    E) far from the sphere

24. A total charge of 7×10^{-8} C is uniformly distributed throughout a non-conducting sphere with a radius of 5 cm. The electric potential at the surface, relative to the potential far away, is about:

    A) -2.1×10^4 V   D) -6.3×10^4 V
   *B) 2.1×10^4 V   E) 0
    C) 7.0×10^5 V

25. Eight identical spherical raindrops are each at a potential V, relative to the potential far away. They coalesce to make one spherical raindrop whose potential is:

    A) V/8   B) V/2   C) 2V   *D) 4V   E) 8V

26. A metal sphere carries a charge of 5×10^{-9} C and is at a potential of 400 V, relative to the potential far away. The potential at the center of the sphere is:

   *A) 400 V   D) zero
    B) -400 V   E) none of these
    C) 2×10^{-6} V

27. A 5-cm radius isolated conducting sphere is charged so its potential is -100 V, relative to the potential far away. The charge density on its surface is:

    A) 2.2×10^{-7} C/m^2 D) -3.5×10^{-7} C/m^2
    B) -2.2×10^{-7} C/m^2 *E) -1.8×10^{-8} C/m^2
    C) 3.5×10^{-7} C/m^2

28. A conducting sphere has charge Q and its electric potential is V, relative to the potential far away. If the charge is doubled to 2Q, the potential is:

    A) V   *B) 2V   C) 4V   D) V/2   E) V/4

29. A 2-meter stick is parallel to a uniform 200 N/C electric field. The potential difference between its ends is:

A) 0
B) 1.6×10^{-17} V
C) 3.2×10^{-17} V
D) 100 V
*E) 400 V

30. In a certain region of space the electric potential increases uniformly from north to south and does not vary in any other direction. The electric field:

A) points north and varies with position
*B) points north and does not vary with position
C) points south and varies with position
D) points south and does not vary with position
E) points east and does not vary with position

31. If the electric field is in the positive x direction and has a magnitude given by E = Cx, where C is a constant, then the electric potential is given by V =:

A) C   B) −C   C) Cx   D) $1/2Cx^2$ *E) $-1/2Cx^2$

32. The work in joules required to carry a 6.0-C charge from a 5.0-V equipotential surface to a 6.0-V equipotential surface and back again to the 5.0-V surface is:

*A) zero   B) 1.2×10^{-5} C) 3.0×10^{-5} D) 6.0×10^{-5} E) 6.0×10^{-6}

33. The equipotential surfaces associated with an isolated point charge are:

A) radially outward from the charge
B) vertical planes
C) horizontal planes
*D) concentric spheres centered at the charge
E) concentric cylinders with the charge on the axis

34. The electric field in a region around the origin is given by **E** = C(x**î** + y**ĵ**), where C is a constant. The equipotential surfaces are:

*A) concentric cylinders with axes along the z axis
B) concentric cylinders with axes along the x axis
C) concentric spheres centered at the origin
D) planes parallel to the xy plane
E) planes parallel to the yz plane

35. The electric potential in a certain region of space is given by
    $V = -7.5x^2 + 3x$, where V is in volts and x is in meters. In this
    region the equipotential surfaces are:

    A) planes parallel to the x axis
    *B) planes parallel to the yz plane
    C) concentric spheres centered at the origin
    D) concentric cylinders with the x axis as the cylinder axis
    E) unknown unless the charge is given

36. A charge q is to be brought from far away to a point near an
    electric dipole. No work is done if the final position of q is on:

    A) the line through the charges of the dipole
    *B) a line that is perpendicular to the dipole moment
    C) a line that makes an angle of 45° with the dipole moment
    D) a line that makes an angle of 30° with the dipole moment
    E) none of the above

37. Equipotential surfaces associated with an electric dipole are:

    A) spheres centered on the dipole
    B) cylinders with axes along the dipole moment
    C) planes perpendicular to the dipole moment
    D) planes parallel to the dipole moment
    *E) none of the above

Halliday Fund. 4e Chap 27

1. The units of capacitance are equivalent to:

A) J/C   B) V/C   C) J^2/C D) C/J   *E) C^2/J

2. A farad is the same as a:

A) J/V   B) V/J   *C) C/V   D) V/C   E) N/C

3. A capacitor C "has a charge Q". The actual charges on its plates are:

A) Q, Q   D) Q/2, -Q/2
B) Q/2, Q/2   E) Q, 0
*C) Q, -Q

4. Each plate of a capacitor stores a charge of magnitude 1 mC when a 100-V potential difference is applied. The capacitance is:

A) 5 μF   D) 100 μF
*B) 10 μF   E) none of these
C) 50 μF

5. A capacitor stores 0.10 C of charge with a potential difference of 40 V across its plates. Its capacitance is:

A) 40 F   B) 4 F   C) 0.4 F   D) 0.25 F   *E) 0.025 F

6. To charge a 1-F capacitor with 2 C requires a potential difference of:

*A) 2 V   D) 0.5 V
B) 0.2 V   E) none of these
C) 5 V

7. The capacitance of a parallel-plate capacitor with plate area A and plate separation d is given by:

A) $\in_0 d/A$ B) $\in_0 d/2A$ *C) $\in_0 A/d$ D) $\in_0 A/2d$ E) $Ad/\in_0$

301

8. The capacitance of a parallel-plate capacitor is:

*A) proportional to the plate area
 B) proportional to the charge stored
 C) independent of any material inserted between the plates
 D) proportional to the potential difference of the plates
 E) proportional to the plate separation

9. The capacitance of a parallel-plate capacitor can be increased by:

 A) increasing the charge
 B) decreasing the charge
 C) increasing the plate separation
*D) decreasing the plate separation
 E) decreasing the plate area

10. If both the plate area and the plate separation of a parallel-plate capacitor are doubled, the capacitance is:

 A) doubled   D) tripled
 B) halved   E) quadrupled
*C) unchanged

11. If the plate area of an isolated charged parallel-plate capacitor is doubled:

 A) the electric field is doubled
*B) the potential difference is halved
 C) the charge on each plate is halved
 D) the area charge density on each plate is doubled
 E) none of the above

12. If the plate separation of an isolated charged parallel-plate capacitor is doubled:

 A) the electric field is doubled
 B) the potential difference is halved
 C) the charge on each plate is halved
 D) the area charge density on each plate is doubled
*E) none of the above

13. Pulling the plates of an isolated charged capacitor apart:

 A) increases the capacitance
*B) increases the potential difference
 C) does not affect the potential difference
 D) decreases the potential difference
 E) does not affect the capacitance

14. If the charge on a parallel-plate capacitor is doubled:

   A) the capacitance is halved
   B) the capacitance is doubled
   C) the electric field is halved
  *D) the electric field is doubled
   E) the area charge density is not changed on either plate

15. A parallel-plate capacitor has a plate area of 0.2 m^2 and a plate
    separation of 0.1 mm. If the charge on each plate has a magnitude of
    4×10^{-6} C the electric field between the plates is approximately:

   A) 0   *D) 2×10^6 V/m
   B) 4×10^2 V/m   E) 4×10^{12} V/m
   C) 1×10^6 V/m

16. A parallel-plate capacitor has a plate area of 0.2 m^2 and a plate
    separation of 0.1 mm. If the charge on each plate has a magnitude of
    4×10^{-6} C the potential difference across the plates is
    approximately:

   A) 0   B) 4×10^{-2} V   C) 1×10^2 V   *D) 2×10^2 V   E) 4×10^8 V

17. The capacitance of a spherical capacitor with inner radius a and
    outer radius b is proportional to:

   A) a/b   *D) ab/(b-a)
   B) b - a   E) $ab/(b^2-a^2)$
   C) $b^2 - a^2$

18. The capacitance of a single isolated spherical conductor with radius
    R is proportional to:

  *A) R   D) $1/R^2$
   B) R^2 E) none of these
   C) 1/R

19. Two conducting spheres have radii of R_1 and R_2. If they are far
    apart the capacitance is proportional to:

  *A) $R_1R_2/(R_1-R_2)$ D) $R_2^2 - R_1^2$
   B) $R_1^2 - R_2^2$
                                  E) none of these
   C) $(R_1-R_2)/R_1R_2$

20. A 2-μF and a 1-μF capacitor are connected in series and a potential difference is applied across the combination. The 2-μF capacitor has:

   A) twice the charge of the 1-μF capacitor
   B) half the charge of the 1-μF capacitor
   C) twice the potential difference of the 1-μF capacitor
   *D) half the potential difference of the 1-μF capacitor
   E) none of the above

21. A 2-μF and a 1-μF capacitor are connected in parallel and a potential difference is applied across the combination. The 2-μF capacitor has:

   *A) twice the charge of the 1-μF capacitor
   B) half the charge of the 1-μF capacitor
   C) twice the potential difference of the 1-μF capacitor
   D) half the potential difference of the 1-μF capacitor
   E) none of the above

22. Let Q denote charge, V denote potential difference and U denote stored energy. Of these quantities, capacitors in series must have the same:

   *A) Q only   D) Q and U only
   B) V only   E) V and U only
   C) U only

23. Let Q denote charge, V denote potential difference and U denote stored energy. Of these quantities, capacitors in parallel must have the same:

   A) Q only   D) Q and U only
   *B) V only   E) V and U only
   C) U only

24. Capacitor C_1 and C_2 are connected in parallel. The equivalent capacitance is given by:

   A) $C_1 C_2 / (C_1 + C_2)$ D) C_1 / C_2
   B) $(C_1 + C_2) / C_1 C_2$ *E) $C_1 + C_2$
   C) $1 / (C_1 + C_2)$

25. Capacitors C_1 and C_2 are connected in series. The equivalent capacitance is given by:

   *A) $C_1 C_2 / (C_1 + C_2)$ D) C_1 / C_2
   B) $(C_1 + C_2) / C_1 C_2$ E) $C_1 + C_2$
   C) $1 / (C_1 + C_2)$

26. Capacitors C_1 and C_2 are connected in series and a potential difference is applied to the combination. If the capacitor that is equivalent to the combination has the same potential difference, then the charge on the equivalent capacitor is the same as:

 *A) the charge on C_1
  B) the sum of the charges on C_1 and C_2
  C) the difference of the charges on C_1 and C_2
  D) the product of the charges on C_1 and C_2
  E) none of the above

27. Capacitors C_1 and C_2 are connected in parallel and a potential difference is applied to the combination. If the capacitor that is equivalent to the combination has the same potential difference, then the charge on the equivalent capacitor is the same as:

  A) the charge on C_1
 *B) the sum of the charges on C_1 and C_2
  C) the difference of the charges on C_1 and C_2
  D) the product of the charges on C_1 and C_2
  E) none of the above

28. Two identical capacitors are connected in series and two, each identical to the first, are connected in parallel. The equivalent capacitance of the series connection is _____ the equivalent capacitance of parallel connection.

  A) twice   *D) one fourth
  B) four times   E) the same as
  C) half

29. Two identical capacitors (capacitance = C) are connected in parallel and the combination is connected in series to a third identical capacitor. The equivalent capacitance of this arrangement is:

 *A) 2C/3   B) C   C) 3C/2   D) 2C   E) 3C

30. A 2-μF and a 1-μF capacitor are connected in series and charged from a battery. They store charges P and Q respectively. When disconnected and charged separately using the same battery, they have charges R and S respectively. Then:

 *A) R > S > Q = P   D) R = P > S = Q
  B) P > Q > R = S   E) R > P > S = Q
  C) R > P = Q > S

305

31. Each of the four capacitors shown is 500 μF. The voltmeter reads 1000 V. The magnitude of the charge, in coulombs, on each capacitor plate is:

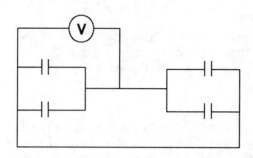

A) 0.2
*B) 0.5
C) 20

D) 50
E) none of these

32. The diagram shows six 6-μF capacitors. The capacitance between "a" and "b" is:

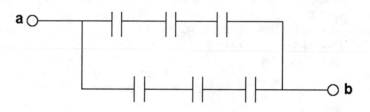

A) 3 μF   *B) 4 μF   C) 6 μF   D) 9 μF   E) 1 μF

33. Each of the three 25-μF capacitors shown is initially uncharged. How many coulombs pass through the ammeter A after the switch S is closed?

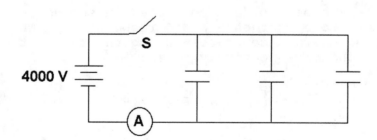

A) 0.10
*B) 0.30
C) 10

D) 0.033
E) none of these

306

34. A 20-F capacitor is charged to 200 V. Its stored energy is:

A) 4000 J   B) 4 J   *C) 0.4 J   D) 2000 J   E) 0.1 J

35. A charged capacitor stores 10 C at 40 V. Its stored energy is:

A) 400 J   B) 4 J   C) 0.2 J   D) 2.5 J   *E) 200 J

36. A 2-μF and a 1-μF capacitor are connected in series and charged by a battery. They store energies P and Q respectively. When disconnected and charged separately using the same battery, they have energies R and S respectively. Then:

A) R > P > S > Q   D) P > R > S > Q
B) P > Q > R > S   *E) R > S > Q > P
C) R > P > Q > S

37. The quantity $(1/2)\epsilon_o E^2$ has the significance of:

A) energy/farad   *D) energy/volume
B) energy/coulomb   E) energy/volt
C) energy

38. Capacitors A and B are identical. Capacitor A is charged so it stores 4 J of energy and capacitor B is uncharged. The capacitors are then connected in parallel. The total stored energy in the capacitors is now:

A) 16 J   B) 8 J   C) 4 J   *D) 2 J   E) 1 J

39. The two capacitors shown each have a capacitance of 1 μF. Their total stored energy is:

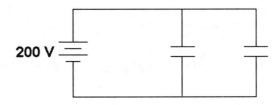

A) 0.01 J   D) 0.06 J
B) 0.02 J   E) none of these
*C) 0.04J

40. A battery is used to charge a parallel-plate capacitor, after which it is disconnected. Then the plates are pulled apart to twice their original separation. This process will double the:

   A) capacitance
   B) surface charge density on each plate
  *C) stored energy
   D) electric field between the two places
   E) charge on each plate

41. A parallel-plate capacitor has a plate area of 0.3 m^2 and a plate separation of 0.1 mm. If the charge on each plate has a magnitude of 5×10^{-6} C then the force exerted by one plate on the other has a magnitude of about:

   A) 0   *B) 5 N   C) 9 N   D) 1×10^4 N   E) 9×10^5 N

42. A certain capacitor has a capacitance of 5 μF. While it is charged to 5 μC and isolated, the plates are pulled apart so its capacitance becomes 2 μF. The work done by the pulling agent is about:

   A) 0   D) 9×10^{-6} J
  *B) 4×10^{-6} J   E) 18×10^{-6} J
   C) 8×10^{-6} J

43. An air-filled parallel-plate capacitor has a capacitance of 1 pF. The plate separation is then doubled and a wax dielectric is inserted, completely filling the space between the plates. As a result, the capacitance becomes 2 pF. The dielectric constant of the wax is:

   A) 0.25   B) 0.5   C) 2.0   *D) 4.0   E) 8.0

44. Suppose one has available:
       two sheets of copper
       a sheet of mica (0.1 mm, κ = 6)
       a sheet of glass (2 mm, κ = 7)
       a slab of paraffin (1 cm, κ = 2)
   To obtain the largest capacitance, place between the two copper sheets:

   A) a 1 mm gap of air   D) the paraffin
  *B) the mica   E) the mica, glass, and paraffin
   C) the glass

45. Two capacitors are identical except that one is filled with air and the other with oil. Both capacitors carry the same charge. The ratio of the electric fields E_{air}/E_{oil} is:

   A) between 0 and 1
   B) 0
   C) 1
   *D) between 1 and infinity
   E) infinite

46. A parallel-plate capacitor, with air dielectric, is charged by a battery, after which the battery is disconnected. A slab of glass dielectric is then slowly inserted between the plates. As it is being inserted:

   A) a force repels the glass out of the capacitor
   *B) a force attracts the glass into the capacitor
   C) no force acts on the glass
   D) a net charge appears on the glass
   E) the glass makes the plates repel each other

47. Two parallel-plate capacitors with the same plate separation but different capacitance are connected in parallel to a battery. Both capacitors are filled with air. The quantity that is NOT the same for both capacitors when they are fully charged is:

   A) potential difference
   B) energy density
   C) electric field between the plates
   *D) charge on the positive plate
   E) dielectric constant

48. Two parallel-plate capacitors with the same plate area but different capacitance are connected in parallel to a battery. Both capacitors are filled with air. The quantity that is the same for both capacitors when they are fully charged is:

   *A) potential difference
   B) energy density
   C) electric field between the plates
   D) charge on the positive plate
   E) plate separation

49. Two parallel-plate capacitors with different plate separation but the same capacitance are connected in series to a battery. Both capacitors are filled with air. The quantity that is NOT the same for both capacitors when they are fully charged is:

   A) potential difference
   B) stored energy
   *C) electric field between the plates
   D) charge on the positive plate
   E) dielectric constant

50. Two parallel-plate capacitors with different capacitance but the same plate separation are connected in series to a battery. Both capacitors are filled with air. The quantity that is the same for both capacitors when they are fully charged is:

   A) potential difference
   B) stored energy
   C) energy density
   D) electric field between the plates
  *E) charge on the positive plate

Halliday Fund. 4e Chap 28

1. A car battery is rated at 80 A ·h. An ampere-hour is a unit of:

A) power   B) energy   C) current   *D) charge   E) force

2. Current has units:

A) kilowatt hour   D) volt
*B) coulomb/second   E) ohm
C) coulomb

3. Current has units:

A) kilowatt hour   D) volt
*B) ampere   E) ohm
C) coulomb

4. The units of resistivity are:

A) ohm   D) ohm/meter^2
*B) ohm ·meter   E) none of these
C) ohm/meter

5. The rate at which electrical energy is used may be measured in:

A) watt/second   D) joule ·second
B) watt ·second   E) kilowatt ·hour
*C) watt

6. Energy may be measured in:

A) kilowatt   *D) watt ·second
B) joule ·second   E) volt/ohm
C) watt

7. Which one of the following quantities is correctly matched to its
   unit?

A) power - kW ·h   D) current - A/s
B) energy - kW   E) resistance - V/C
*C) potential difference - J/C

8. Current is a measure of:

A) force that moves a charge past a point
B) resistance to the movement of a charge past a point
C) energy used to move a charge past a point
*D) amount of charge that moves past a point per unit time
E) speed with which a charge moves past a point

9. A 60-watt light bulb carries a current of 0.5 ampere. The total charge passing through it in one hour is:

A) 120 C   B) 3600 C   C) 3000 C   D) 2400 C   *E) 1800 C

10. A 10-ohm resistor has a constant current of 5 A. How many coulombs flow through this resistor in 4 minutes?

A) 20   B) 40   C) 200   *D) 1200   E) 2400

11. Two wires made of different materials have the same uniform current density. They carry the same current only if:

A) their lengths are the same
*B) their cross-sectional areas are the same
C) both their lengths and cross-sectional areas are the same
D) the potential differences across them are the same
E) the electric fields in them are the same

12. A wire with a length of 1.5 m and a radius of 0.15 mm carries a current of 2.0 A. The current density is about:

A) 0.28 A/m^2 *D) 3.1×10^6 A/m^2
B) 1.3 A/m^2 E) 4.7×10^6 A/m^2
C) 2.1×10^6 A/m^2

13. In a conductor carrying a current we expect the electron drift speed to be:

A) much greater than the average electron speed
*B) much less than the average electron speed
C) about the same as the average electron speed
D) less than the electron speed at low temperature and greater than the electron speed at high temperature
E) less than the electron speed at high temperature and greater than the electron speed at low temperature

14. Two substances are identical except that the electron mean free time for substance A is twice the electron mean free time for substance B. If the same electric field exists in both substances the electron drift speed in A is:

   A) the same as in B
   *B) twice that in B
   C) half that in B
   D) four times that in B
   E) one fourth that in B

15. The current is zero in a conductor when no potential difference is applied because:

   A) the electrons are not moving
   B) the electrons are not moving fast enough
   *C) for every electron with a given velocity there is another with a velocity of equal magnitude and opposite direction.
   D) equal numbers of electrons and protons are moving together
   E) otherwise Ohm's law would not be valid

16. The current density is the same in two wires. Wire A has twice the free electron concentration of wire B. The drift speed of electrons in A is:

   A) twice that of electrons in B
   B) four times that of electrons in B
   *C) half that of electrons in B
   D) one fourth that of electrons in B
   E) the same as that of electrons in B

17. Copper contains 8.4×10^{28} free electrons/m^3. A copper wire of cross-sectional area 1 mm^2 carries a current of 1 A. The electron drift speed is approximately:

   A) 3×10^8 m/s
   B) 10^3 m/s
   C) 1 m/s
   *D) 10^{-4} m/s
   E) 10^{-23} m/s

18. If **J** is the current density and d**A** is a vector element of area then the integral $\int \mathbf{J} \cdot d\mathbf{A}$ over an area represents:

   A) the electric flux through the area
   B) the average current density at the position of the area
   C) the resistance of the area
   D) the resistivity of the area
   *E) the current through the area

313

19. If the potential difference across a resistor is doubled:

  *A) only the current is doubled
   B) only the current is halved
   C) only the resistance is doubled
   D) only the resistance is halved
   E) both the current and resistance are doubled

20. Of the following the copper conductor that has the least resistance
    is:

   A) thin, long and hot   D) thin, short and cool
  *B) thick, short and cool   E) thin, short and hot
   C) thick, long and hot

21. A cylindrical copper rod has resistance R. It is reformed to twice
    its original length with no change of volume. Its new resistance is:

   A) R   B) 2R   *C) 4R   D) 8R   E) R/2

22. The resistance of a rod does NOT depend on its:

   A) temperature
   B) material
   C) length
   D) conductivity
  *E) shape of its (fixed) cross-sectional area

23. A certain wire has resistance R. Another wire, of the same material,
    has half the length and half the diameter of the first wire. The
    resistance of the second wire is:

   A) R/4   B) R/2   C) R   *D) 2R   E) 4R

24. A nichrome wire is 1 m long and 1 mm^2 in cross-sectional area. When
    connected to a potential difference of 2 V, a current of 4 A exists
    in the wire. The resistivity of this nichrome is:

   A) 10^{-7} Ω ·m   *D) 5×10^{-7} Ω ·m
   B) 2×10^{-7} Ω ·m   E) 8×10^{-7} Ω ·m
   C) 4×10^{-7} Ω ·m

25. Two conductors are made of the same material and have the same
    length. Conductor A is a solid wire of diameter 1 mm. Conductor B is
    a hollow tube of inside diameter 1 mm and outside diameter 2 mm. The
    ratio of their resistance, RA/RB, is:

   A) 1   B) $\sqrt{2}$ C) 2   *D) 3   E) 4

26. "Conductivity" is:

   A) the same as resistivity, it is just more convenient to use for good
      conductors
   B) expressed in Ω^{-1}
   C) equal to 1/resistance
   *D) expressed in $(\Omega \cdot m)^{-1}$
   E) not a meaningful quantity for an insulator

27. A certain sample carries a current of 2 A when the potential
    difference is 1 V and a current of 5 A when the potential difference
    is 2 V. This sample:

   A) obeys Ohm's law
   B) has a resistance of 0.5 Ω at 1 V
   *C) has a resistance of 2.5 Ω at 2 V
   D) has a resistance of 0.4 Ω at 2 V
   E) does not have a resistance

28. A current of 0.5 ampere exists in a 60-ohm lamp. The applied
    potential difference is:

   A) 15 V   D) 120 V
   *B) 30 V   E) none of these
   C) 60 V

29. Which of the following graphs best represents the current-voltage
    relationship of an incandescent light bulb?

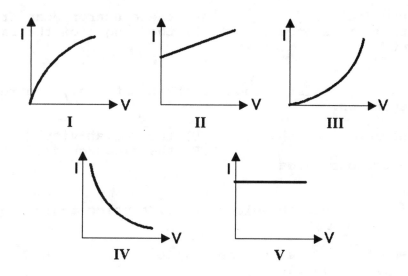

*A) I.   B) II.   C) III.   D) IV.   E) V.

30. Two wires are made of the same material and have the same length but different radii. The are joined end-to-end and a potential difference is maintained across the combination. Of the following the quantity that is the same for both wires is:

A) potential difference
*B) current
C) current density
D) electric field
E) none of the above

31. For an ohmic substance the resistivity is the proportionality constant for:

A) current and potential difference
B) current and electric field
C) current density and potential difference
*D) current density and electric field
E) potential difference and electric field

32. For an ohmic resistor, resistance is the proportionality constant for:

A) potential difference and electric field
B) current and electric field
C) current and length
D) current and cross-sectional area
*E) current and potential difference

33. For an ohmic substance the resistivity depends on:

A) the electric field
B) the potential difference
C) the current
*D) the electron mean free time
E) the length of the sample

34. For a cylindrical resistor made of ohmic material, the resistance does NOT depend on:

*A) the current
B) the length
C) the cross-sectional area
D) the resistivity
E) the electron drift velocity

35. For an ohmic substance the electron drift velocity is proportional to:

A) the cross-sectional area of the sample
B) the length of the sample
C) the mass of an electron
*D) the electric field in the sample
E) none of the above

36. A student kept her 60 watt 120 volt study lamp turned on from 2 PM until 2 AM. How many coulombs went through it?

A) 150   B) 3600   C) 7200   *D) 9000   E) 18,000

37. A flat iron is marked "120 volt, 600 watt". In normal use, the current in it is:

A) 2 A   B) 4 A   *C) 5 A   D) 7.2 A   E) 0.2 A

38. An unknown resistor dissipates 0.5 W when connected to a 3 V potential difference. When connected to a 1 V potential difference, this resistor will dissipate:

A) 0.5 W   *D) 0.056 W
B) 0.167 W   E) none of these
C) 1.5 W

39. An ordinary light bulb is marked "60 watt, 120 volt". Its (heated) resistance is:

A) 60 Ω   B) 120 Ω   C) 180 Ω   *D) 240 Ω   E) 15 Ω

40. The mechanical equivalent of heat is 1 cal = 4.18 J. An electric immersion water heater, rated at 400 W, should heat a liter of water from 10°C to 30°C in about:

*A) 3.5 min   B) 1 min   C) 15 min   D) 45 min   E) 15 s

41. It is better to send 10,000 kW of electric power long distances at 10,000 V rather than at 220 V because:

*A) there is less heating in the transmission wires
 B) the resistance of the wires is less at high voltages
 C) more current is transmitted at high voltages
 D) the insulation is more effective at high voltages
 E) the "iR" drop along the wires is greater at high voltage

42. Suppose the electric company charges 10 cents per kW·h. How much does it cost to use a 125 watt lamp 4 hours a day for 30 days?

A) $1.20   D) $7.20
*B) $1.50   E) none of these
C) $1.80

43. A certain x-ray tube requires a current of 7 mA at a voltage of 80 kV. The power (in watts) dissipated is:

*A) 560   B) 5600   C) 26   D) 11.4   E) 87.5

317

44. The mechanical equivalent of heat is 1 cal = 4.18 J. A heating coil, connected to a 120-V source, develops 60,000 calories in 10 minutes. The current in the coil is:

A) 0.83 A   B) 2 A   *C) 3.5 A   D) 20 A   E) 50 A

45. You buy a "75 watt" light bulb. The label means that:

A) no matter how you use the bulb, the power will be 75 W
B) the bulb was filled with 75 W at the factory
C) the actual power dissipated will be much higher than 75 W since most of the power appears as heat
D) the bulb is expected to "burn out" after you use up its 75 watts
*E) none of the above

46. A current of 0.3 A is passed through a lamp for 2 minutes using a 6 V power supply. The energy dissipated by this lamp during the 2 minutes is:

A) 1.8 J   B) 12 J   C) 20 J   D) 36 J   *E) 216 J

1. "The sum of the currents into a junction equals the sum of the currents out of the junction" is a result of:

A) Newton's third law
B) Ohm's law
C) Newton's second law

D) conservation of energy
*E) conservation of charge

2. "The sum of the emf's and potential differences around a closed loop equals zero" is a result of:

A) Newton's third law
B) Ohm's law
C) Newton's second law

*D) conservation of energy
E) conservation of charge

3. Four wires meet at a junction. The first carries 4 A into the junction, the second carries 5 A out of the junction, and the third carries 2 A out of the junction. The fourth carries:

A) 7 A out of the junction
B) 7 A into the junction
C) 3 A out of the junction

*D) 3 A into the junction
E) 1 A into the junction

4. In the context of Kirchhoff's rules a junction is:

A) where a wire is connected to a resistor
B) where a wire is connected to a battery
C) where only two wires are joined
*D) where three or more wires are joined
E) where a wire is bent

5. For any circuit the number of independent equations containing emf's, resistances, and currents equals:

A) the number of junctions
B) the number of junctions minus 1
*C) the number of branches
D) the number of branches minus 1
E) the number of closed loops

6. If a circuit has L closed loops, B branches, and J junctions the number of independent loop equations is:

*A) B-J+1   B) B-J   C) B   D) L   E) L-J

7. A total resistance of 3.0 Ω is to be produced by combining an unknown resistor R with a 12 Ω resistor. What is the value of R and how is it to be connected to the 12 Ω resistor?

*A) 4.0 Ω, parallel   D) 2.4 Ω, series
 B) 4.0 Ω, series   E) 9.0 Ω, series
 C) 2.4 Ω, parallel

8. By using only two resistors, R_1 and R_2 a student is able to obtain resistances of 3 Ω, 4 Ω, 12 Ω, and 16 Ω. The values of R_1 and R_2 (in ohms) are:

A) 3, 4   B) 2, 12   C) 3, 16   *D) 4, 12   E) 4, 16

9. Four 20-Ω resistors are connected in parallel and the combination is connected to a 20-V emf device. The current in the device is:

A) 0.25 A   B) 1.0 A   *C) 4.0 A   D) 5.0 A   E) 100 A

10. Four 20-Ω resistors are connected in parallel and the combination is connected to a 20-V emf device. The current in any one of the resistors is:

A) 0.25 A   *B) 1.0 A   C) 4.0 A   D) 5.0 A   E) 100 A

11. Four 20-Ω resistors are connected in series and the combination is connected to a 20-V emf device. The current in any one of the resistors is:

*A) 0.25 A   B) 1.0 A   C) 4.0 A   D) 5.0 A   E) 100 A

12. Four 20-Ω resistors are connected in series and the combination is connected to a 20-V emf device. The potential difference across any one of the resistors is:

A) 4 V   *B) 5 V   C) 8 V   D) 20 V   E) 80 V

13. Nine identical wires, each of diameter d and length L, are connected in parallel. The combination has the same resistance as a single similar wire of length L but whose diameter is:

*A) 3d   B) 9d   C) d/3   D) d/9   E) d/81

14. Nine identical wires, each of diameter d and length L, are connected in series. The combination has the same resistance as a single similar wire of length L but whose diameter is:

A) 3d   B) 9d   *C) d/3   D) d/9   E) d/81

15. Two wires made of the same material have the same length but different diameter. They are connected in parallel to a battery. The quantity that is NOT the same for the wires is:

  A) the end-to-end potential difference
 *B) the current
  C) the current density
  D) the electric field
  E) the electron drift velocity

16. Two wires made of the same material have the same length but different diameter. They are connected in series to a battery. The quantity that is the same for the wires is:

  A) the end-to-end potential difference
 *B) the current
  C) the current density
  D) the electric field
  E) the electron drift velocity

17. The resistance of resistor A is twice the resistance of resistor B. The two are connected in parallel and a potential difference is maintained across the combination. Then:

  A) the current in A is twice that in B
 *B) the current in A is half that in B
  C) the potential difference across A is twice that across B
  D) the potential difference across A is half that across B
  E) none of the above are true

18. The resistance of resistor A is twice the resistance of resistor B. The two are connected in series and a potential difference is maintained across the combination. Then:

  A) the current in A is twice that in B
  B) the current in A is half that in B
 *C) the potential difference across A is twice that across B
  D) the potential difference across A is half that across B
  E) none of the above are true

19. Resistor A has twice the resistance of resistor B. The two are connected in series and a potential difference is maintained across the combination. The rate of thermal dissipation in A is:

  A) the same as that in B   D) four times that in B
 *B) twice that in B   E) one fourth that in B
  C) half that in B

321

20. Resistor A has twice the resistance of resistor B. The two are connected in parallel and a potential difference is maintained across the combination. The rate of thermal dissipation in A is:

A) the same as that in B
B) twice that in B
*C) half that in B

D) four times that in B
E) one fourth that in B

21. The equivalent resistance between points A and B of the circuit shown is:

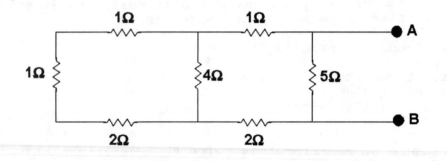

A) 4 Ω
B) 4.5 Ω
C) 6 Ω
D) 3 Ω
*E) 2.5 Ω

22. Each of the resistors in the diagram is 12 Ω. The resistance of the entire circuit is:

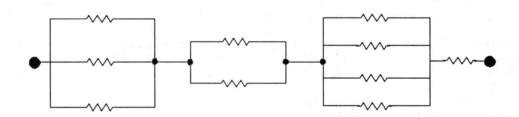

A) 5.76 Ω
*B) 25 Ω
C) 48 Ω

D) 120 Ω
E) none of these

23. The emf of a battery is equal to its terminal potential difference:

A) under all conditions
B) only when the battery is being charged
C) only when a large current is in the battery
*D) only when there is no current in the battery
E) under no conditions

322

24. The terminal potential difference of a battery is greater than its
    emf:

   A) under all conditions
  *B) only when the battery is being charged
   C) only when the battery is being discharged
   D) only when there is no current in the battery
   E) under no conditions

25. A battery of emf 24 V is connected to a 6-Ω resistor. As a result,
    current of 3 A exists in the resistor. The terminal potential
    difference of the battery is:

   A) 0   B) 6 V   C) 12 V   *D) 18 V   E) 24 V

26. Resistances of 2.0 Ω, 4.0 Ω, and 6.0 Ω and a 24 V battery are all in
    series. The current in the 2.0 Ω resistor is:

   A) 12 A   B) 4.0 A   C) 2.4 A   *D) 2.0 A   E) 0.50 A

27. Resistances of 2.0 Ω, 4.0 Ω, and 6.0 Ω and a 24 V battery are all in
    series. The potential difference across the 2.0 Ω resistor is:

  *A) 4 V   B) 8 V   C) 12 V   D) 24 V   E) 48 V

28. A battery with an emf of 12 V and an internal resistance of 1 Ω is
    used to charge a battery with an emf of 10 V and an internal
    resistance of 1 Ω. The current in the circuit is:

  *A) 1 A   B) 2 A   C) 4 A   D) 11 A   E) 22 A

29. In the diagram, the current in the 3-Ω resistor is 4 A. The
    potential difference between points A and B is:

   A) 0.75 V   B) 0.8 V   C) 1.25 V   D) 12 V   *E) 20 V

30. The current in the 5.0-Ω resistor in the circuit shown is:

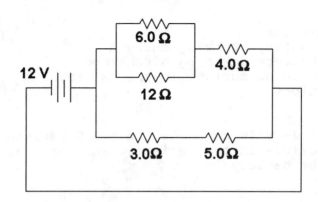

A) 0.42 A   B) 0.67 A   *C) 1.5 A   D) 2.4 A   E) 3.0 A

31. A 3-Ω and a 1.5-Ω resistor are wired in parallel and the combination is wired in series to a 4-Ω resistor and a 10-V emf device. The current in the 3-Ω resistor is:

A) 0.33 A   *B) 0.67 A   C) 2.0 A   D) 3.3 A   E) 6.7 A

32. A 3-Ω and a 1.5-Ω resistor are wired in parallel and the combination is wired in series to a 4-Ω resistor and a 10-V emf device. The potential difference across the 3-Ω resistor is:

*A) 2.0 V   B) 6.0 V   C) 8.0 V   D) 10 V   E) 12 V

33. Two identical batteries, each with an emf of 18 V and an internal resistance of 1 Ω, are wired in parallel by connecting their positive terminals together and connecting their negative terminals together. The combination is then wired across a 4 Ω resistor. The current in the 4 Ω resistor is:

A) 1.0 A   B) 2.0 A   *C) 4.0 A   D) 3.6 A   E) 7.2 A

34. Two identical batteries, each with an emf of 18 V and an internal resistance of 1 Ω, are wired in parallel by connecting their positive terminals together and connecting their negative terminals together. The combination is then wired across a 4 Ω resistor. The current in each battery is:

A) 1.0 A   *B) 2.0 A   C) 4.0 A   D) 3.6 A   E) 7.2 A

35. Two identical batteries, each with an emf of 18 V and an internal resistance of 1 Ω, are wired in parallel by connecting their positive terminals together and connecting their negative terminals together. The combination is then wired across a 4 Ω resistor. The potential difference across the 4 Ω resistor is:

A) 4.0 V   B) 8.0 V   C) 14 V   *D) 16 V   E) 29 V

36. In the diagrams, all light bulbs are identical and all emf devices are identical. In which circuit (I, II, III, IV, V) will the bulbs glow with the same brightness as in circuit X?

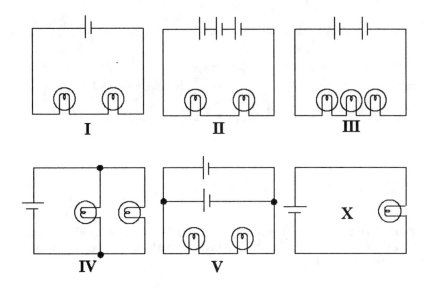

A) I.   B) II.   C) III.   *D) IV.   E) V.

37. In the diagrams, all light bulbs are identical and all emf devices are identical. In which circuit (I, II, III, IV, V) will the bulbs be dimmest?

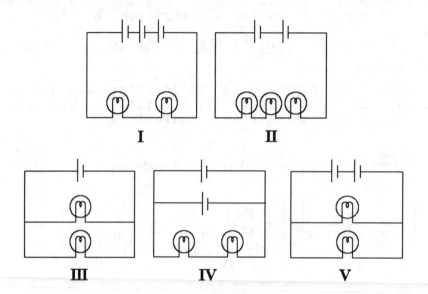

A) I.   B) II.   C) III.   *D) IV.   E) V.

38. A 120-V power line is protected by a 15-A fuse. What is the maximum number of "120 V, 500 W" light bulbs that can be operated at full brightness from this line?

A) 1   B) 2   *C) 3   D) 4   E) 5

39. Two 110-V light bulbs, one "25 W" and the other "100 W", are connected in series to a 110 V source. Then:

A) the current in the 100 W bulb is greater than that in the 25 W bulb
B) the current in the 100 W bulb is less than that in the 25 W bulb
C) both bulbs will light with equal brightness
D) each bulb will have a potential difference of 55 V
*E) none of the above

40. A 2-ohm resistor and a 4-ohm resistor are connected in parallel to a 6-volt battery. The power dissipated by the 2-ohm resistor is:

A) 8 W   *D) 18 W
B) 6 W   E) none of these
C) 9 W

326

41. In an antique automobile, a 6-V battery supplies a total of 48 W to two identical headlights in parallel. The resistance (in ohms) of each bulb is:

A) 0.67   *B) 1.5   C) 3   D) 4   E) 8

42. Resistor A has twice the resistance of resistor B. They are connected in parallel to a battery. The ratio of the power dissipated by A to that by B is:

A) 1:4   *B) 1:2   C) 1:1   D) 2:1   E) 4:1

43. A series circuit consists of a battery with internal resistance r and an external resistor R. If these two resistances are equal (r = R) then the energy dissipated per unit time by the internal resistance r is:

 *A) the same as by R
  B) half that by R
  C) twice that by R
  D) one third that by R
  E) unknown unless the emf is given

44. The positive terminals of two batteries with emf's of 14 V and 10 V respectively are connected together. The circuit is completed by connecting the negative terminals. If each battery has an internal resistance of 1.0 ohm, the rate in watts at which electrical energy is converted to chemical energy in the smaller battery is:

A) 4   B) 14   *C) 20   D) 120   E) 144

45. In the figure, voltmeter V_1 reads 600 V, voltmeter V_2 reads 580 V, and ammeter A reads 100 A. The power wasted in the transmission line connecting the power house to the consumer is:

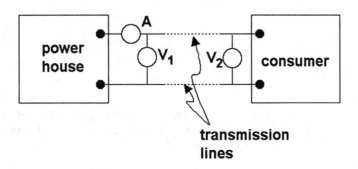

A) 1 kW   *B) 2 kW   C) 58 kW   D) 59 kW   E) 60 kW

327

46. The circuit shown was wired for the purpose of measuring the resistance of the lamp L. Inspection shows that:

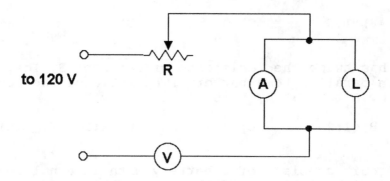

to 120 V

A) voltmeter V and rheostat R should be interchanged
B) the circuit is satisfactory
C) the ammeter A should be in parallel with R, not L
*D) the meters, V and A, should be interchanged
E) L and V should be interchanged

47. When switch S is open, the ammeter in the circuit shown reads 2.0 A. When S is closed, the ammeter reading will:

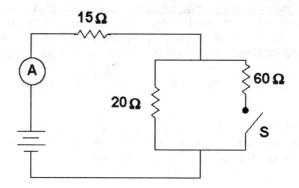

*A) increase slightly   D) double
B) remain the same   E) halve
C) decrease slightly

48. A certain galvanometer has a resistance of 100 Ω and requires 1 mA for full scale deflection. To make this into a voltmeter reading 1 V full scale, connect a resistance of:

A) 1000 Ω in parallel   D) 0.1 Ω in series
*B) 10 Ω in parallel   E) 1000 Ω in series
C) 900 Ω in series

49. To make a galvanometer into an ammeter, connect:

A) a high resistance in parallel   *D) a low resistance in parallel
B) a high resistance in series   E) a source of emf in series
C) a low resistance in series

50. A certain voltmeter has an internal resistance of 10,000 Ω and a range from 0 to 100 V. To give it a range from 0 to 1000 V, one should connect:

A) 100,000 Ω in series   D) 90,000 Ω in series
B) 1000 Ω in parallel   *E) 1000 Ω in series
C) 100,000 Ω in parallel

51. A certain ammeter has an internal resistance of 1 Ω and a range from 0 to 50 mA. To make its range from 0 to 5 A, use:

A) a series resistance of 99 Ω
B) an extremely large (say 10^6 Ω) series resistance
C) a resistance of 99 Ω in parallel
*D) a resistance of 1/99 Ω in parallel
E) a resistance of 1/1000 Ω in parallel

52. A galvanometer has an internal resistance of 12 Ω and requires 0.01 A for full scale deflection. To convert it to a voltmeter reading 3 V full scale, one must use a series resistance of:

A) 102 Ω   *B) 288 Ω   C) 300 Ω   D) 360 Ω   E) 412 Ω

53. A certain voltmeter has an internal resistance of 10,000 Ω and a range from 0 to 12 V. To extend its range to 120 V, use a series resistance of:

A) 1,111 Ω   D) 108,000 Ω
*B) 90,000 Ω   E) 120,000 Ω
C) 100,000 Ω

54. In the circuit shown, both resistors have the same value R. Suppose switch S is initially closed. When it is then opened, the circuit has a time constant τ_a Conversely, suppose S is initially open. When it is then closed, the circuit has a time constant τ_b The ratio $\tau_a \tau_b$ is:

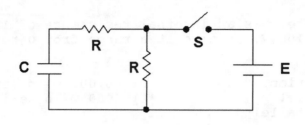

A) 1   *B) 2   C) 0.5   D) 0.667   E) 1.5

55. In the circuit shown, the capacitor is initially uncharged. At time t = 0, switch S is closed. If τ denotes the time constant, the approximate current through the 3 Ω resistor when t = τ/100 is:

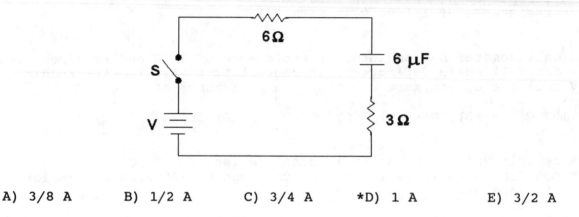

A) 3/8 A   B) 1/2 A   C) 3/4 A   *D) 1 A   E) 3/2 A

56. Suppose the current charging a capacitor is kept constant. Which graph below correctly gives the potential difference V across the capacitor as a function of time?

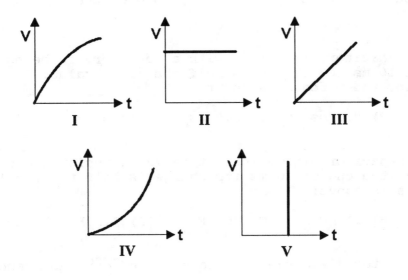

A) I.   B) II.   *C) III.   D) IV.   E) V.

57. A charged capacitor is being discharged through a resistor. At the end of one time constant the charge has been reduced by $(1 - 1/e) = 63\%$ of its initial value. At the end of two time constants the charge has been reduced by what percent of its initial value?

   A) 82%
  *B) 86%
   C) 100%
   D) between 90% and 100%
   E) need to know more data to answer the question

58. An initially uncharged capacitor C is connected in series with resistor R. This combination is then connected to a battery of emf V_o Sufficient time elapses so that a steady state is reached. Which of the following statements is NOT true:

   A) the time constant is independent of V_o
   B) the final charge on C is independent of R
  *C) the total energy dissipated by R is independent of R
   D) the total energy dissipated by R is independent of V_o
   E) the initial current (just after the battery was connected) is independent of C

59. The time constant RC has units of:

A) second/farad
B) second/ohm
C) 1/second

D) second/watt
*E) none of these

60. A certain capacitor, in series with a resistor, is being charged. At the end of 10 ms its charge is half the final value. The time constant for the process is about:

A) 0.43 ms   B) 2.3 ms   C) 6.9 ms   D) 10 ms   *E) 14 ms

61. A certain capacitor, in series with a 720 Ω resistor, is being charged. At the end of 10 ms its charge is half the final value. The capacitance is about:

A) 9.6 μF B) 14 μF *C) 20 μF D) 7.2 F   E) 10 F

62. In the capacitor discharge formula $q = q_o e^{-t/RC}$ the symbol "t" represents:

A) the time constant
B) the time it takes for C to lose the fraction $1/e$ of its initial charge
C) the time it takes for C to lose the fraction $(1 - 1/e)$ of its initial charge
D) the time it takes for C to lose essentially all of its initial charge
*E) none of the above

332

Halliday Fund. 4e Chap 30

1. Units of a magnetic field might be:

A) C ·m/s   B) C ·s/m   C) C/kg   *D) kg/C ·s   E) N/C ·m

2. In the formula **F** = q**v**x**B**:

A) **F** must be perpendicular to **v** but not necessarily to **B**
B) **F** must be perpendicular to **B** but not necessarily to **v**
C) **v** must be perpendicular to **B** but not necessarily to **F**
D) all three vectors must be mutually perpendicular
*E) none of the above

3. At any point the magnetic field lines are in the direction of:

A) the magnetic force on a moving positive charge
B) the magnetic force on a moving negative charge
C) the velocity of a moving positive charge
D) the velocity of a moving negative charge
*E) none of the above

4. The magnetic force on a charged particle is in the direction of its velocity:

A) if it is moving in the direction of the field
B) if it is moving opposite to the direction of the field
C) if it is moving perpendicular to the field
D) if it is moving in some other direction
*E) never

5. A magnetic field exerts a force on a charged particle:

A) always
B) never
*C) if the particle is moving across the field lines
D) if the particle is moving along the field lines
E) if the particle is at rest

6. The direction of the magnetic field in a certain region of space is determined by firing a test charge into the region with its velocity in various directions in different trials. The field direction is:

*A) one of the directions of the velocity when the magnetic force is zero
 B) the direction of the velocity when the magnetic force is a maximum
 C) the direction of the magnetic force
 D) perpendicular to the velocity when the magnetic force is zero
 E) none of the above

7. An electron is moving north in a region where the magnetic field is south. The magnetic force exerted on the electron is:

*A) zero   B) up   C) down   D) east   E) west

8. A magnetic field CANNOT:

 A) exert a force on a charge
 B) accelerate a charge
 C) change the momentum of a charge
*D) change the kinetic energy of a charge
 E) exist

9. A proton (charge e), traveling perpendicular to a magnetic field, experiences the same force as an alpha particle (charge 2e) which is also traveling perpendicular to the same field. The ratio of their speeds, v_{proton}/v_{alpha} is:

 A) 0.5   B) 1   *C) 2   D) 4   E) 8

10. A hydrogen atom that has lost its electron is moving east in a region where the magnetic field is directed from south to north. It will be deflected:

*A) up   D) south
 B) down   E) not at all
 C) north

11. A beam of electrons is sent horizontally down the axis of a tube to strike a fluorescent screen at the end of the tube. On the way, the electrons encounter a magnetic field directed vertically downward. The spot on the screen will therefore be deflected:

 A) upward
 B) downward
*C) to the right as seen from the electron source
 D) to the left as seen from the electron source
 E) not at all

12. An electron (charge = -1.6x10^{-19} C) is moving at 3x10^5 m/s in the positive x direction. A magnetic field of 0.8 T is in the positive z direction. The magnetic force on the electron is:

A) 0
B) 4x10^{-14} N in the positive z direction
C) 4x10^{-14} N in the negative z direction
D) 4x10^{-14} N in the positive y direction
*E) 4x10^{-14} N in the negative y direction

13. At one instant an electron (charge = -1.6x10^{-19} C) is moving in the xy plane, the components of its velocity being v_x = 5x10^5 m/s and v_y = 3x10^5 m/s. A magnetic field of 0.8 T is in the positive z direction. At that instant the magnitude of the magnetic force on the electron is:

A) 0
B) 3.8x10^{-14} N
C) 5.1x10^{-14} N

D) 6.4x10^{-14} N
*E) 7.5x10^{-14} N

14. At one instant an electron (charge = -1.6x10^{-19} C) is moving in the xy plane, the components of its velocity being v_x = 5x10^5 m/s and v_y = 3x10^5 m/s. A magnetic field of 0.8 T is in the positive x direction. At that instant the magnitude of the magnetic force on the electron is:

A) 0
*B) 3.8x10^{-14} N
C) 5.1x10^{-14} N

D) 6.4x10^{-14} N
E) 7.5x10^{-14} N

15. An electron travels due north through a vacuum in a region of uniform magnetic field **B** that is also directed due north. It will:

*A) be unaffected by the field
B) speed up
C) slow down
D) follow a right-handed corkscrew path
E) follow a left-handed corkscrew path

16. At one instant an electron is moving in the positive x direction along the x axis in a region where there is a uniform magnetic field in the positive z direction. When viewed from a point on the positive z axis, it subsequent motion is:

A) straight ahead
*B) counterclockwise around a circle in the xy plane
C) clockwise around a circle in the xy plane
D) in the positive z direction
E) in the negative z direction

17. A uniform magnetic field is directed into the page. A charged particle, moving in the plane of the page, follows a clockwise spiral of decreasing radius as shown. A reasonable explanation is:

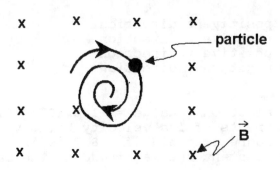

A) the charge is positive and slowing down
*B) the charge is negative and slowing down
C) the charge is positive and speeding up
D) the charge is negative and speeding up
E) none of the above

18. An electron is launched with velocity **v** in a uniform magnetic field **B**. The angle θ between **v** and **B** is between 0 and 90°. As a result, the electron follows a helix, its velocity vector **v** returning to its initial value in a time interval of:

*A) 2m/eB
B) 2mv/eB
C) 2mv sinθ/eB
D) 2mv cosθ/eB
E) none of these

19. An electron and a proton are both initially moving with the same speed and in the same direction at 90° to the same uniform magnetic field. They experience magnetic forces, which are initially:

A) identical
*B) equal in magnitude but opposite in direction
C) in the same direction and differing in magnitude by a factor of 1840
D) in opposite directions and differing in magnitude by a factor of 1840
E) equal in magnitude but perpendicular to each other

20. An electron enters a region of uniform perpendicular **E** and **B** fields. It is observed that the velocity **v** of the electron is unaffected. A possible explanation is:

A) **v** is parallel to **E** and has magnitude E/B
B) **v** is parallel to **B**
C) **v** is perpendicular to both **E** and **B** and has magnitude B/E
*D) **v** is perpendicular to both **E** and **B** and has magnitude E/B
E) the given situation is impossible

21. A charged particle is projected into a region of uniform, parallel,
    E and **B** fields. The force on the particle is:

    A) zero
    *B) at some angle < 90° with the field lines
    C) along the field lines
    D) perpendicular to the field lines
    E) unknown (need to know the sign of the charge)

22. A uniform magnetic field is in the positive z direction. A
    positively charged particle is moving in the positive x direction
    through the field. The net force on the particle can be made zero by
    applying an electric field in what direction?

    A) positive y   D) negative x
    *B) negative y   E) positive z
    C) positive x

23. A proton is in a region where a uniform electric field of 5×10^4 V/m
    is perpendicular to a uniform magnetic field of 0.8 T. If its
    acceleration is zero then its speed must be:

    A) 0   *D) 6.3×10^5 m/s
    B) 1.6×10^4 m/s   E) any value but 0
    C) 4.0×10^5 m/s

24. The current is from left to right in the conductor shown. The
    magnetic field is into the page and point S is at a higher potential
    than point T. The charge carriers are:

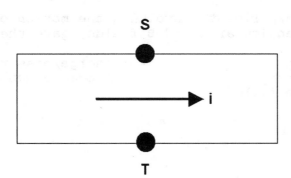

    *A) positive   D) absent
    B) negative   E) moving near the speed of light
    C) neutral

25. Electrons (mass m, charge -e) are accelerated from rest through a potential difference V and are then deflected by a magnetic field **B** that is perpendicular to their velocity. The radius of the resulting electron trajectory is:

$$\text{A)}\,(\sqrt{2eV/m})/B \quad \text{B)}\,B\sqrt{2eV/m} \quad \text{C)}\,(\sqrt{2mV/e})/B \quad \text{D)}\,B\sqrt{2mV/e}$$

Ans. c

26. In a certain mass spectrograph, an ion beam passes through a velocity filter consisting of mutually perpendicular fields **E** and **B**. The beam then enters a region of another magnetic field **B′** perpendicular to the beam. The radius of curvature of the resulting ion beam is proportional to:

A) EB′/B   B) EB/B′   C) BB′/E   D) B/EB′   *E) E/BB′

27. A cyclotron operates with a given magnetic field and at a given frequency. If R denotes the radius of the final orbit, the final particle energy is proportional to:

A) 1/R   B) R   *C) R^2 D) R^3 E) R^4

28. J. J. Thomson's experiment, involving the motion of an electron beam in mutually perpendicular E and B fields, gave the value of:

A) mass of electron   *D) charge/mass ratio for electron
B) charge of electron   E) Avogadro number
C) earth's magnetic field

29. The diagram shows a straight wire carrying a flow of electrons into the page. The wire is between the poles of a permanent magnet. The direction of the magnetic force exerted on the wire is:

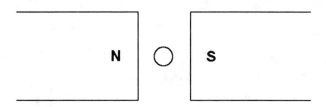

*A) ↑
 B) ↓
 C) ←

D) →
E) into the page

30. The figure shows the motion of electrons in a wire which is near the N pole of a magnet. The wire will be pushed:

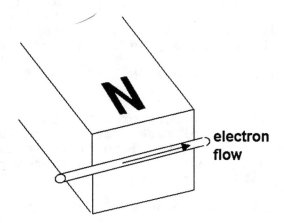

electron flow

A) toward the magnet
B) away from the magnet
C) downwards

*D) upwards
 E) along its length

31. The figure shows a uniform magnetic field **B** directed to the left and a wire carrying a current into the page. The magnetic force acting on the wire is:

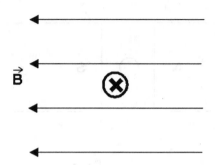

  *A) toward the top of the page   D) toward the right
   B) toward the bottom of the page   E) zero
   C) toward the left

32. A loop of wire carrying a current of 2.0 A is in the shape of a right triangle with two equal sides, each 15 cm long. A 0.7 T uniform magnetic field is parallel to the hypotenuse. The resultant magnetic force on the two sides has a magnitude of:

  *A) 0   B) 0.21 N   C) 0.30 N   D) 0.41 N   E) 0.51 N

33. A loop of wire carrying a current of 2.0 A is in the shape of a right triangle with two equal sides, each 15 cm long. A 0.7 T uniform magnetic field is in the plane of the triangle and is perpendicular to the hypotenuse. The resultant magnetic force on the two sides has a magnitude of:

   A) 0   B) 0.21 N   *C) 0.30 N   D) 0.41 N   E) 0.51 N

34. A current is clockwise around the outside edge of this page and a uniform magnetic field is directed parallel to the page, from left to right. If the magnetic force is the only force acting on the page, the page will turn so the right edge:

  *A) moves toward you   D) moves to your left
   B) moves away from you   E) does not move
   C) moves to your right

35. A square loop of wire lies in the plane of the page and carries a current I as shown. There is a uniform magnetic field **B** parallel to the side MK as indicated. The loop will tend to rotate:

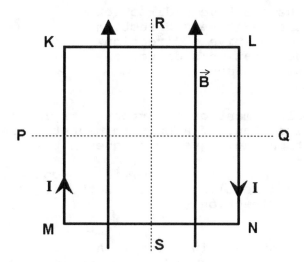

*A) about PQ with KL coming out of the page
 B) about PQ with KL going into the page
 C) about RS with MK coming out of the page
 D) about RS with MK going into the page
 E) about an axis perpendicular to the page

36. The units of magnetic dipole moment are:

A) ampere   D) ampere/meter
B) ampere ·meter   E) ampere/meter^2
*C) ampere ·meter^2

37. A current of 3.0 A is clockwise around the outside edge of this page, which has an area of 5.8×10^{-2} m^2. The magnetic dipole moment is:

A) 3.0 A ·m^2, into the page   D) 0.17 A ·m^2, out of the page
B) 3.0 A ·m^2, out of the page   E) 0.17 A ·m^2, left to right
*C) 0.17 A ·m^2, into the page

38. The magnetic torque exerted on a flat current-carrying loop of wire by a uniform magnetic field **B** is:

A) maximum when the plane of the loop is perpendicular to **B**
*B) maximum when the plane of the loop is parallel to **B**
C) dependent on the shape of the loop for a fixed loop area
D) independent of the orientation of the loop
E) such as to rotate the loop around the magnetic field lines

39. A circular loop of wire with a radius of 20 cm lies in the xy plane and carries a current of 2 A, counterclockwise when viewed from a point on the positive z axis. Its magnetic dipole moment is:

*A) 0.25 A $\cdot m^2$, in the positive z direction
 B) 0.25 A $\cdot m^2$, in the negative z direction
 C) 2.5 A $\cdot m^2$, in the positive z direction
 D) 2.5 A $\cdot m^2$, in the negative z direction
 E) 0.25 A$\cdot m^2$, in the xy plane

40. The magnetic dipole moment of a current-carrying loop of wire is in the positive z direction. If a uniform magnetic field is in the positive x direction the magnetic torque on the loop is:

 A) 0
*B) in the positive y direction
 C) in the negative y direction
 D) in the positive z direction
 E) in the negative z direction

41. For a loop of current-carrying wire in a uniform magnetic field the potential energy is a minimum if the magnetic dipole moment of the loop is:

*A) in the same direction as the field
 B) in the direction opposite to that of the field
 C) perpendicular to the field
 D) at an angle of 45° to the field
 E) none of the above

42. A loop of current-carrying wire has a magnetic dipole moment of 5×10^{-4} A $\cdot m^2$. The moment initially makes an angle of 90° with a 0.5-T magnetic field. As it turns to become aligned with the field, the work done by the field is:

 A) 0
*B) 2.5×10^{-4} J
 C) -2.5×10^{-4} J
 D) 1.0×10^{-3} J
 E) -1.0×10^{-3} J

1. Suitable units for μ_0 are:

A) tesla
B) newton/ampere^2
C) weber/meter
D) kilogram ·ampere/meter
*E) tesla ·meter/ampere

2. A "coulomb" is:

A) one ampere per second
B) the quantity of charge which will exert a force of 1 N on a similar charge at a distance of 1 m
C) the amount of current in each of two long parallel wires separated by 1 m, which produces a force of 2×10^{-7} N per meter
*D) the amount of charge which flows past a point in one second when the current is 1 A
E) an abbreviation for a certain combination of kilogram, meter and second

3. Electrons are going around a circle in a counterclockwise direction as shown. They produce a magnetic field whose direction at the center of the circle is:

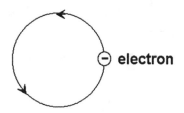

*A) into the page
B) out of the page
C) to the left
D) to the right
E) the field is zero at the center

4. In the figure, the current element i $d\vec{l}$, the point P, and the three
   vectors (1, 2, 3) are all in the plane of the page. The direction of
   d**B**, due to this current element, at the point P is:

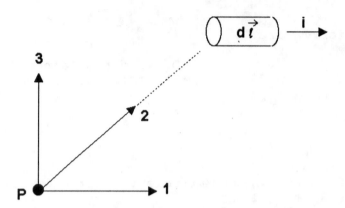

A) in the direction marked "1"   D) out of the page
B) in the direction marked "2"   *E) into the page
C) in the direction marked "3"

5. The magnitude of the magnetic field at point P, at the center of the
   semicircle shown, is given by:

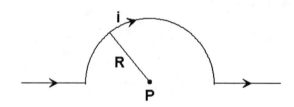

A) $\mu_0 i/R^2$ B) $\mu_0 i/2\pi R$ C) $\mu_0 i/4\pi R$ D) $\mu_0 i/2R$ *E) $\mu_0 i/4R$

6. Lines of the magnetic field produced by a long straight wire
   carrying a current:

A) are in the direction of the current
B) are opposite to the direction of the current
C) leave the wire radially
*D) are circles concentric with the wire
E) are lines similar to those produced by a bar magnet

7. In an overhead straight wire, the current is north. The magnetic field due to this current, at our point of observation, is:

A) east   B) up   C) north   D) down   *E) west

8. A wire carrying a large current i from east to west is placed over an ordinary magnetic compass. The end of the compass needle marked "N" will point:

A) north
*B) south
C) east
D) west
E) the compass will act as an electric motor, hence the needle will keep rotating

9. The magnetic field outside a long straight current-carrying wire depends on the distance R from the wire axis according to:

A) R   *B) $1/R$ C) $1/R^2$ D) $1/R^3$ E) $1/R^{3/2}$

10. Which graph correctly gives the magnitude of the magnetic field outside an infinitely long straight current-carrying wire as a function of the distance r from the wire?

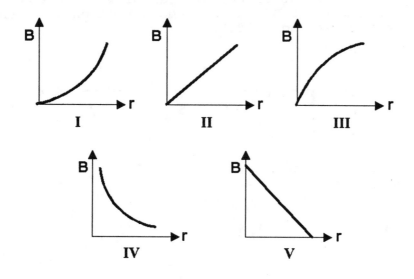

A) I.   B) II.   C) III.   *D) IV.   E) V.

11. The magnetic field (in T) a distance 2 cm from a long straight wire carrying a current of 2 A is about:

A) 2×10^{-7} B) 1×10^{-5} *C) 2×10^{-5} D) 1×10^{-3} E) 10

12. Two long parallel straight wires carry equal currents in opposite directions. At a point midway between the wires, the magnetic field they produce is:

  A) zero
  B) non-zero and along a line connecting the wires
  C) non-zero and parallel to the wires
 *D) non-zero and perpendicular to the plane of the two wires
  E) none of the above

13. Two long straight wires are parallel and carry current in the same direction. The currents are 8.0 A and 12 A and the wires are separated by 0.40 cm. The magnetic field in tesla at a point midway between the wires is:

  A) 0   *B) 4.0×10^{-4} C) 8.0×10^{-4} D) 12×10^{-4} E) 20×10^{-4}

14. Two long straight wires are parallel and carry current in opposite directions. The currents are 8.0 A and 12 A and the wires are separated by 0.40 cm. The magnetic field in tesla at a point midway between the wires is:

  A) 0   B) 4.0×10^{-4} C) 8.0×10^{-4} D) 12×10^{-4} *E) 20×10^{-4}

15. Two long straight current-carrying parallel wires cross the x axis and carry currents I and 3I in the same direction, as shown. At what value of x is the net magnetic field zero?

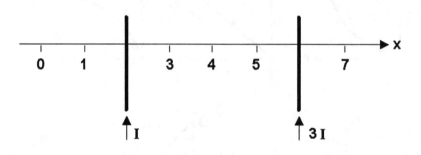

  A) 0   *B) 3   C) 6   D) 10   E) 13

346

16. Two long straight wires pierce the plane of the paper at vertices of an equilateral triangle as shown below. They each carry 2 A, out of the paper. The magnetic field at the third vertex (P) has magnitude (in T):

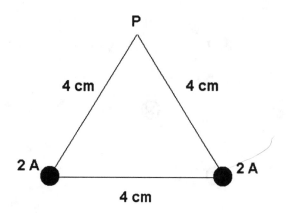

A) 1.0×10^{-5} *B) 1.7×10^{-5} C) 2.0×10^{-5} D) 5.0×10^{-6} E) 8.7×10^{-6}

17. Two parallel wires carrying equal currents of 10 A attract each other with a force of 1 mN. If both currents are doubled, the force of attraction will be:

A) 1 mN   *B) 4 mN   C) 0.5 mN   D) 0.25 mN   E) 2 mN

18. Two parallel long wires carry the same current and repel each other with a force F per unit length. If both these currents are doubled and the wire separation tripled, the force per unit length becomes:

A) 2F/9   B) 4F/9   C) 2F/3   *D) 4F/3   E) 6F

19. Two parallel wires, 4 cm apart, carry currents of 2 A and 4 A respectively, in the same direction. The force per unit length in N/m of one wire on the other is:

A) 1×10^{-3}, repulsive   *D) 4×10^{-5}, attractive
B) 1×10^{-3}, attractive   E) none of these
C) 4×10^{-5}, repulsive

20. Two parallel wires, 4 cm apart, carry currents of 2 A and 4 A respectively, in opposite directions. The force per unit length in N/m of one wire on the other is:

A) 1×10^{-3}, repulsive   D) 4×10^{-5}, attractive
B) 1×10^{-3}, attractive   E) none of these
*C) 4×10^{-5}, repulsive

21. Four long straight wires carry equal currents into the page as shown. The magnetic force exerted on wire F is:

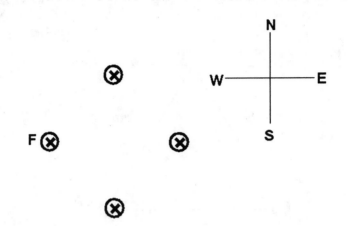

A) north   *B) east   C) south   D) west   E) zero

22. A constant current is sent through a helical coil. The coil:

*A) tends to get shorter
 B) tends to get longer
 C) tends to rotate about its axis
 D) produces zero magnetic field at its center
 E) none of the above

23. Helmholtz coils are commonly used in the laboratory because the magnetic field between them:

 A) can be varied more easily than the fields of other current arrangements
 B) is especially strong
 C) nearly cancels the earth's magnetic field
 D) is parallel to the plane of the coils
*E) is nearly uniform

24. If the radius of a pair of Helmholtz coils is R then the distance between the coils is:

 A) R/4   B) R/2   *C) R   D) 2R   E) 4R

25. If R is the distance from a magnetic dipole, then the magnetic field it produces is proportional to:

 A) R   B) 1/R   C) R^2 D) $1/R^2$ *E) $1/R^3$

26. A square loop of current-carrying wire with edge length a is in the xy plane, the origin being at its center. Along which of the following lines can a charge move without experiencing a magnetic force?

A) x = 0, y = a/2
B) x = a/2, y = a/2
C) x = a/2, y = 0
*D) x = 0, y = 0
E) x = 0, z = 0

27. In Ampere's law, $\oint \mathbf{B} \cdot d\mathbf{s} = \mu_0 i$, the integration must be over:

A) any surface
B) any closed surface
C) any path
*D) any closed path
E) any closed path that surrounds all the current producing **B**

28. In Ampere's law, $\oint \mathbf{B} \cdot d\mathbf{s} = \mu_0 i$, the symbol d**s** is:

A) an infinitesimal piece of the wire that carries current i
B) in the direction of **B**
C) perpendicular to **B**
D) a vector whose magnitude is the length of the wire that carries current i
*E) none of the above

29. In Ampere's law, $\oint \mathbf{B} \cdot d\mathbf{s} = \mu_0 i$, the direction of the integration around the path:

A) must be clockwise
B) must be counterclockwise
C) must be such as to follow the magnetic field lines
D) must be along the wire in the direction of the current
*E) none of the above

30. A long straight wire carrying a 3.0 A current enters a room through a window 1.5 m high and 1.0 m wide. The path integral $\oint \mathbf{B} \cdot d\mathbf{s}$ around the window frame has the value (in T ·m):

A) 0.20
B) 2.5×10^{-7}
C) 3.0×10^{-7}
*D) 3.8×10^{-6}
E) none of these

31. Two long straight wires enter a room through a window. One carries a current of 3.0 A into the room while the other carries a current of 5.0 A out. The magnitude in T ·m of the path integral $\oint \mathbf{B} \cdot d\mathbf{s}$ around the window frame is:

*A) 2.5×10^{-6}
B) 3.8×10^{-6}
C) 6.3×10^{-6}
D) 1.0×10^{-5}
E) none of these

32. If the magnetic field **B** is uniform over the area bounded by a square with edge length a, the net current through the square is:

*A) 0   B) $4Ba/\mu_0$ C) Ba^2/μ_0 D) Ba/μ_0 E) B/μ_0

33. The magnetic field at any point is given by **B** = $Ar \times \hat{k}$, where **r** is the position vector of the point and A is a constant. The net current through a circle of radius R, in the xy plane and centered at the origin is given by:

A) $\pi AR^2/\mu_0$ B) $2\pi AR/\mu_0$ C) $4\pi AR^3/3\mu_0$ *D) $2\pi AR^2/\mu_0$ E) $\pi AR^2/2\mu_0$

34. A hollow cylindrical conductor (inner radius = a, outer radius = b) carries a current i uniformly spread over its cross-section. Which graph below correctly gives B as a function of the distance r from the center of the cylinder?

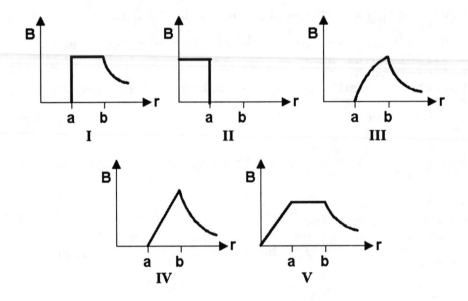

    I   II   III

            IV   V

A) I.   B) II.   *C) III.   D) IV.   E) V.

35. A long straight cylindrical shell carries current i uniformly distributed over its cross section. The magnitude of the magnetic field is greatest:

*A) inside the shell near its inner surface
 B) inside the shell near its outer surface
 C) inside the shell near the middle
 D) in hollow region near the inner surface
 E) near the center of the hollow region

36. A long straight cylindrical shell has an inner radius R_i and an outer radius R_o. It carries a current i, uniformly distributed over its cross section. A wire is parallel to the cylinder axis, in the hollow region ($r < R_i$). The magnetic field is zero everywhere outside the shell ($r > R_o$). We conclude that the wire:

   A) is on the cylinder axis and carries current i in the same direction as the current in the shell
   B) may be anywhere in the hollow region but must be carrying current i in the direction opposite to that of the current in the shell
   C) may be anywhere in the hollow region but must be carrying current i in the same direction as the current in the shell
   *D) is on the cylinder axis and carries current i in the direction opposite to that of the current in the shell
   E) does not carry any current

37. A long straight cylindrical shell has an inner radius R_i and an outer radius R_o. It carries a current i, uniformly distributed over its cross section. A wire is parallel to the cylinder axis, in the hollow region ($r < R_i$). The magnetic field is zero everywhere in the hollow region. We conclude that the wire:

   A) is on the cylinder axis and carries current i in the same direction as the current in the shell
   B) may be anywhere in the hollow region but must be carrying current i in the direction opposite to that of the current in the shell
   C) may be anywhere in the hollow region but must be carrying current i in the same direction as the current in the shell
   D) is on the cylinder axis and carries current i in the direction opposite to that of the current in the shell
   *E) does not carry any current

38. The magnetic field B inside a long ideal solenoid is independent of:

   A) the current   *D) the cross-sectional area
   B) the core material   E) the direction of the current
   C) the spacing of the windings

39. Two long ideal solenoids (with radii 20 mm and 30 mm respectively) carry the same current. The smaller solenoid is mounted inside the larger, along a common axis. It is observed that there is zero magnetic field within the inner solenoid. Therefore the inner solenoid must have X times as many turns per length as the outer solenoid, where X is:

   A) 4/9   B) 2/3   *C) 1   D) 3/2   E) 9/4

40. Magnetic field lines inside the solenoid shown are:

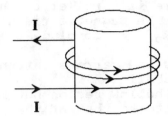

A) clockwise circles as one looks down the axis from the top of the page
B) counterclockwise circles as one looks down the axis from the top of the page
*C) toward the top of the page
D) toward the bottom of the page
E) in no direction since B = 0

41. Solenoid B has twice the radius and six times the number of turns per unit length as solenoid A. The ratio of the magnetic field in the interior of B to that in the interior of A is:

A) 2   B) 4   *C) 6   D) 1   E) 1/3

42. A solenoid is 3.0 cm long and has a radius of 0.50 cm. It is wrapped with 500 turns of wire carrying a current of 2.0 A. The magnetic field in tesla at the center of the solenoid is:

A) 9.9×10^{-8} D) 16
B) 1.3×10^{-3} E) none of these
*C) 4.2×10^{-2}

43. A toroid with a square cross section carries current i. The magnetic field has its largest magnitude:

A) at the center of the hole
*B) just inside the toroid at its inner surface
C) just inside the toroid at its outer surface
D) at any point inside (the field is uniform)
E) none of the above

44. A toroid has a square cross section with the length of an edge equal to the radius of the inner surface. The ratio of the magnitude of the magnetic field at the inner surface to the magnitude of the field at the outer surface is:

A) 1/4   B) 1/2   C) 1   *D) 2   E) 4

1. The normal to a certain 1-m^2 area makes an angle of 60° with a uniform magnetic field. The magnetic flux through this area is the same as the flux through a second area that is perpendicular to the field if the second area is:

A) 0.866 m^2 B) 1.15 m^2 *C) 0.5 m^2 D) 2 m^2 E) 1 m^2

2. Suppose this page is perpendicular to a uniform magnetic field and the magnetic flux through it is 5 Wb. If the page is turned by 30° around an edge the flux through it will be:

A) 2.5 Wb   *B) 4.3 Wb   C) 5 Wb   D) 5.8 Wb   E) 10 Wb

3. A 2-T uniform magnetic field makes an angle of 30° with the z axis. The magnetic flux through a 3-m^2 portion of the xy plane is:

A) 2 Wb   B) 3 Wb   *C) 5.2 Wb   D) 6 Wb   E) 12 Wb

4. A uniform magnetic field makes an angle of 30° with the z axis. If the magnetic flux through a 1-m^2 portion of the xy plane is 5 Wb then the magnetic flux through a 2-m^2 portion of the same plane is:

A) 2.5 Wb   B) 4.3 Wb   C) 5 Wb   D) 5.8 Wb   *E) 10 Wb

5. 1 weber is the same as:

A) 1 V/s   B) 1 T/s   C) 1 T/m   *D) 1 T ·m^2 E) 1 T/m^2

6. 1 weber is the same as:

*A) 1 V ·s   B) 1 T ·s   C) 1 T/m   D) 1 V/s   E) 1 T/m^2

7. "emf" means:

A) electromagnetic field   *D) electromotive force
B) E M flow   E) erg ·mole ·farad
C) everyone's male or female

8. The units of motional emf are:

A) volt/second   D) tesla/second
B) volt ·meter/second   *E) tesla ·meter^2/second
C) volt/tesla

9. Faraday's law states that an induced emf is proportional to:

   A) the rate of change of the magnetic field
   B) the rate of change of the electric field
 *C) the rate of change of the magnetic flux
   D) the rate of change of the electric flux
   E) zero

10. The emf that appears in Faraday's law is:

   A) around a conducting circuit
 *B) around the boundary of the surface used to compute the magnetic flux
   C) throughout the surface used to compute the magnetic flux
   D) perpendicular to the surface used to compute the magnetic flux
   E) none of the above

11. If the magnetic flux through a certain region is changing with time:

   A) energy must be dissipated as heat
   B) an electric field must exist at the boundary
   C) a current must flow around the boundary
 *D) an emf must exist around the boundary
   E) a magnetic field must exist at the boundary

12. A square loop of wire lies in the plane of the page. A decreasing
    magnetic field is directed into the page. The induced current in
    the loop is:

   A) counterclockwise
 *B) clockwise
   C) zero
   D) depends upon whether or not B is decreasing at a constant rate
   E) clockwise in two of the loop sides and counterclockwise in the other
      two

13. As an externally generated magnetic field through a certain
    conducting loop increases in magnitude the field produced at points
    inside the loop by the current induced in the loop:

   A) must be increasing in magnitude
   B) must be decreasing in magnitude
   C) must be in the same direction as the applied field
 *D) must be directed opposite to the applied field
   E) must be perpendicular to the applied field

14. At any instant of time the total magnetic flux through a stationary conducting loop is less in magnitude than the flux associated with an externally applied field. This might occur because:

*A) the applied field is normal to the loop and increasing in magnitude
 B) the applied field is normal to the loop and decreasing in magnitude
 C) the applied field is parallel to the plane of the loop and increasing in magnitude
 D) the applied field is parallel to the plane of the loop and decreasing in magnitude
 E) the applied field is tangent to the loop

15. A long straight wire is in the plane of a rectangular conducting loop. The straight wire carries a constant current i, as shown. While the wire is being moved toward the rectangle the current in the rectangle is:

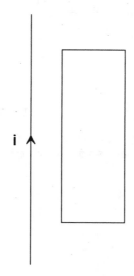

 A) zero
 B) clockwise
*C) counterclockwise
 D) clockwise in the left side and counterclockwise in the right side
 E) counterclockwise in the left side and clockwise in the right side

16. A long straight wire is in the plane of a rectangular conducting loop. The straight wire carries an increasing current in the direction shown. The current in the rectangle is:

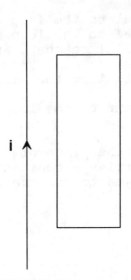

   A) zero
   B) clockwise
*C) counterclockwise
   D) clockwise in the left side and counterclockwise in the right side
   E) counterclockwise in the left side and clockwise in the right side

17. A long straight wire is in the plane of a rectangular conducting loop. The straight wire initially carries a constant current i in the direction shown. While the current i is being shut off, the current in the rectangle is:

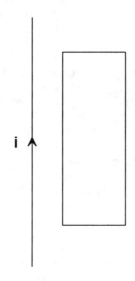

A) zero
*B) clockwise
C) counterclockwise
D) clockwise in the left side and counterclockwise in the right side
E) counterclockwise in the left side and clockwise in the right side

18. A rectangular loop of wire is placed midway between two long straight parallel conductors as shown. The conductors carry currents i_1 and i_2 as indicated. If i_1 is increasing and i_2 is constant, then the induced current in the loop is:

A) zero
B) clockwise
*C) counterclockwise

D) depends on $i_1 - i_2$
E) depends on $i_1 + i_2$

19. You push a permanent magnet with its north pole away from you toward a loop of conducting wire in front of you. Before the north pole enters the loop the current in the loop is:

A) zero
B) clockwise
*C) counterclockwise
D) to your left
E) to your right

20. A vertical bar magnet is dropped through the center of a horizontal loop of wire, with its north pole leading. At the instant when the midpoint of the magnet is in the plane of the loop, the induced current at point P, viewed from above, is:

A) maximum and clockwise
B) maximum and counterclockwise
C) not maximum but clockwise
D) not maximum but counterclockwise
*E) essentially zero

21. A circular loop of wire rotates about a diameter in a magnetic field that is perpendicular to the axis of rotation. Looking in the direction of the field at the loop the induced current is:

A) always clockwise
B) always counterclockwise
C) clockwise in the lower half of the loop and counterclockwise in the upper half
D) clockwise in the upper half of the loop and counterclockwise in the lower half
*E) sometimes clockwise and sometimes counterclockwise

22. In the experiment shown:

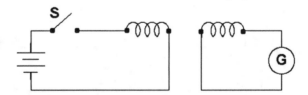

A) there is a steady reading in G as long as S is closed
B) a motional emf is generated when S is closed
C) the current in the battery goes through G
*D) there is a current in G just after S is opened or closed
E) since the two loops are not connected, the current in G is always zero

23. The emf developed in a coil "X" due to the current in a neighboring coil "Y" is proportional to the:

 A) magnetic field in X
 *B) rate of change of magnetic field in X
 C) resistance of X
 D) thickness of the wire in X
 E) current in Y

24. One hundred turns of insulated copper wire are wrapped around an iron core of cross-sectional area 0.100 m². The circuit is completed by connecting the coil to a 10 Ω resistor. The magnetic field along the coil axis is made to change from 1.00 T in one direction to 1.00 T is the other direction. The total charge that flows through the resistor in this process is:

 A) 10^{-2} C   B) 2×10^{-2} C   C) 1 C   *D) 2 C   E) 0.20 C

25. In the circuit shown, there will be a non-zero reading in galvanometer G:

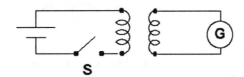

 A) only just after S is closed
 B) only just after S is opened
 C) only while S is kept closed
 D) never
 *E) only just after S is opened or closed

26. A magnet moves inside a coil. Consider the following factors:
         I.   strength of the magnet
         II. number of turns in the coil
         III. speed at which the magnet moves
    Which can affect the emf induced in the coil?

 A) I only   D) I and II only
 B) II only   *E) I, II, III
 C) III only

27. The circuit shown is in a uniform magnetic field that is into the
    page and is decreasing in magnitude at the rate 150 T/s. The current
    in the circuit (in amperes) is:

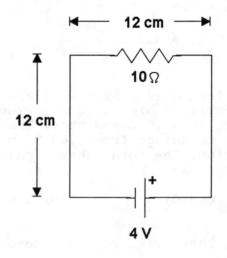

*A) 0.18   D) 0.62
 B) 0.22   E) none of these
 C) 0.40

28. A changing magnetic field pierces the interior of a circuit
    containing three identical resistors. Two voltmeters are connected
    to the same points, as shown. V_1 reads 1 mV. V_2 reads:

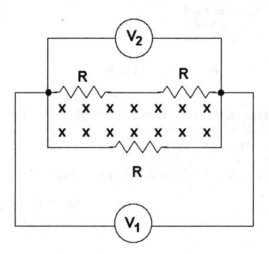

A) 0   B) 1/3 mV   C) 1/2 mV   D) 1 mV   *E) 2 mV

29. A circular loop of wire is positioned half in and half out of a
    square region of uniform B field directed into the page, as shown.
    To induce a clockwise current in this loop:

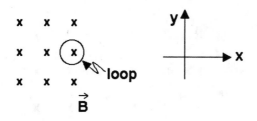

*A) move it in +x direction
 B) move it in +y direction
 C) move it in -y direction

D) move it in -x direction
E) increase the strength of B

30. A square loop of wire moves with a constant speed v from a field-free region into a region of uniform B field, as shown. Which of the five graphs correctly shows the induced current i in the loop as a function of time t?

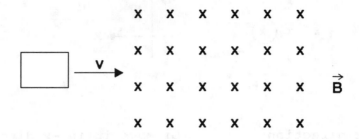

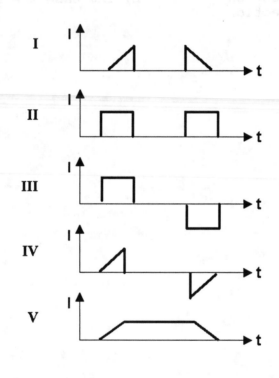

A) I.   B) II.   *C) III.   D) IV.   E) V.

31. The figure shows a bar moving to the right on two conducting rails.
    To make an induced current i in the direction indicated, a constant
    magnetic field in region "A" should be in what direction?

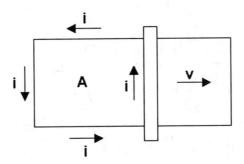

   A) right
   B) left
  *C) into the page
   D) out of the page
   E) impossible, cannot be done with a constant magnetic field

32. A car travels northward at 75 km/h along a straight road in a region
    where the earth's magnetic field has a vertical component of
    0.50×10^{-4} T. The emf induced between the left and right side,
    separated by 1.7 m, is:

   A) 0   *B) 1.8 mV   C) 3.6 mV   D) 6.4 mV   E) 13 mV

33. Coils P and Q each have a large number of turns of insulated wire. When switch S is closed, the pointer of galvanometer G is deflected toward the left. With S now closed, to make the pointer of G deflect toward the right one could:

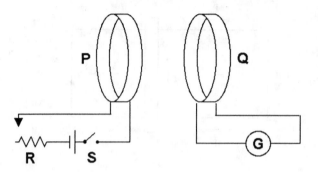

A) move the slide of the rheostat R quickly to the right
B) move coil P toward coil Q
C) move coil Q toward coil P
*D) open S
E) do none of the above

34. A rod lies across frictionless rails in a uniform magnetic field B, as shown. The rod moves to the right with speed v. In order for the emf around the circuit to be zero, the magnitude of the magnetic field should:

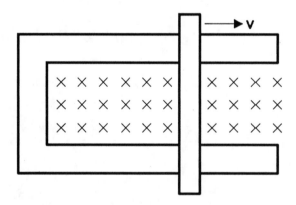

A) not change
B) increase linearly with time
*C) decrease linearly with time
D) increase quadratically with time
E) decrease quadratically with time

35. A rectangular loop of wire has area A. It is placed perpendicular to
    a uniform magnetic field B and then spun around one of its sides at
    frequency f. The maximum induced emf is:

   A) BAf   B) BAf   C) 2BAf   *D) 2πBAf   E) 4πBAf

36. A rectangular loop of wire is placed perpendicular to a uniform
    magnetic field and then spun around one of its sides at frequency f.
    The induced emf is a maximum when:

   *A) the flux is zero
    B) the flux is a maximum
    C) the flux is half its maximum value
    D) the derivative of the flux with respect to time is zero
    E) none of the above

37. The diagram shows a circular loop of wire which rotates at a steady
    rate about a diameter O which is perpendicular to a uniform B field.
    The maximum induced emf occurs when the point X on the loop passes:

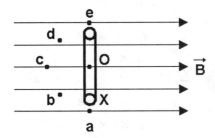

   A) a   B) b   *C) c   D) d   E) e

38. A copper hoop is held in a vertical east-west plane in a uniform
    magnetic field whose field lines run along the north-south
    direction. The largest induced emf is produced when the hoop is:

    A) rotated about a north-south axis
   *B) rotated about an east-west axis
    C) moved rapidly, without rotation, toward the east
    D) moved rapidly, without rotation, toward the south
    E) moved rapidly, without rotation, toward the northwest

39. A 10 turn conducting loop with a radius of 3.0 cm spins at 60
    revolutions per second in a magnetic field of 0.50 T. The maximum
    emf generated is:

   A) 0.014 V   B) 0.53 V   *C) 5.3 V   D) 18 V   E) 180 V

365

40. A single loop of wire with a radius of 7.5 cm rotates about a
    diameter in a uniform magnetic field of 1.6 T. To produce a maximum
    emf of 1.0 V, it should rotate at:

 A) 0   *D) 35 rad/s
 B) 2.7 rad/s   E) 71 rad/s
 C) 5.6 rad/s

41. A merry-go-round has an area of 300 m^2 and spins at 2 rpm about a
    vertical axis at a place where the earth's magnetic field is
    vertical and has a magnitude of 5x10^{-5} T. The emf around the rim is:

 *A) 0   B) 0.5 mV   C) 3.1 mV   D) 15 mV   E) 30 mV

42. A copper penny slides on a horizontal frictionless table. There is
    a square region of uniform magnetic field perpendicular to the
    table, as shown. Which graph correctly shows the speed v of the
    penny as a function of time t?

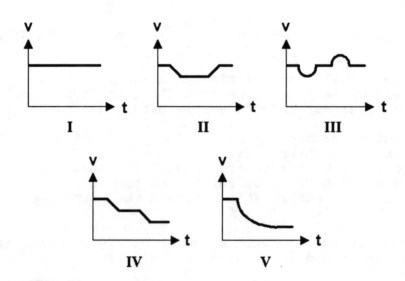

 A) I.   B) II.   C) III.   *D) IV.   E) V.

43. A rod with resistance R lies across frictionless conducting rails in a uniform magnetic field B, as shown. Assume the rails have negligible resistance. The force that must be applied by a person to pull the rod to the right at constant speed v is:

A) 0   B) BLv   C) BLv/R   *D) B^2L^2v/R E) B^2Lxv/R

44. A rectangular loop of wire with resistance R moves through a uniform magnetic field **B**, perpendicular to the loop. If L is the length of each side, the force that must be applied by a person to keep the rod moving with constant velocity **v** is:

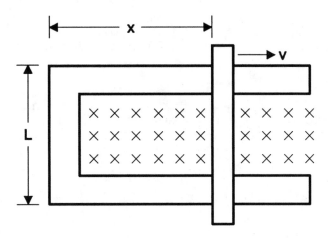

*A) 0   B) BLv   C) BLv/R   D) B^2L^2v/R E) B^2Lxv/R

45. As a loop of wire with a resistance of 10 ohms moves in a non-uniform magnetic field, it loses kinetic energy at a uniform rate of 5 mJ/s. The induced current in the loop:

A) is 0
B) is 2 mA
C) is 2.8 mA
*D) is 20 mA
E) cannot be calculated from the given data

46. As a loop of wire with a resistance of 10 ohms moves in a non-uniform magnetic field, it loses kinetic energy at a uniform rate of 5 mJ/s. The induced emf in the loop:

A) is 0
*B) is 0.22 V
C) is 0.28 V
D) is 2.2V 7.1
E) cannot be calculated from the given data

$P = 5 \times 10^{-3} \, W = \frac{\varepsilon^2}{R}$

$\varepsilon = \sqrt{5 \times 10^{-2}} = 0.22$

367

47. An electric field is associated with:

A) every magnetic field
*B) every time-dependent magnetic field
C) every time-dependent magnetic flux
D) every object moving in a magnetic field
E) every conductor moving in a magnetic field

48. A cylindrical region of radius R = 3.0 cm contains a uniform magnetic field parallel to its axis. If the field is changing at the rate 0.60 T/s, the electric field induced at a point R/2 from the cylinder axis is:

A) 0
*B) 0.0045 V
C) 0.0090 V

D) 0.018 V
E) none of these

49. A cylindrical region of radius R = 3.0 cm contains a uniform magnetic field parallel to its axis. The field is 0 outside the cylinder. If the field is changing at the rate 0.60 T/s, the electric field induced at a point 2R from the cylinder axis is:

A) 0
*B) 0.0045 V
C) 0.0090 V

D) 0.018
E) none of these

50. A cylindrical region of radius R contains a uniform magnetic field, parallel to its axis, with magnitude that is changing linearly with time. If r is the radial distance from the cylinder axis, the magnitude of the induced electric field inside the cylinder is proportional to:

A) R   *B) r   C) r^2 D) $1/r$ E) $1/r^2$

51. A cylindrical region of radius R contains a uniform magnetic field, parallel to its axis, with magnitude that is changing linearly with time. If r is the radial distance from the cylinder axis, the magnitude of the induced electric field outside the cylinder is proportional to:

A) R   B) r   C) r^2 *D) $1/r$ E) $1/r^2$

1. The unit "henry" is equivalent to:

*A) volt ·second/ampere
 B) volt/second
 C) ohm

D) ampere ·volt/second
E) ampere ·second/volt

2. A 10-turn ideal solenoid has an inductance of 3.5 mH. When the solenoid carries a current of 2.0 A the magnetic flux through each turn is:

A) 0
B) 3.5×10^{-4} wb
*C) 7.0×10^{-4} wb

D) 7.0×10^{-3} wb
E) 7.0×10^{-2} wb

3. A 10-turn ideal solenoid has an inductance of 3.5 mH. When the solenoid carries a current that is changing at 200 A/s the emf of the solenoid is:

A) 0   B) 0.070 V   *C) 0.70 V   D) 7.0 V   E) 70 V

4. A long narrow solenoid has length ℓ and a total of N turns, each of which has cross-sectional area A. Its inductance is:

A) $\mu_o N^2 A \ell$
*B) $\mu_o N^2 A / \ell$
 C) $\mu_o NA / \ell$

D) $\mu_o N^2 \ell / A$
E) none of these

5. A flat coil of wire, having 5 turns, has an inductance L. The inductance of a similar coil having 20 turns is:

A) 4L   B) L/4   *C) 16L   D) L/16   E) L

6. An inductance L, resistance R, and ideal battery of emf E are wired in series. A switch in the circuit is closed at time 0, at which time the current is 0. At any later time t the current i is given by:

A) $(E/R)(1 - e^{-Lt/R})$
B) $(E/R) e^{-Lt/R}$
C) $(E/R)(1 + e^{-RT/L})$

D) $(E/R) e^{-RT/L}$
*E) $(E/R)(1 - e^{-Rt/L})$

7. An inductance L, resistance R, and ideal battery of emf E are wired in series. A switch in the circuit is closed at time 0, at which time the current is 0. At any later time t the emf of the inductor is given by:

A) $E(1 - e^{-Lt/R})$
B) $Ee^{-Lt/R}$
C) $E(1 + e^{-RT/L})$

*D) $Ee^{-RT/L}$
E) $E(1 - e^{-Rt/L})$

8. An inductance L, resistance R, and ideal battery of emf E are wired in series. A switch in the circuit is closed at time 0, at which time the current is 0. At any later time t the potential difference across the resistor is given by:

A) $E(1 - e^{-Lt/R})$
B) $Ee^{-Lt/R}$
C) $E(1 + e^{-RT/L})$

D) $Ee^{-RT/L}$
*E) $E(1 - e^{-Rt/L})$

9. An 8.0-mH inductor and a 2.0-Ω resistor are wired in series to an ideal battery. A switch in the circuit is closed at time 0, at which time the current is 0. The current reaches half its final value at time:

*A) 2.8 ms   B) 4.0 ms   C) 3 s   D) 170 s   E) 250 s

10. An 8.0-mH inductor and a 2.0-Ω resistor are wired in series to a 20-V ideal battery. A switch in the circuit is closed at time 0. After a long time the potential difference across the resistor and the emf of the inductor are:

A) 20 V, 20 V
B) 0, 20 V
C) 10 V, 10 V

*D) 20 V, 0
E) 0, 0

11. An 8.0-mH inductor and a 2.0-Ω resistor are wired in series to a 20-V ideal battery. A switch in the circuit is closed at time 0, at which time the current is 0. After a long time the current in the resistor and the current in the inductor are:

A) 0, 0
*B) 10 A, 10A
C) 2.5 A, 2.5 A

D) 10 A, 2.5 A
E) 10 A, 0

12. An 8.0-mH inductor and a 2.0-Ω resistor are wired in series to a 20-V ideal battery. A switch in the circuit is closed at time 0, at which time the current is 0. A long time after the switch is thrown the potential differences across the inductor and resistor are:

  A) 0, 20 V
 *B) 20 V, 0
  C) 10 V, 10 V
  D) 16 V, 4 V
  E) unknown since the rate of change of the current is not given

13. An 8.0-mH inductor and a 2.0-Ω resistor are wired in series to a 20-V ideal battery. A switch in the circuit is closed at time 0, at which time the current is 0. A long time after the switch is thrown the potential differences across the inductor and resistor are:

 *A) 0, 20 V
  B) 20 V, 0
  C) 10 V, 10 V
  D) 16 V, 4 V
  E) unknown since the rate of change of the current is not given

14. If both the resistance and the inductance in an LR series circuit are doubled the new inductive time constant will be:

  A) twice the old   D) one-fourth the old
  B) four times the old   *E) unchanged
  C) half the old

15. When the switch S in the circuit shown is closed, the time constant for the growth of current in R_2 is:

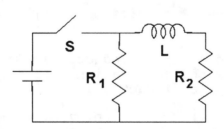

  A) L/R_1 D) $L(R_1 + R_2)/(R_1 R_2)$
 *B) L/R_2 E) $(L/R_1 + L/R_2)/2$
  C) $L/(R_1 + R^2)$

16. Immediately after switch S in the circuit shown is closed, the current through the battery shown is:

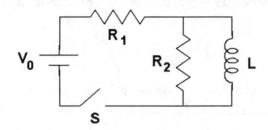

A) 0
B) V_O/R_1
C) V_O/R_2

*D) $V_O/(R_1 + R_2)$
E) $V_O(R_2 + R_2)/(R_1R_2)$

17. A 3.5 mH inductor and a 4.5 mH inductor are connected in series. The equivalent inductance is:

A) 2.0 mH   B) 0.51 mH   C) 0.13 mH   D) 1.0 mH   *E) 8.0 mH

18. A 3.5 mH inductor and a 4.5 mH inductor are connected in series and a time varying current is established. When the total emf of the combination is 16 V, the emf of the larger inductor is:

A) 7.0 V   *B) 9.0 V   C) 2.3 V   D) 28 V   E) 36 V

19. A 3.5 mH inductor and a 4.5 mH inductor are connected in parallel. The equivalent inductance is:

*A) 2.0 mH   B) 0.51 mH   C) 0.13 mH   D) 1.0 mH   E) 8.0 mH

20. A 3.5 mH inductor and a 4.5 mH inductor are connected in parallel. When the total emf of the combination is 16 V, the rate of change of the current in the larger inductor is:

A) 2.0×10^3 A/s
*B) 3.6×10^3 A/s
C) 4.6×10^3 A/s

D) 7.0×10^3 A/s
E) 8.1×10^3 A/s

21. A 3.0 mH inductor and a 6.0 mH inductor are connected in parallel. When the rate of change of the current in the larger inductor is 2000 A/s the rate of change of the current in the smaller is:

A) 2000 A/s   *B) 4000 A/s   C) 1000 A/s   D) 6000 A/s   E) 6700 A/s

22. The stored energy in an inductor:

   A) depends, in sign, upon the direction of the current
   B) depends on the rate of change of current
   C) is proportional to the square of the inductance
   D) has units J/H
  *E) none of the above

23. An inductance L and a resistance R are connected in series to an
    ideal battery. A switch in the circuit is closed at time 0, at which
    time the current is 0. The energy stored in the inductor is a
    maximum:

   A) just after the switch is closed
   B) at the time $t = L/R$ after the switch is closed
   C) at the time $t = L/R^2$ after the switch is closed
   D) at the time $t = 2L/R$ after the switch is closed
  *E) a long time after the switch is closed

24. An inductance L and a resistance R are connected in series to an
    ideal battery. A switch in the circuit is closed at time 0, at which
    time the current is 0. The rate of increase of the energy stored in
    the inductor is a maximum:

   A) just after the switch is closed
   B) at the time $t = L/R$ after the switch is closed
   C) at the time $t = 2L/R$ after the switch is closed
  *D) at the time $t = (L/R)\ln 2$ after the switch is closed
   E) a long time after the switch is closed

25. In each of the following operations, energy is expended. The LEAST
    percentage of returnable electrical energy will be yielded by:

   A) charging a capacitor
   B) charging a storage battery
  *C) sending current through a resistor
   D) establishing a current through an inductor
   E) moving a conducting rod through a magnetic field

26. A current of 10 A in a certain inductor results in a stored energy
    of 40 J. When the current is changed to 5 A in the opposite
    direction, the stored energy changes by:

   A) 20 J   *B) 30 J   C) 40 J   D) 50 J   E) 60 J

27. A 6.0 mH inductor is in a series circuit with a resistor and a seat
    of emf. At the instant the current in the circuit is 5.0 A the
    energy stored in the inductor is:

   A) 0
   *B) 7.5×10^{-2} J
   C) 15×10^{-2} J
   D) 30×10^{-2} J
   E) unknown since the rate of change of the current is not given

28. A 6.0 mH inductor is in a circuit. At the instant the current is 5.0
    A and its rate of change is 200 A/s, the rate at which the energy
    stored in the inductor is increasing is:

   A) 7.5×10^{-2} W   D) 3.0 W
   B) 120 W   *E) 6.0 W
   C) 240 W

29. An 6.0-mH inductor and a 3.0-Ω resistor are wired in series to a
    12-V ideal battery. A switch in the circuit is closed at time 0, at
    which time the current is 0. 2.0 ms later the energy stored in the
    inductor is:

   A) 0   D) 1.8×10^{-3} J
   *B) 8.8×10^{-4} J   E) 2.2×10^{-3} J
   C) 1.1×10^{-3} J

30. The quantity (B^2/μ_o) has units of:

   A) J   B) J/H   C) J/m   *D) J/m^3 E) H/m^3

31. A 0.20-cm radius cylinder, 3.0 cm long, is wrapped with wire to form
    an inductor. At the instant the magnetic field in the interior is
    5.0 mT the energy stored in the field is:

   A) 0   D) 7.5×10^{-4} J
   *B) 3.8×10^{-6} J   E) 9.9 J
   C) 7.5×10^{-6} J

33

32. In the diagram, assume that all the lines of B generated by coil #1 pass through coil #2. Coil #1 has 100 turns and coil #2 has 400 turns. Then:

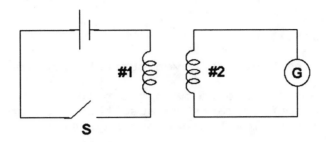

A) the power supplied to coil #1 is equal to the power delivered by coil #2
B) the emf around coil #1 will be 1/4 that around coil #2
C) the current in coil #1 will be 1/4 that in coil #2
D) the emfs will be the same in the two coils
*E) none of the above

1. Gauss' law for magnetism:

 A) can be used to find **B** due to given currents provided there is enough symmetry
 B) is false because there are no magnetic poles
 C) can be used with open surfaces because there are no magnetic poles
 D) contradicts Faraday's law because one says $\Phi_B = 0$ and the other says emf $= -d\Phi_B/dt$
*E) none of the above

2. Gauss' law for magnetism tells us:

 A) the net charge in any given volume
 B) that the line integral of a magnetic field around any closed loop must vanish
 C) the magnetic field of a current element
*D) that magnetic monopoles do not exist
 E) charges must be moving to produce magnetic fields

3. The statement that magnetic field lines form closed loops is a direct consequence of:

 A) Faraday's law
 B) Ampere's law
 C) Gauss' law for electricity
*D) Gauss' law for magnetism
 E) the Lorentz force

4. A magnetic field parallel to the x axis with a magnitude that decreases with increasing x but does not change with y and z is impossible according to:

 A) Faraday's law
 B) Ampere's law
 C) Gauss' law for electricity
*D) Gauss' law for magnetism
 E) Newton's second law

5. According to Gauss' law for magnetism, magnetic field lines:

*A) form closed loops
 B) start at south poles and end at north poles
 C) start at north poles and end at south poles
 D) start at both north and south poles and end at infinity
 E) do not exist

6. The **B** field lines due to an ordinary bar magnet:

*A) form closed curves
 B) cross one another near the poles
 C) are more numerous near the N pole than near the S pole
 D) leave the S pole, loop around the outside of the magnet, and enter
    the N pole
 E) none of the above

7. The polarity of an unmarked magnet can be determined using:

 A) a charged glass rod   D) another unmarked magnet
*B) a compass   E) iron filings
 C) an electroscope

8. A bar magnet is placed vertically with its S pole up and its N pole
   down. Its **B** field at its center is:

 A) zero
*B) down
 C) up due to the weight of the magnet
 D) horizontal
 E) slightly below the horizontal

9. A bar magnet is broken in half. Each half is broken in half again,
   etc. The observation is that each piece has both a north and south
   pole. This is usually explained:

*A) by Ampere's theory that all magnetic phenomena result from electric
    currents
 B) by our inability to divide the magnet into small enough pieces
 C) by Coulomb's law
 D) by Lenz' law
 E) by conservation of charge

10. A small bar magnet is suspended horizontally by a string. When
    placed in a uniform horizontal magnetic field, it will:

 A) translate in the direction of **B**
 B) translate in the opposite direction of **B**
 C) rotate so as to be at right angles to **B**
 D) rotate so as to be vertical
*E) none of the above

11. Magnetic dipole X is fixed and dipole Y free to move. Dipole Y will initially:

 *A) move toward X but not rotate
  B) move away from X but not rotate
  C) move toward X and rotate
  D) move away from X and rotate
  E) rotate but not move

12. Magnetic dipole X is fixed and dipole Y free to move. Dipole Y will initially:

  A) move toward X but not rotate
  B) move away from X but not rotate
  C) move toward X and rotate
  D) move away from X and rotate
 *E) rotate but not move toward or away from X

13. The energy of a magnetic dipole in an external magnetic field is least when:

 *A) the dipole moment is parallel to the field
  B) the dipole moment is antiparallel to the field
  C) the dipole moment is perpendicular to the field
  D) none of the above (the same energy is associated with all orientations)
  E) none of the above (no energy is associated with the dipole-field interaction)

14. The magnetic properties of materials stem chiefly from:

  A) particles with north poles
  B) particles with south poles
  C) motions of protons within nuclei
  D) proton spin angular momentum
 *E) electron magnetic dipole moments

15. Magnetization is:

   A) the current density in an object
   B) the charge density of moving charges in an object
   C) the magnetic dipole moment of an object
  *D) the magnetic dipole moment per unit volume of an object
   E) the magnetic field per unit volume produced by an object

16. The units of magnetization are:

   A) ampere   *D) ampere/meter
   B) ampere ·meter   E) ampere/meter^2
   C) ampere ·meter^2

17. If **L** is the orbital angular momentum of an electron, the magnetic
    dipole moment associated with its orbital motion:

   A) is in the direction of **L** and has magnitude proportional to L
  *B) is opposite to the direction of **L** and has magnitude proportional to
       L
   C) is in the direction of **L** and has magnitude proportional to L^2
   D) is opposite to the direction of **L** and has magnitude proportional to
       L^2
   E) does not depend on **L**

18. If an electron has an orbital angular momentum with magnitude L the
    magnitude of the orbital contribution to its magnetic dipole moment
    is given by:

   A) eL/m
  *B) eL/2m
   C) mL/e
   D) mL/2e
   E) none of the above (it does not depend on L)

19. An electron traveling with speed v around a circle of radius r is
    equivalent to a current of:

   A) evr/2   B) ev/r   *C) ev/2πr   D) 2πer/v   E) 2πev/r

20. The intrinsic magnetic dipole moments of protons and neutrons are
    much less than that of an electron because:

  *A) their masses are greater
   B) their angular momenta are much less
   C) their angular momenta are much greater
   D) their charges are much less
   E) their radii are much less

21. The spin magnetic dipole moment of an electron:

   A) is in the same direction as the spin angular momentum
   B) is zero
  *C) is opposite the direction of the spin angular momentum
   D) has a magnitude that depends on the orbital angular momentum
   E) has a magnitude that depends on the applied magnetic field

22. If an electron has zero orbital angular momentum, the magnitude of
    its magnetic dipole moment equals:

   A) zero   D) twice a Bohr magneton
   B) half the Bohr magneton   E) none of these
  *C) a Bohr magneton

23. The magnetic dipole moment of an atomic electron is typically:

   A) much less than a Bohr magneton
  *B) a few Bohr magnetons
   C) much greater than a Bohr magneton
   D) much greater or much less than a Bohr magneton, depending on the
      atom
   E) not related to the value of the Bohr magneton

24. The magnitude of the Bohr magneton in J/T is about:

   A) 10^{-15} B) 10^{-19} *C) 10^{-23} D) 10^{-27} E) 10^{-31}

25. The molecular theory of magnetism can explain each of the following
    EXCEPT:

  *A) an N pole attracts a S pole
   B) stroking an iron bar with a magnet will magnetize the bar
   C) when a bar magnet is broken in two, each piece is a bar magnet
   D) heating tends to destroy magnetization
   E) hammering tends to destroy magnetization

26. Lenz' law can explain:

   A) paramagnetism only
  *B) diamagnetism only
   C) ferromagnetism only
   D) only two of the three types of magnetism
   E) all three of the types of magnetism

27. Paramagnetism is closely associated with:

 *A) the tendency of electron dipole moments to align with an applied
     magnetic field
  B) the tendency of electron dipole moments to align opposite to an
     applied magnetic field
  C) the exchange force between electrons
  D) the force exerted by electron dipole moments on each other
  E) the torque exerted by electron dipole moments on each other

28. A paramagnetic substance is placed in a weak magnetic field and its
    absolute temperature T is increased. As a result, its magnetization:

  A) increases in proportion to T   *D) decreases in proportion to $1/T$
  B) increases in proportion to T^2 E) decreases in proportion to $1/T^2$
  C) remains the same

29. A magnetic field B_0 is applied to a paramagnetic substance. In the
    interior the magnetic field produced by the magnetic dipoles of the
    substance is:

  A) greater than B_0 and in the opposite direction
  B) less than B_0 and in the opposite direction
 *C) greater than B_0 and in the same direction
  D) less than B_0 and in the same direction
  E) the same as B_0

30. A paramagnetic substance, in an external magnetic field, is
    thermally isolated. The field is then removed. As a result:

  A) the magnetic energy of the magnetic dipoles decreases
  B) the temperature of the substance increases
  C) the magnetization decreases, but only slightly
  D) the magnetization reverses direction
 *E) none of the above

31. A magnetic field B_0 is applied to a diamagnetic substance. In the
    interior the magnetic field produced by the magnetic dipoles of the
    substance is:

  A) greater than B_0 and in the opposite direction
 *B) less than B_0 and in the opposite direction
  C) greater than B_0 and in the same direction
  D) less than B_0 and in the same direction
  E) the same as B_0

32. Ferromagnetism is closely associated with:

  A) the tendency of electron dipole moments to align with an applied
     magnetic field
  B) the tendency of electron dipole moments to align opposite to an
     applied magnetic field
  C) the tendency of electron dipole moments to change magnitude in an
     applied magnetic field
 *D) the tendency of electron dipole moments to align with each other
  E) the force exerted by electron dipole moments on each other

33. Of the three chief kinds of magnetic materials (diamagnetic,
    paramagnetic, and ferromagnetic) which are used to make permanent
    magnets?

  A) only diamagnetic
 *B) only ferromagnetic
  C) only paramagnetic
  D) only paramagnetic and ferromagnetic
  E) all three

34. When a permanent magnet is strongly heated:

  A) nothing happens   D) its magnetism increases
  B) it becomes an induced magnet   E) its polarity reverses
 *C) it loses its magnetism

35. Magnetization vectors in neighboring ferromagnetic domains are:

  A) always in opposite directions
  B) always in the same direction
 *C) always in different directions
  D) sometimes in different directions and sometimes in the same
     direction
  E) sometimes in opposite directions and sometimes in the same direction

36. The behavior of ferromagnetic domains in an applied magnetic field
    gives rise to:

 *A) hysteresis
  B) ferromagnetism
  C) the Curie law
  D) a lowering of the Curie temperature
  E) Gauss' law for magnetism

34

Because ferromagnets exhibit hysteresis, the magnetization:

) can never be in the same direction as an applied field
) may not vanish when an applied field is reduced to zero
) can never vanish
) is proportional to any applied magnetic field
) is always opposite to the direction of any applied magnetic field

The soft iron core in the solenoid shown is removable. Then:

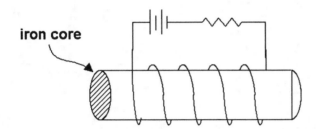

iron core

) the current will be larger without the core
) the current will be larger with the core
) one must do work to remove the core
) the circuit will do work in expelling the core
) the stored energy is the same with or without the core

An unmagnetized steel bar is placed inside a solenoid. As the current in the solenoid is slowly increased from zero to some large value, the magnetization of the bar:

) increases proportionally with the current
) remains zero for awhile and then increases linearly with any further increase in current
) increases with increasing current at first but later is much less affected by it
) is unaffected by the current
) increases quadratically with the current

The magnetic field of the earth is roughly the same as that of a magnetic dipole with a dipole moment of about:

) 10^{17} J/T   B) 10^{19} J/T   C) 10^{21} J/T   *D) 10^{23} J/T   E) 10^{25} J/T

Of the following places one would expect that the horizontal component of the earth's magnetic field to be largest in:

) Maine   *B) Florida   C) Maryland   D) New York   E) Iowa

42. A positively charged ion, due to a cosmic ray, is headed through the earth's atmosphere toward the center of the earth. Due to the earth's magnetic field, the ion will be deflected:

   A) south
   B) north
   C) west
  *D) east
   E) not at all since it is a charge and not a pole

35

Halliday Fund. 4e Chap 35

1. Which of the following has the greatest effect in decreasing the oscillation frequency of an LC circuit? Using instead:

A) L/2 and C/2   *D) 2L and 2C
B) L/2 and 2C   E) none of these
C) 2L and C/2

2. We desire to make an LC circuit that oscillates at 100 Hz using an inductance of 2.5 H. We also need a capacitance of:

A) 1 F   B) 1 mF   *C) 1 µF   D) 100 µF   E) 1 pF

3. An LC circuit consists of a 1 µF capacitor and a 4 mH inductor. Its oscillation frequency is approximately:

A) 0.025 Hz   *D) 2500 Hz
B) 25 Hz   E) 15,800 Hz
C) 60 Hz

4. An LC circuit has an oscillation frequency of 10^5 Hz. If C = 0.1 µF, then L must be about:

A) 10 mH   B) 1 mH   *C) 25 µH   D) 2.5 µH   E) 1 pH

5. In the circuit shown, switch S is first pushed up to charge the capacitor. When S is then pushed down, the current in the circuit will oscillate at a frequency of:

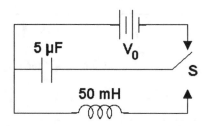

*A) 318 Hz   D) 2000 Hz
B) 0.01 Hz   E) depends on V_0
C) 12.500 Hz

6. Radio receivers are usually tuned by adjusting the capacitor of an LC circuit. If $C = C_1$ for a frequency of 600 kHz, then for a frequency of 1200 kHz one must adjust C to:

A) $C_1/2$ *B) $C_1/4$ C) $2C_1$ D) $4C_1$ E) $\sqrt{2}C_1$

7. An LC series circuit with an inductance L and a capacitance C has an oscillation frequency f. Two inductors, each with inductance L, and two capacitors, each with capacitance C, are all wired in series and the circuit is completed. The oscillation frequency is:

A) f/4   B) f/2   *C) f   D) 2f   E) 4f

8. The electrical analog of a spring constant "k" is:

A) L   B) 1/L   C) C   *D) 1/C   E) R

9. Consider the mechanical system consisting of two springs and a block as shown in "X". Which one of the five electrical circuits (I, II, III, IV, V) is the analog of X?

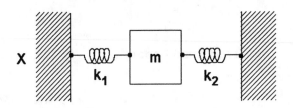

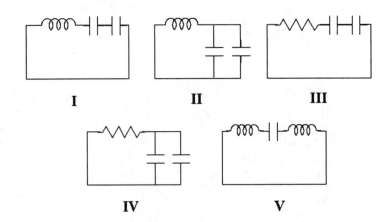

*A) I.   B) II.   C) III.   D) IV.   E) V.

10. A 150-g block on the end of a spring with a spring constant of 35 N/m is pulled aside 25 cm and released from rest. In the electrical analog the initial charge on the capacitor is:

A) 0.15 C   B) 6.67 C   *C) 0.025 C   D) 40 C   E) 35 C

11. A 150-g block on the end of a spring with a spring constant of 35 N/m is pulled aside 25 cm and released from rest. In the electrical analog the maximum current in the LC circuit is:

*A) 0.38 A   B) 0.025 A   C) 40 A   D) 2.3 A   E) 5.3 A

12. In an oscillating LC circuit, the total stored energy is U. The maximum energy stored in the capacitor during one cycle is:

A) U/2   B) $U/\sqrt{2}$ *C) U   D) $U/(2\pi)$ E) U/π

13. In an oscillating LC circuit, the total stored energy is U. When $q = Q/2$, U_B is:

A) U/2   B) U/4   *C) $(\sqrt{3}/2)U$ D) $U/\sqrt{2}$ E) 3U/4

14. The total energy in an LC circuit is 5.0×10^{-6} J. If C = 15 μF the charge on the capacitor is:

A) 0.82 μC   B) 8.5 μC   *C) 12 μC   D) 17 μC   E) 24 μC

15. The total energy in an LC circuit is 5.0×10^{-6} J. If L = 25 mH the maximum current is:

A) 10 mA   B) 14 mA   *C) 20 mA   D) 28 mA   E) 40 mA

16. At time t = 0 the charge on the 50-μF capacitor in an LC circuit is 15 μC and there is no current. If the inductance is 20 mH the maximum current is:

A) 15 nA   B) 15 μA   C) 6.7 mA   *D) 15 mA   E) 15 A

17. An LC circuit has an inductance of 20 mH and a capacitance of 5.0 μF. At time t = 0 the charge on the capacitor is 3.0 μC and the current is 7.0 mA. The total energy is:

A) 4.1×10^{-7} A   *D) 1.4×10^{-6} A
B) 4.9×10^{-7} A   E) 2.8×10^{-6} A
C) 9.0×10^{-7} A

18. An LC circuit has a capacitance of 30 μF and an inductance of 15 mH. AT time t = 0 the charge on the capacitor is 10 μC and the current is 20 mA. The maximum charge on the capacitor is:

A) 8.9 μC   B) 10 μC   C) 12 μC   *D) 17 μC   E) 24 μC

19. An LC circuit has an inductance of 15 mH and a capacitance of 10 μF. At one instant the charge on the capacitor is 25 μC. At that instant the current is changing at the rate:

A) 0
B) 1.7×10^{-8} A/s
C) 5.9×10^{-3} A/s

D) 3.8×10^{-2} A/s
*E) 170 A/s

20. An LC circuit has a capacitance of 30 μF and an inductance of 15 mH. At time t = 0 the charge on the capacitor is 10 μC and the current is 20 mA. The maximum current is:

A) 18 mA   B) 20 mA   *C) 25 mA   D) 35 mA   E) 42 mA

21. An RLC circuit has a resistance of 200 Ω and an inductance of 15 mH. Its oscillation frequency is 7000 Hz. At time t = 0 the charge on the capacitor is 50 μC and there is no current. After 5 complete cycles the charge on the capacitor is:

A) 0
B) 3.7×10^{-9} C
*C) 4.3×10^{-7} C

D) 4.6×10^{-6} C
E) 5.0×10^{-5} C

22. An RLC circuit has an inductance of 25 mH and a capacitance of 5.0 μF. The charge on the capacitor does NOT oscillate but rather decays exponentially to 0. The resistance in the circuit must be:

*A) greater than or equal to 20,000 Ω
B) less than 20,000 Ω but greater than 10,000Ω
C) less than 10,000 Ω but greater than 5,000Ω
D) less than 5,000 Ω but greater than 0
E) 0

23. A series circuit with an inductance of 15 mH, a capacitance of 35 μF, and a resistance of 5.0 Ω, contains a sinusoidal source of emf with a frequency of 500 Hz. The frequency with which the charge on the capacitor oscillates is:

*A) 500 Hz
B) 1.4 kHz
C) greater than 1.4 kHz

D) less than 500 Hz
E) between 500 Hz and 1.4 kHz

24. The rapid exponential decay in just a few cycles of the charge on the plates of capacitor in an RLC circuit might due to:

A) a large inductance   *D) a large resistance
B) a large capacitance   E) a small resistance
C) a small capacitance

25. An RLC circuit has a capacitance of 12 μF, an inductance of 25 mH, and a resistance of 60 Ω. The current oscillates with an angular frequency of:

A) 1.2×10^3 rad/s   D) 2.2×10^3 rad/s
*B) 1.4×10^3 rad/s   E) 2.6×10^3 rad/s
C) 1.8×10^3 rad/s

26. The angular frequency of a certain RLC series circuit is ω_0. A source of sinusoidal emf, with angular frequency 2ω, is inserted into the circuit. After transients die out the angular frequency of the current oscillations is:

A) $\omega_0/2$ B) ω_0 *C) $2\omega_0$ D) $1.5\omega_0$ E) $3\omega_0$

27. The angular frequency of a certain RLC series circuit is ω_0. A source of sinusoidal emf, with angular frequency ω, is inserted into the circuit and ω is varied while the amplitude of the source is held constant. For which of the following values of ω is the amplitude of the current oscillations the greatest?

A) $\omega_0/5$
B) $\omega_0/2$
*C) ω_0
D) $2\omega_0$
E) none of them (they all produce the same current amplitude)

28. An RLC circuit has a sinusoidal source of emf. The average rate at which the source supplies energy is 5 nW. This must also be:

A) the average rate at which energy is stored in the capacitor
B) the average rate which energy is stored in the inductor
*C) the average rate at which energy is dissipated in the resistor
D) twice the average rate at which energy is stored in the capacitor
E) three times the average rate at which energy is stored in the inductor

1. In a purely capacitive circuit the current:

*A) leads the voltage by 1/4 cycle   D) lags the voltage by 1/2 cycle
 B) leads the voltage by 1/2 cycle   E) is in phase with the voltage
 C) lags the voltage by 1/4 cycle

2. In a purely resistive circuit the current:

 A) leads the voltage by 1/4 cycle   D) lags the voltage by 1/2 cycle
 B) leads the voltage by 1/2 cycle   *E) is in phase with the voltage
 C) lags the voltage by 1/4 cycle

3. In a purely inductive circuit, the current lags the voltage by:

*A) 1/4 cycle
 B) 1/2 cycle
 C) 3/4 cycle
 D) 1 cycle
 E) an amount that depends on the frequency

4. A series RL circuit is connected to an emf source of angular
   frequency ω. The current leads the applied emf by:

 A) $\tan^{-1}(\omega L/R)$ D) $-\tan^{-1}(\omega R/L)$
*B) $-\tan^{-1}(\omega L/R)$ E) zero
 C) $\tan^{-1}(\omega R/L)$

5. An RC series circuit is connected to an emf source having angular
   frequency ω. The current leads the source voltage by:

*A) $\tan^{-1}(1/\omega CR)$ D) $-\tan^{-1}(\omega CR)$
 B) $-\tan^{-1}(1/\omega CR)$ E) $\pi/4$
 C) $\tan^{-1}(\omega CR)$

6. In an RLC series circuit, which is connected to a source of emf
   $\epsilon_m\cos(\omega t)$, the current lags the voltage by 45° if:

 A) $R = 1/\omega C - \omega L$ D) $R = \omega C - 1/\omega L$
 B) $R = 1/\omega L - \omega C$ E) $\omega L = 1/\omega C$
*C) $R = \omega L - 1/\omega C$

7. A coil has a resistance of 60Ω and an impedance of 100Ω. Its reactance, in ohms, is:

A) 40   B) 60   *C) 80   D) 117   E) 160

8. The reactance in ohms of a 35-μF capacitor connected to a 400-Hz generator is:

A) 0   B) 0.014   C) 0.088   *D) 11   E) 71

9. A 35-μF capacitor is connected to an ac source of emf with a frequency of 400 Hz and a maximum emf of 20 V. The maximum current is:

A) 0   B) 0.28 A   *C) 1.8 A   D) 230 A   E) 1400 A

10. A 45-mH inductor is connected to an ac source of emf with a frequency of 400 Hz and a maximum emf of 20 V. The maximum current is:

A) 0   *B) 0.18 A   C) 1.1 A   D) 360 A   E) 2300 A

11. The impedance of an RLC series circuit is definitely increased if:

A) C decreases   *D) R increases
B) L increases   E) R decreases
C) L decreases

12. An RLC series circuit has R = 4 Ω, X_C = 3 Ω, and X_L = 6 Ω. The impedance of this circuit is:

*A) 5Ω   B) 7Ω   C) 9.8Ω   D) 13Ω   E) 7.8Ω

13. The impedance of the circuit shown is:

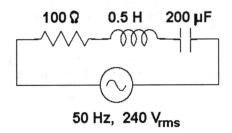

100 Ω   0.5 H   200 μF

50 Hz, 240 V_{rms}

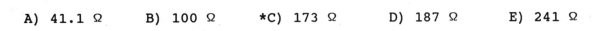

A) 41.1 Ω   B) 100 Ω   *C) 173 Ω   D) 187 Ω   E) 241 Ω

391

14. An electric motor, under load, has an effective resistance of 30 Ω and an inductive reactance of 40 Ω. When powered by a source with a maximum voltage of 420 V, the maximum current is:

A) 6.0 A   *B) 8.4 A   C) 10.5 A   D) 12.0 A   E) 14.0 A

15. An RL series circuit is connected to an ac generator. If ϵ_m = 20 V and the maximum potential difference across the resistor is 16 V, then the maximum potential difference across the inductor is:

A) 2 V   B) 4 V   *C) 12 V   D) 25.6 V   E) 36 V

16. When the amplitude of the oscillator in a series RLC circuit is doubled:

  A) the impedance is doubled
  B) the voltage across the capacitor is halved
  C) the capacitive reactance is halved
  D) the power factor is doubled
 *E) the current amplitude is doubled

17. When the frequency of the oscillator in a series RLC circuit is doubled:

  A) the capacitive reactance is doubled
 *B) the capacitive reactance is halved
  C) the impedance is doubled
  D) the current amplitude is doubled
  E) the current amplitude is halved

18. In an RLC series circuit, the source voltage is leading the current at a given frequency f. If f is lowered slightly, then the circuit impedance will:

  A) increase
 *B) decrease
  C) remain the same
  D) need to know the amplitude of the source voltage
  E) need to know whether the phase angle is larger or smaller than 45°

19. An RLC series circuit has L = 100 mH and C = 1 μF. It is connected to a 1000 Hz source and the phase angle is observed to be 75°. The value of R is:

A) 12.6 Ω *B) 126 Ω C) 175 Ω D) 1750 Ω E) 1810 Ω

20. An RLC series circuit, connected to a source E, is at resonance. Then:

  A) the voltage across R is zero
 *B) the voltage across R equals the applied voltage
  C) the voltage across C is zero
  D) the voltage across L equals the applied voltage
  E) the applied voltage and current differ in phase by 90°

21. An RLC series circuit is connected to an oscillator with ϵ_m = 100 V. If the voltage amplitudes V_R, V_L, and V_C are all equal to each other, then V_R must be:

  A) 33 V   B) 50 V   C) 67 V   D) 87 V   *E) 100 V

22. A resistor, an inductor, and a capacitor are connected in parallel to a sinusoidal source of emf. Which of the following is true?

  A) The currents in all branches are in phase.
 *B) The potential differences across all branches are in phase.
  C) The current in the capacitor branch leads the current in the inductor branch by 1/4 cycle
  D) The potential difference across the capacitor branch leads the potential difference across the inductor branch by 1/4 cycle.
  E) The current in the capacitor branch lags the current in the inductor branch by 1/4 cycle.

23. The rms value of an ac current is:

  A) its peak value
  B) its average value
 *C) that steady current which produces the same rate of heating in a resistor
  D) that steady current which will charge a battery at the same rate
  E) zero

24.
  The rms value of a sinusoidal voltage is $V_0/\sqrt{2}$, where V_0 is the amplitude. What is the rms value of its fully rectified wave? Recall that $V_{rect}(t) = |V(t)|$.

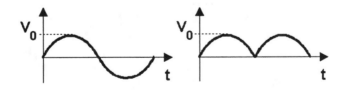

A) $V_0^2/\sqrt{2}$ B) $V_0^2/2$ C) $\sqrt{2}V_0$ *D) $V_0/\sqrt{2}$ E) $V_0/(2\sqrt{2})$

25. A sinusoidal voltage V(t) has an rms value of 100 V. Its maximum value is:

   A) 100 V   B) 707 V   C) 70.7 V   *D) 141 V   E) 200 V

26. An ac generator produces 10 volts (rms) at 400 rad/s. It is connected to a series RL circuit (R = 17.3Ω, L = 0.025 H). The rms current is:

   A) 0.50 A, i leads ∈ by 30°   *D) 0.50 A, i lags ∈ by 30°
   B) 0.71 A, i lags ∈ by 30°   E) 0.58 A, i leads ∈ by 90°
   C) 1.40 A, i lags ∈ by 60°

27. An ac generator producing 10 volts (rms) at 200 rad/s is connected in series with a 50 Ω resistor, a 400 mH inductor, and a 200 μF capacitor. The rms current in amperes is:

   A) 0.125   *B) 0.135   C) 0.18   D) 0.20   E) 0.40

28. An ac generator producing 10 volts (rms) at 200 rad/s is connected in series with a 50 Ω resistor, a 400 mH inductor, and a 200 μF capacitor. The rms voltage (in volts) across the resistor is:

   A) 2.5   B) 3.4   *C) 6.7   D) 10.0   E) 10.8

29. An ac generator producing 10 volts (rms) at 200 rad/s is connected in series with a 50 Ω resistor, a 400 mH inductor, and a 200 μF capacitor. The rms voltage (in volts) across the capacitor is:

   A) 2.5   *B) 3.4   C) 6.7   D) 10.0   E) 10.8

30. An ac generator producing 10 volts (rms) at 200 rad/s is connected in series with a 50 Ω resistor, a 400 mH inductor, and a 200 μF capacitor. The rms voltage (in volts) across the inductor is:

   A) 2.5   B) 3.4   C) 6.7   D) 10.0   *E) 10.8

31. The ideal meters shown read rms current and voltage. The average power delivered to the load is:

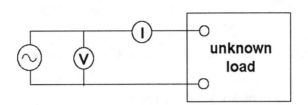

   A) definitely equal to VI
   B) perhaps more than VI
  *C) possibly equal to VI even if the load contains L and C
   D) definitely less than VI
   E) zero as is the average of any sine wave

32. The average power supplied to the circuit shown passes through a maximum when which one of the following is increased continuously from a very low to a very high value?

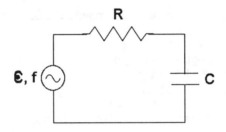

   A) source emf   D) source frequency
  *B) R   E) none of these
   C) C

33. In a series RCL circuit the rms value of the generator emf is E and the rms value of the current is i. The current lags the emf by Φ. The average power supplied by the generator is given by:

   A) (iE/2)cosΦ   D) i^2z
   B) iE   *E) i^2R
   C) i^2/z

34. The units of the "power factor" are:

   A) ohm   D) ohm(1/2)
   B) watt   *E) none of these
   C) radian

395

35. A series circuit consists of a 15-Ω resistor, a 25-mH inductor, and a 35-μF capacitor. If the frequency is 100 Hz the power factor is:

A) 0   B) 0.20   *C) 0.45   D) 0.89   E) 1.0

36. The main reason that alternating current replaced direct current for general use is:

A) ac generators do not need slip rings
*B) ac voltages may be conveniently transformed
C) electric clocks do not work on dc
D) a given ac current does not heat a power line as much as the same dc current
E) ac minimizes magnetic effects

37. A "step-down" transformer is used to:

A) increase the power   *D) decrease the voltage
B) decrease the power   E) change ac to dc
C) increase the voltage

38. Iron, rather than copper, is used in the core of transformers because:

A) iron can withstand a higher temperature
B) iron has a greater resistivity
*C) iron has a very high permeability
D) iron makes a good permanent magnet
E) iron insulates the primary from the secondary

39. The core of a transformer is made in a laminated form to:

A) facilitate easy assembly   D) save weight
B) reduce i^2R losses in the coils *E) prevent eddy currents
C) increase the magnetic flux

40. A generator supplies 100 V to the primary coil of a transformer. The primary has 50 turns and the secondary has 500 turns. The secondary voltage is:

*A) 1000 V   B) 500 V   C) 250 V   D) 100 V   E) 10 V

41. The resistance of the primary coil of a well designed, 1:10 step-down transformer is 1 ohm. With the secondary circuit open, the primary is connected to a 12 V ac generator. The primary current is:

 *A) very small
  B) about 12 A
  C) about 120 A
  D) depends on the actual number of turns in the primary coil
  E) depends on the core material

42. The primary of an ideal transformer has 100 turns and the secondary has 600 turns. Then:

  A) the power in the primary circuit is less than that in the secondary circuit
  B) the currents in the two circuits are the same
  C) the voltages in the two circuits are the same
 *D) the primary current is six times the secondary current
  E) the frequency in the secondary circuit is six times that in the primary circuit

43. The primary of a 3:1 step-up transformer is connected to a source and the secondary is connected to a resistor R. The power dissipated by R in this situation is P. If R is connected directly to the source it will dissipate a power of:

 *A) P/9   B) P/3   C) P   D) 3P   E) 9P

44. In an ideal 1:8 step-down transformer, the primary power is 10 kW and the secondary current is 25 A. The primary voltage is:

  A) 25,600 V   *B) 3200 V   C) 400 V   D) 50 V   E) 6.25 V

45. A source with an impedance of 100 Ω is connected to the primary coil of a transformer and a resistance R is connected to the secondary coil. If the transformer has 500 turns in its primary coil and 100 turns in its secondary coil the greatest power will be dissipated in the resistor if R =:

  A) 0   B) 0.25 Ω   *C) 4.0 Ω   D) 50 Ω   E) 100 Ω

1. Maxwell's great contribution to electromagnetic theory was his hypothesis that:

 A) work is required to move a magnetic pole through a closed path surrounding a current
*B) a time-varying electric flux acts as a current for purposes of producing a magnetic field
 C) the speed of light could be determined from simple electrostatic and magnetostatic experiments (finding the values of μ_o and ϵ_o)
 D) the magnetic force on a moving charge particle is perpendicular to both **v** and **B**
 E) magnetism could be explained in terms of circulating currents in atoms

2. "Displacement current" is:

 A) $d\Phi_E/dt$
*B) $\epsilon_o d\Phi_E/dt$
 C) $\mu_o d\Phi_E/dt$
 D) $\mu_o \epsilon_o d\Phi_E/dt$
 E) $-d\Phi_B/dt$

3. Displacement current exists wherever:

 A) there is a magnetic field
 B) there is moving charge
 C) there is a changing magnetic field
 D) there is an electric field
*E) there is a changing electric field

4. Displacement current exists in the region between the plates of a parallel plate capacitor if:

 A) the capacitor leaks charge across the plates
*B) the capacitor is being discharged
 C) the capacitor is fully charged
 D) the capacitor is fully discharged
 E) none of the above are true

5. A 1.2-m radius cylindrical region contains a uniform electric field that is increasing uniformly with time. At t = 0 the field is 0 and at t = 5.0 s the field is 200 V/m. The total displacement current through a cross section of the region is:

 A) 4.5×10^{-16} A
 B) 2.0×10^{-15} A
 C) 3.5×10^{-10} A
*D) 1.6×10^{-9} A
 E) 8.0×10^{-9} A

6. A current of 1 A is used to charge a parallel plate capacitor with square plates. If the area of each plate is 0.6 m^2 the displacement current through a 0.3 m^2 area wholly between the capacitor plates and parallel to them is:

A) 1 A   B) 2 A   C) 0.7 A   *D) 0.5 A   E) 0.25 A

7. A 1-μF capacitor is connected to an emf that is increasing uniformly with time at a rate of 100 V/s. The displacement current between the plates is:

A) 0   B) 1x10^{-8} A   C) 1x10^{-6} A   *D) 1x10^{-4} A   E) 100 A

8. A magnetic field exists between the plates of a capacitor:

A) always
B) never
C) when the capacitor is fully charged
*D) while the capacitor is being charged
E) only when the capacitor is starting to be charged

9. Suppose you are looking into one end of a long cylindrical tube in which there is a uniform electric field, pointing away from you. If the magnitude of the field is decreasing with time the direction of the induced magnetic field is:

A) toward you   *D) counterclockwise
B) away from you   E) to your right
C) clockwise

10. Suppose you are looking into one end of a long cylindrical tube in which there is a uniform electric field, pointing away from you. If the magnitude of the field is decreasing with time the field lines of the induced magnetic field are:

*A) circles
B) ellipses
C) straight lines parallel to the electric field
D) straight lines perpendicular to the electric field
E) none of the above

11. A cylindrical region contains a uniform electric field that is along the cylinder axis and is changing with time. If r is distance from the cylinder axis the magnitude of the magnetic field within the region is:

A) uniform   D) proportional to 1/r^2
B) proportional to 1/r   *E) proportional to r
C) proportional to r^2

399

12. A cylindrical region contains a uniform electric field that is parallel to the axis and is changing with time. If r is distance from the cylinder axis the magnitude of the magnetic field outside the region is:

A) 0
*B) proportional to 1/r
C) proportional to r^2
D) proportional to 1/r^2
E) proportional to r

13. A 0.70-m radius cylindrical region contains a uniform electric field that is parallel to the axis and is increasing at the rate 5.0x10^{12} V/m ·s. The magnetic field at a point 0.25 m from the axis has a magnitude of:

A) 0
*B) 7.0x10^{-6} T
C) 2.8x10^{-5} T
D) 5.4x10^{-5} T
E) 7.0x10^{-5} T

14. A 0.70-m radius cylindrical region contains a uniform electric field that is parallel to the axis and is increasing at the rate 5.0x10^{12} V/m ·s. The magnetic field at a point 1.2 m from the axis has a magnitude of:

A) 0
B) 7.0x10^{-6} T
*C) 1.1x10^{-5} T
D) 2.3x10^{-5} T
E) 2.8x10^{-5} T

15. A 1-A current is used to charge a parallel plate capacitor. A large square piece of paper is placed between the plates and parallel to them so it sticks out on all sides. The value of the integral $\oint$**B** ·d**s** around the perimeter of the paper is:

A) 2 T ·m
*B) 4πx10^{-7} T ·m
C) 8.85x10^{-12} T ·m
D) 10^{-7} T ·m
E) not determined from the given quantities

16. A sinusoidal emf is connected to a parallel plate capacitor. The magnetic field between the plates:

A) is 0
B) is constant
C) is sinusoidal and its amplitude does not depend on the frequency of the source
*D) is sinusoidal and its amplitude is proportional to the frequency of the source
E) is sinusoidal and its amplitude is inversely proportional to the frequency of the source

17. An electron is on the z axis moving toward the xy plane but it has not reached that plane yet. At that instant:

  A) there is only a true current through the xy plane
 *B) there is only a displacement current through the xy plane
  C) there are both true and displacement currents through the xy plane
  D) there is neither a true nor a displacement current through the xy plane
  E) none of the above are true

18. Consider the four Maxwell equations:
    I. $\oint \mathbf{E} \cdot d\mathbf{A} = q/\epsilon_o$
    II. $\oint \mathbf{B} \cdot d\mathbf{A} = 0$
    III. $\oint \mathbf{E} \cdot d\mathbf{s} = -d\Phi_B/dt$
    IV. $\oint \mathbf{B} \, yd\mathbf{s} = \mu_o i + \mu_o \epsilon_o d\Phi_E/dt$
  Which of these must be modified if magnetic poles are discovered?

  A) only I   D) only III and IV
  B) only II   E) only II, III, IV
 *C) only II and III

19. One of the Maxwell equations begins with $\oint \mathbf{B} \cdot d\mathbf{s} = \ldots$. The symbol "d**s**" means:

  A) an infinitesimal displacement of a charge
  B) an infinitesimal displacement of a magnetic pole
  C) an infinitesimal inductance
  D) an infinitesimal surface area
 *E) none of the above

20. One of the Maxwell equations begins with $\oint \mathbf{E} \cdot d\mathbf{s} = \ldots$. The "o" symbol in the integral sign means:

  A) the same as the subscript in μ_o
  B) integrate clockwise around the path
  C) integrate counterclockwise around the path
 *D) integrate around a closed path
  E) integrate over a closed surface

21. One of the Maxwell equations begins with $\oint \mathbf{B} \cdot d\mathbf{A} = \ldots$. The "o" symbol in the integral sign means:

  A) the same as the subscript in μ_o
  B) integrate clockwise around the path
  C) integrate counterclockwise around the path
  D) integrate around a closed path
 *E) integrate over a closed surface

22. One of the crucial facts upon which the Maxwell equations are based is:

A) the numerical value of the electron charge
B) charge is quantized
C) the numerical value of the charge/mass ratio of the electron
D) there are three types of magnetic materials
*E) none of the above

23. Two of Maxwell's equations contain a path integral on the left side and an area integral on the right. For them:

A) the path must pierce the area
B) the path must be well-separated from the area
C) the path must be along a field line and the area must be perpendicular to the field line
*D) the path must be the boundary of the area
E) the path must lie in the area, away from its boundary

24. Two of Maxwell's equations contain an integral over a closed surface. For them the infinitesimal vector area d**A** is always:

A) tangent to the surface
*B) perpendicular to the surface and pointing outward
C) perpendicular to the surface and pointing inward
D) tangent to a field line
E) perpendicular to a field line

25. Two of Maxwell's equations contain a path integral on the left side and an area integral on the right. The directions of the infinitesimal path element d**s** and infinitesimal area element d**A** are:

A) always in the same direction
B) always in opposite directions
C) always perpendicular to each other
D) never perpendicular to each other
*E) none of the above

26. Two of Maxwell's equations contain a path integral on the left side and an area integral on the right. Suppose the area is the surface of a piece of paper at which you are looking and d**A** is chosen to point away from you. Then the path integral is:

*A) clockwise around the circumference of the paper
B) counterclockwise around the circumference of the paper
C) from left to right
D) from right to left
E) from top to bottom

402

27. Which of the following equations can be used, along with a symmetry argument, to calculate the electric field of a point charge?

*A) $\oint \mathbf{E} \cdot d\mathbf{A} = q/\epsilon_o$
 B) $\oint \mathbf{B} \cdot d\mathbf{A} = 0$
 C) $\oint \mathbf{E} \cdot d\mathbf{s} = -d\Phi_B/dt$

D) $\oint \mathbf{B} \cdot d\mathbf{s} = \mu_o i + \mu_o \epsilon_o d\Phi_E/dt$
E) none of these

28. Which of the following equations can be used, along with a symmetry argument, to calculate the magnetic field of a long straight wire carrying current?

A) $\oint \mathbf{E} \cdot d\mathbf{A} = q/\epsilon_o$
B) $\oint \mathbf{B} \cdot d\mathbf{A} = 0$
C) $\oint \mathbf{E} \cdot d\mathbf{s} = -d\Phi_B/dt$

*D) $\oint \mathbf{B} \cdot d\mathbf{s} = \mu_o i + \mu_o \epsilon_o d\Phi_E/dt$
E) none of these

29. Which of the following equations can be used to show that magnetic field lines form closed loops?

 A) $\oint \mathbf{E} \cdot d\mathbf{A} = q/\epsilon_o$
*B) $\oint \mathbf{B} \cdot d\mathbf{A} = 0$
 C) $\oint \mathbf{E} \cdot d\mathbf{s} = -d\Phi_B/dt$

D) $\oint \mathbf{B} \cdot d\mathbf{s} = \mu_o i + \mu_o \epsilon_o d\Phi_E/dt$
E) none of these

30. Which of the following equations, along with a symmetry argument, can be used to calculate the magnetic field produced by a uniform time-varying electric field?

A) $\oint \mathbf{E} \cdot d\mathbf{A} = q/\epsilon_o$
B) $\oint \mathbf{B} \cdot d\mathbf{A} = 0$
C) $\oint \mathbf{E} \cdot d\mathbf{s} = -d\Phi_B/dt$

*D) $\oint \mathbf{B} \cdot d\mathbf{s} = \mu_o i + \mu_o \epsilon_o d\Phi_E/dt$
E) none of these

31. Which of the following equations, along with a symmetry argument, can be used to calculate the electric field produced by a uniform time-varying magnetic field?

 A) $\oint \mathbf{E} \cdot d\mathbf{A} = q/\epsilon_o$
 B) $\oint \mathbf{B} \cdot d\mathbf{A} = 0$
*C) $\oint \mathbf{E} \cdot d\mathbf{s} = -d\Phi_B/dt$

D) $\oint \mathbf{B} \cdot d\mathbf{s} = \mu_o i + \mu_o \epsilon_o d\Phi_E/dt$
E) none of these

32. Which of the following equations, along with a symmetry argument, can be used to calculate the magnetic field between the plates of a charging parallel plate capacitor with circular plates?

A) $\oint \mathbf{E} \cdot d\mathbf{A} = q/\epsilon_o$
B) $\oint \mathbf{B} \cdot d\mathbf{A} = 0$
C) $\oint \mathbf{E} \cdot d\mathbf{s} = -d\Phi_B/dt$

*D) $\oint \mathbf{B} \cdot d\mathbf{s} = \mu_o i + \mu_o \epsilon_o d\Phi_E/dt$
E) none of these

403

33. Maxwell's equations, along with an appropriate symmetry argument, can be used to calculate:

  A) the electric force on a given charge
  B) the magnetic force on a given moving charge
  C) the flux of a given electric field
  D) the flux of a given magnetic field
 *E) none of these

Halliday Fund. 4e Chap 38

1. Select the correct statement:

  A) ultra-violet light has a longer wavelength than infra-red
  B) blue light has a higher frequency than x rays
  C) radio waves have higher frequency than gamma rays
  *D) gamma rays have higher frequency than infra-red waves
  E) electrons are a type of electromagnetic wave

2. Consider: radio waves (r), visible light (v), infra-red (i), x-rays (x), and ultraviolet (u). In order of increasing frequency, they are:

  A) r, v, i, x, u   D) i, v, r, u, x
  *B) r, i, v, u, x   E) r, i, v, x, u
  C) i, r, v, u, x

3. The order of increasing wavelength for blue (b), green (g), red (r), and yellow (y) light is:

  A) r, y, g, b   *D) b, g, y, r
  B) r, g, y, b   E) b, y, g, r
  C) g, y, b, r

4. Of the following human eyes are most sensitive to:

  A) red light
  B) violet light
  C) blue light
  *D) green light
  E) none of these (they are equally sensitive to all colors)

5. Which of the following is NOT true for electromagnetic waves?

  A) they consist of changing electric and magnetic fields
  *B) they travel at different speeds in vacuum, depending on their frequency
  C) they transport energy
  D) they transport momentum
  E) they can be reflected

6. The dimensions of the product $\mu_0 \epsilon_0$ are related to those of velocity as:

A) $(\text{velocity})^2$
B) velocity
C) $1/\text{velocity}$

*D) $1/(\text{velocity})^2$
E) $1/(\text{velocity})^{(1/2)}$

7. Maxwell's equations predict that the speed of electromagnetic waves in free space is given by:

A) $\mu_0 \epsilon_0$
B) $(\mu_0 \epsilon_0)^{1/2}$
C) $1/\mu_0 \epsilon_0$

*D) $1/(\mu_0 \epsilon_0)^{1/2}$
E) $1/(\mu_0 \epsilon_0)^2$

8. Maxwell's equations predict that the speed of light in free space is:

A) an increasing function of frequency
B) a decreasing function of frequency
*C) independent of frequency
D) a function of the distance from the source
E) a function of the size of the source

9. The speed of light in vacuum is about:

A) 1100 ft/s
B) 93×10^6 mi/s
C) 6×10^{23} m/s

*D) 3×10^{10} cm/s
E) 186,000 mph

10. The sun is about 1.5×10^{11} m away. The time for light to travel this distance is about:

A) 4.5×10^{18} s
B) 8 s
*C) 8 min

D) 8 hr
E) 8 yr

11. The time for a radar signal to travel to the moon and back, a one-way distance of about 3.8×10^8 m, is:

A) 1.3 s   *B) 2.5 s   C) 8 s   D) 8 min   E) 1×10^6 s

12. Which of the following types of electromagnetic radiation travels at the greatest speed in vacuum?

A) radio waves
B) visible light
C) x rays
D) gamma rays
*E) all of these travel at the same speed

13. Radio waves differ from visible light waves in that radio waves:

    A) travel slower
    B) have a higher frequency
    C) travel faster
    *D) have a lower frequency
    E) require a material medium

14. Visible light has a frequency of about:

    A) 5×10^{18} Hz
    B) 5×10^{16} Hz
    *C) 5×10^{14} Hz
    D) 5×10^{12} Hz
    E) 5×10^{10} Hz

15. The theoretical upper limit for the frequency of electromagnetic waves is:

    A) just slightly greater than that of red light
    B) just slightly less than that of blue light
    C) the greatest x-ray frequency
    *D) none of the above (there is no upper limit)
    E) none of the above but there is an upper limit

16. Radio waves of wavelength 3 cm have a frequency of:

    A) 1 MHz
    B) 9 MHz
    C) 100 MHz
    *D) 10,000 MHz
    E) 900 MHz

17. Radio waves of wavelength 300 m have a frequency of:

    A) 10^{-6} kHz   B) 500 kHz   *C) 1000 kHz   D) 9000 kHz   E) 108 kHz

18. If the electric field in a plane electromagnetic wave is given by $E_m \sin(3 \times 10^6 x - \omega t)$, in SI units, the value of ω is:

    A) 0.01 rad/s
    B) 10 rad/s
    C) 100 rad/s
    *D) 9×10^{14} rad/s
    E) 9×10^{16} rad/s

19. An electromagnetic wave is generated by:

    A) any moving charge
    *B) any accelerating charge
    C) only a charge with changing acceleration
    D) only a charge moving in a circle
    E) only a charge moving in a straight line

20. The electric field for a plane electromagnetic wave traveling in the +y direction is shown. Consider a point where **E** is in the +z direction. The **B** field is:

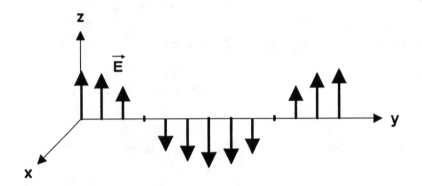

 *A) in the +x direction and in phase with the **E** field
  B) in the -x direction and in phase with the **E** field
  C) in the +x direction and 1/4 wave out of phase with the **E** field
  D) in the +z direction and in phase with the **E** field
  E) in the +z direction and 1/4 wave out of phase with the **E** field

21. In a plane electromagnetic wave in vacuum, the ratio E/B of the amplitudes in SI units of the two fields is:

 *A) the speed of light
  B) an increasing function of frequency
  C) a decreasing function of frequency
  D)
    $\sqrt{2}$
  E)
    $1/\sqrt{2}$

22. If the electric field in a plane electromagnetic wave is along the y axis and its component is given by $E_m \sin(kx - \omega t)$, in SI units, then the magnetic field is along the z axis and its component is given by:

  A) $(E_m/c)\cos(kx - \omega t)$ D) $E_m\cos(kx - \omega t)$
  B) $-(E_m/c)\cos(kx - \omega t)$ *E) $(E_m/c)\sin(kx - \omega t)$
  C) $-(E_m/c)\sin(kx - \omega t)$

23. If the electric field in a plane electromagnetic wave is along the y axis and its component is given by $E_m \sin(kx + \omega t)$, in SI units, then the magnetic field is along the z axis and its component is given by:

  A) $(E_m/c)\cos(kx + \omega t)$ D) $E_m\cos(kx + \omega t)$
  B) $-(E_m/c)\cos(kx + \omega t)$ E) $(E_m/c)\sin(kx + \omega t)$
 *C) $-(E_m/c)\sin(kx + \omega t)$

24. An electromagnetic wave is traveling in the positive x direction with its electric field along the z axis and its magnetic field along the y axis. The fields are related by:

A) $\partial E/\partial x = \mu_0 \epsilon_0 \partial B/\partial x$
B) $\partial E/\partial x = \mu_0 \epsilon_0 \partial B/\partial t$
C) $\partial B/\partial x = \mu_0 \epsilon_0 \partial E/\partial x$
D) $\partial B/\partial x = \mu_0 \epsilon_0 \partial E/\partial t$
*E) $\partial B/\partial x = -\mu_0 \epsilon_0 \partial E/\partial t$

25. If the amplitude of the electric field in a plane electromagnetic wave is 100 V/m then the amplitude of the magnetic field is:

*A) 3.3×10^{-7} T
B) 6.7×10^{-7} T
C) 0.27 T
D) 8.0×10^{7} T
E) 3.0×10^{9} T

26. For an electromagnetic wave the direction of the vector **ExB** gives:

A) the direction of the electric field
B) the direction of the magnetic field
*C) the direction of wave propagation
D) the direction of the electromagnetic force on a proton
E) the direction of the emf induced by the wave

27. The dimensions of **S** $= (1/\mu_0)$**ExB** are:

A) J/m^2 B) J/s C) W/s *D) W/m^2 E) J/m^3

28. The time averaged energy in a sinusoidal electromagnetic wave is:

A) overwhelmingly electrical
B) slightly more electrical than magnetic
*C) equally divided between the electric and magnetic fields
D) slightly more magnetic than electrical
E) overwhelmingly magnetic

29. A point source emits electromagnetic energy at a rate of 100 W. The intensity 10 m from the source is:

A) 10 W/m^2
B) 1.6 W/m^2
C) 1 W/m^2
D) 0.024 W/m^2
*E) 0.080 W/m^2

30. The light intensity 10 m from a point source is 1000 W/m^2. The intensity 100 m from the same source is:

A) 1000 W/m^2 B) 100 W/m^2 *C) 10 W/m^2 D) 1 W/m^2 E) 0.1 W/m^2

31. When the distance between a point source of light and a light meter is reduced from 6.0 m to 3.0 m, the intensity of illumination at the meter will be the original value multiplied by:

  *A) 4   B) 2   C) 1/2   D) 1/4   E) 9

32. The electric field in a sinusoidal light wave has an amplitude of 100 V/m. The intensity of the wave is:

  A) 1.7×10^{-5} W/m^2 D) 1.0×10^4 W/m^2
 *B) 1.3 W/m^2 E) 4.0×10^9 W/m^2
  C) 2.7 W/m^2

33. A sinusoidal electromagnetic wave with an electric field amplitude of 100 V/m is incident normally on a surface with an area of 1 cm^2 and is completely absorbed. The energy absorbed in 10 s is:

  A) 0.13 mJ   *B) 1.3 mJ   C) 2.7 mJ   D) 13 mJ   E) 27 mJ

34. Evidence that electromagnetic waves carry momentum is:

 *A) the tail of a comet points away from the sun
  B) electron flow through a wire generates heat
  C) a charged particle in a magnetic field moves in a circular orbit
  D) heat can be generated by rubbing two sticks together
  E) the Doppler effect

35. Light with an intensity of 1 kW/m^2 falls normally on a surface and is completely absorbed. The radiation pressure is:

  A) 1 kPa   *D) 3.3×10^{-6} Pa
  B) 3×10^{11} Pa   E) 6.7×10^{-6} Pa
  C) 1.7×10^{-6} Pa

36. Light with an intensity of 1 kW/m^2 falls normally on a surface and is completely reflected. The radiation pressure is:

  A) 1 kPa   D) 3.3×10^{-6} Pa
  B) 3×10^{11} Pa   *E) 6.7×10^{-6} Pa
  C) 1.7×10^{-6} Pa

37. Light with an intensity of 1 kW/m^2 falls normally on a surface with an area of 1 cm^2 and is completely absorbed. The force of the radiation on the surface is:

  A) 1.0×10^{-4} N   *D) 3.3×10^{-10} N
  B) 3.3×10^{-11} N   E) 6.7×10^{-10} N
  C) 1.7×10^{-10} N

38. Light with an intensity of 1 kW/m^2 falls normally on a surface with an area of 1 cm^2 and is completely reflected. The force of the radiation on the surface is:

A) 1.0×10^{-4} N
B) 3.3×10^{-11} N
C) 1.7×10^{-10} N
D) 3.3×10^{-10} N
*E) 6.7×10^{-10} N

39. A company claims to have developed material that absorbs light energy without a transfer of momentum. Such material is:

*A) impossible
B) possible, but very expensive
C) inexpensive and already in common use
D) in use by NASA but is not commercially available
E) a break-through in high technology

40. Polarization experiments provide evidence that light is:

A) a longitudinal wave
B) a stream of particles
*C) a transverse wave
D) some type of wave
E) nearly monochromatic

41. A vertical automobile radio antenna is sensitive to electric fields that are polarized:

A) horizontally
B) in circles around the antenna
*C) vertically
D) normal to the antenna in the forward direction
E) none of the above

42. For linearly polarized light the plane of polarization is:

A) perpendicular to both the direction of polarization and the direction of propagation
B) perpendicular to the direction of polarization and parallel to the direction of propagation
C) parallel to the direction of polarization and perpendicular to the direction of propagation
*D) parallel to both the direction of polarization and the direction of propagation
E) none of the above

43. Light from any ordinary source (such as a flame) is usually:

*A) unpolarized
B) plane polarized
C) circularly polarized
D) elliptically polarized
E) monochromatic

44. The electric field in unpolarized light:

   A) has no direction at any time
   B) rotates rapidly
   C) is always parallel to the direction of propagation
   *D) changes direction randomly and often
   E) remains along the same line but reverses direction randomly and often

45. A clear sheet of polaroid is placed on top of a similar sheet so that their polarizing axes make an angle of 30° with each other. The ratio of the intensity of emerging light to incident unpolarized light is:

   A) 1:4   B) 1:3   C) 1:2   D) 3:4   *E) 3:8

46. An unpolarized beam of light has intensity I_O. It is incident on two ideal polarizing sheets. The angle between the axes of polarization of these sheets is θ. Find θ if the emerging light has intensity $I_O/4$:

   A) $\sin^{-1}(1/2)$ *D)
   B) $\cos^{-1}(1/\sqrt{2})$
       $\sin^{-1}(1/\sqrt{5})$ E) $\tan^{-1}(1/4)$
   C) $\cos^{-1}(1/2)$

47. In a stack of three polarizing sheets the first and third are crossed while the middle one has its axis at 45° to the axes of the other two. The fraction of the intensity of an incident unpolarized beam of light that is transmitted by the stack is:

   A) 1/2   B) 1/3   C) 1/4   *D) 1/8   E) zero

48. Three polarizing sheets are placed in a stack with the polarizing directions of the first and third perpendicular to each other. What angle should the polarizing direction of the middle sheet make with the polarizing direction of the first sheet to obtain maximum transmitted intensity when unpolarized light is incident on the stack?

   A) 0   B) 30°   *C) 45°   D) 60°   E) 90°

49. Three polarizing sheets are placed in a stack with the polarizing directions of the first and third perpendicular to each other. What angle should the polarizing direction of the middle sheet make with the polarizing direction of the first sheet to obtain zero transmitted intensity when unpolarized light is incident on the stack?

*A) 0
 B) 30°
 C) 45°
 D) 60°
 E) all angles allow light to pass through

1. The relation $\theta_{incident} = \theta_{reflected}$, which applies as a ray of light strikes an interface between two media, is known as:

A) Faraday's law
B) Snell's law
C) Ampere's law

D) Cole's law
*E) none of these

2. The relation $n_1\sin\theta_1 = n_2 \sin\theta_2$ which applies as a ray of light strikes an interface between two media, is known as:

A) Gauss' law
*B) Snell's law
C) Faraday's law

D) Cole's law
E) law of sines

3. As used in the laws of reflection and refraction, the "normal" direction is:

A) any convenient direction
B) tangent to the interface
C) along the incident ray
D) perpendicular to the electric field vector of the light
*E) perpendicular to the interface

4. When an electromagnetic wave meets a reflecting surface, the direction taken by the reflected wave is determined by:

A) the material of the reflecting surface
*B) the angle of incidence
C) the index of the medium
D) the intensity of the wave
E) the wavelength

5. A virtual image is one:

A) toward which light rays converge but do not pass through
*B) from which light rays diverge but do not pass through
C) from which light rays diverge as they pass through
D) toward which light rays converge and pass through
E) with a ray normal to a mirror passing through it

6. Which of the following is true of all virtual images?

A) they can be seen but not photographed
B) they are ephemeral
C) they are smaller than the objects
D) they are larger than the objects
*E) none of the above

7. When you stand in front of a plane mirror, your image is:

A) real, erect, and smaller than you
B) real, erect, and the same size as you
C) virtual, erect, and smaller than you
*D) virtual, erect, and the same size as you
E) real, inverted, and the same size as you

8. An object is 2 m in front of a plane mirror. Its image is:

A) virtual, inverted, and 2 m behind the mirror
B) virtual, inverted, and 2 m in front of the mirror
C) virtual, erect, and 2 m in front of the mirror
D) real, erect, and 2 m behind the mirror
*E) none of the above

9. A ball is held 50 cm in front of a plane mirror. The distance
   between the ball and its image is:

*A) 100 cm   B) 150 cm   C) 200 cm   D) zero   E) 50 cm

10. A card marked IAHIO8 is standing upright in front of a plane mirror.
    Which of the following is NOT true?

A) the image is virtual
*B) the image shifts its position as the observer shifts his position
C) the image appears as 8OIHAI to a person looking in the mirror
D) the image is caused mostly by specular rather than diffuse
   reflection
E) the image is the same size as the object

11. The angle between a horizontal ruler and a vertical plane mirror is
    30°. The angle between the ruler and its image is:

A) 15°   B) 30°   *C) 60°   D) 90°   E) 180°

12. A 5.0-ft woman wishes to see a full length image of herself in a plane mirror. The minimum length mirror required is:

  A) 5 ft
  B) 10 ft
  *C) 2.5 ft
  D) 3.54 ft
  E) no answer: the farther away she stands the smaller the required mirror length

13. A man holds a rectangular card in front of and parallel to a plane mirror. In order for him to see the entire image of the card, the least mirror area needed is:

  A) that of the whole mirror, regardless of its size
  B) that of the pupil of his eye
  C) one-half that of the card
  *D) one-fourth that of the card
  E) an amount which decreases with his distance from the mirror

14. A light bulb burns in front of the center of a 40-cm wide mirror that is hung vertically on a wall. A man walks in front of the mirror along a line that is parallel to the mirror and twice as far from it as the bulb. The greatest distance he can walk and still see the image of the bulb is:

  A) 20 cm   B) 40 cm   C) 60 cm   D) 80 cm   *E) 120 cm

15. A plane mirror is in a vertical plane and is rotating about a vertical axis at 100 rpm. A horizontal beam of light is incident on the mirror. The reflected beam will rotate at:

  A) 100 rpm   *D) 200 rpm
  B) 141 rpm   E) 10,000 rpm
  C) zero rpm

16. Two plane mirrors make an angle of 120° with each other. The maximum number of images of an object placed between them is:

  A) one   D) four
  *B) two   E) more than four
  C) three

17. The index of refraction of a substance is:

  A) the speed of light in the substance
  B) the angle of refraction
  C) the angle of incidence
  *D) the speed of light in vacuum divided by the speed of light in the substance
  E) measured in radians

18. The units of index of refraction are:

A) m/s
B) s/m
C) radian

D) m/s^2
*E) none of these

19. The diagram shows the passage of a ray of light from air into a substance X. The index of refraction of X is:

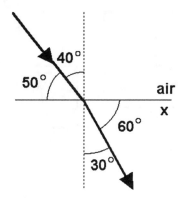

A) 0.74   B) 1.15   *C) 1.29   D) 1.35   E) 1.47

20. If n_{water} = 1.33, what is the angle of refraction for the ray shown?

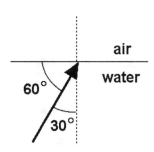

A) 19°   B) 22°   C) 36°   *D) 42°   E) 48°

417

21. Which diagram below illustrates the path of a light ray as it travels from a given point X in air to another given point Y in glass?

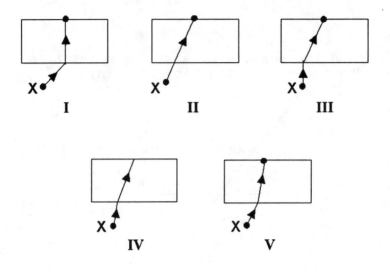

A) I.　　　　B) II.　　　　C) III.　　　　D) IV.　　　　*E) V.

22. The index of refraction for diamond is 2.5. Which of the following is correct for the situation shown?

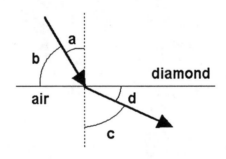

A) (sin a)/(sin b) = 2.5
B) (sin b)/(sin d) = 2.5
C) (cos a)/(cos c) = 2.5

*D) (sin a)/(sin c) = 1/(2.5)
 E) a/c = 2.5

23. When light travels from medium X to medium Y as shown:

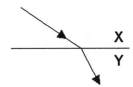

   A) both the speed and the frequency decrease
   B) both the speed and the frequency increase
  *C) both the speed and the wavelength decrease
   D) both the speed and the wavelength increase
   E) both the wavelength and the frequency are unchanged

24. A ray of light passes obliquely through a plate of glass having
    parallel faces. The emerging ray:

   A) is totally internally reflected
   B) is bent more toward the normal than the incident ray
   C) is bent further away from the normal than the incident ray
  *D) is parallel to the incident ray but displaced sideways
   E) lies on the same straight line as the incident ray

25. When light passes from air to glass, it:

   A) bends toward the normal without changing speed
  *B) bends toward the normal and slows down
   C) bends toward the normal and speeds up
   D) bends away from the normal and slows down
   E) bends away from the normal and speeds up

26. A ray of light passes through three media as shown. The speed of
    light in these media obey:

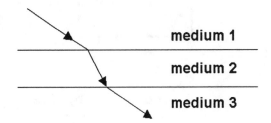

   A) $v_1 > v_2 > v_3$ D) $v_2 > v_1 > v_3$
   B) $v_3 > v_2 > v_1$ E) $v_1 > v_3 > v_2$
  *C) $v_3 > v_1 > v_2$

419

27. As light goes from one medium to another, it is bent away from the normal. Then:

  *A) the speed of the light has increased
  B) dispersion must occur
  C) the second medium has a higher index of refraction
  D) no change in speed has occurred
  E) refraction has not occurred because refraction means a bending toward the normal

28. A parallel beam of monochromatic light in air is incident on a plane glass surface. In the glass, the beam:

  *A) remains parallel   D) follows a parabolic path
  B) undergoes dispersion   E) becomes converging
  C) becomes diverging

29. A pole stands in a river, half in and half out of the water. Another pole of the same length stands vertically on the shore at a place where the ground is level. The shadow cast by the pole in the river on the river bottom is:

  A) slightly longer than the shadow of the pole on land
  B) much longer than the shadow of the pole on land
  *C) shorter than the shadow of the pole on land
  D) shorter than the shadow of the pole on land if the sun is high and longer if the sun is low
  E) the same length as the shadow of the pole on land

30. The rectangular metal tank shown is filled with an unknown liquid. The observer, whose eye is level with the top of the tank, can just see corner E. The index of refraction of this liquid is:

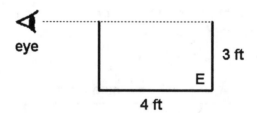

  A) 1.75   B) 1.67   C) 1.50   D) 1.33   *E) 1.25

31. The index of refraction of benzene is 1.80. The critical angle for total internal reflection, at a benzene-air interface, is about:

  A) 56°   B) 47°   *C) 34°   D) 22°   E) 18°

34

32. The index of refraction of a certain glass is 1.50. The sine of the critical angle for total internal reflection at a glass-air interface is:

A) 0.50   *B) 0.67   C) 0.75   D) 1.00   E) 1.50

33. The illustration shows total internal reflection taking place in a glass prism. The index of refraction of this glass is:

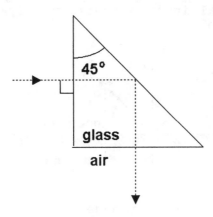

A) at least 1.50
B) at most 1.50
*C) at least 1.41
D) at most 1.41
E) impossible, total internal reflection cannot occur as shown

34. The critical angle for total internal reflection at a diamond-air interface is 25°. Suppose light is incident at an angle of θ with the normal. Total internal reflection will occur if the incident medium is:

A) air and θ = 25°
B) diamond and θ < 25°
C) air and θ > 25°
D) diamond and θ > 25°
*E) air and θ < 25°

35. If n_{water} = 1.50 and n_{glass} = 1.33, then total internal reflection at an interface between this glass and water:

A) occurs whenever the light goes from glass to water
B) occurs whenever the light goes from water to glass
C) may occur when the light goes from glass to water
*D) may occur when the light goes from water to glass
E) can never occur at this interface

421

36. The separation of white light into colors by a prism is associated with:

   A) total internal reflection
   B) partial reflection from each surface
   *C) variation of index of refraction with wavelength
   D) a decrease in the speed of light in the glass
   E) selective absorption of various colors

37. The diagram shows total internal reflection. Which of the following statements is NOT true?

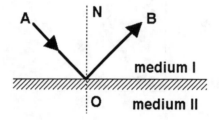

   A) angle AON is the angle of incidence
   B) angle AON = angle BON
   *C) angle AON must be the critical angle
   D) the speed of light in medium II is greater than that in medium I
   E) if angle AON were increased, there would still be total internal reflection

38. A ray of light in water (index n_1) is incident on its surface (with air) at the critical angle. Some oil (index n_2) is now floated on the water. The angle between the ray in the oil and the normal is:

   A) $\sin^{-1}(1.00)$
   B) $\sin^{-1}(1/n_1)$
   *C) $\sin^{-1}(1/n_2)$
   D) $\sin^{-1}(n_1/n_2)$
   E) $\sin^{-1}(n_2/n_1)$

39. The focal length of a spherical mirror is N times its radius of curvature where N is:

   A) 1/4   *B) 1/2   C) 1   D) 2   E) 4

40. Real images formed by a spherical mirror are always:

   A) on the side of the mirror opposite the source
   B) on the same side of the mirror as the source but closer to the
      mirror than the source
   C) on the same side of the mirror as the source but closer to the
      mirror than the focal point
   D) on the same side of the mirror as the source but further from the
      mirror than the focal point
  *E) none of the above

41. The image produced by a convex mirror of an erect object in front of
    the mirror is always:

   A) virtual, erect, and larger than the object
  *B) virtual, erect, and smaller than the object
   C) real, erect, and larger than the object
   D) real, erect, and smaller than the object
   E) none of the above

42. An erect object is located between a concave mirror and its focal
    point. Its image is:

   A) real, erect, and larger than the object
   B) real, inverted, and larger than the object
  *C) virtual, erect, and larger than the object
   D) virtual, inverted, and larger than the object
   E) virtual, erect, and smaller than the object

43. An erect object is in front of a convex mirror a distance greater
    than the focal length. The image is:

   A) real, inverted, and smaller than the object
   B) virtual, inverted, and larger than the object
   C) real, inverted, and larger than the object
  *D) virtual, erect, and smaller than the object
   E) real, erect, and larger than the object

44. As an object is moved from the center of curvature of a concave
    mirror toward its focal point its image:

   A) remains virtual and becomes larger
   B) remains virtual and becomes smaller
  *C) remains real and becomes larger
   D) remains real and becomes smaller
   E) remains real and approaches the same size as the object

45. As an object is moved from a distant location toward the center of curvature of a concave mirror its image:

   A) remains virtual and becomes smaller
   B) remains virtual and becomes larger
   C) remains real and becomes smaller
   *D) remains real and becomes larger
   E) changes from real to virtual

46. The image of an erect candle, formed using a convex mirror, is always:

   A) virtual, inverted, and smaller than the candle
   B) virtual, inverted, and larger than the candle
   C) virtual, erect, and larger than the candle
   *D) virtual, erect, and smaller than the candle
   E) real, erect, and smaller than the candle

47. Where must an object be placed in front of a concave mirror so that the image and object are the same size? (F is the focal point and C is the center of curvature.)

   A) at F   D) between F and C
   *B) at C   E) beyond C
   C) between F and the mirror

48. A point source is to be used with a concave mirror to produce a beam of parallel light. The source should be placed:

   A) as close to the mirror as possible
   B) at the center of curvature
   C) midway between the center of curvature and the focal point
   *D) midway between the center of curvature and the mirror
   E) midway between the focal point and the mirror

49. A concave mirror forms a real image which is twice the size of the object. If the object is 20 cm from the mirror, the radius of curvature of the mirror must be about:

   A) 13 cm   B) 20 cm   *C) 27 cm   D) 40 cm   E) 80 cm

50. A man stands with his nose 4 inches from a concave shaving mirror of radius 16 inches. The distance from the mirror to the image of his nose is:

   A) 4 in   B) 6 in   *C) 8 in   D) 12 in   E) 16 in

51. The figure shows a concave mirror with a small object located at the point marked 6. If the image is also at this point, then the center of curvature of the mirror is at the point marked:

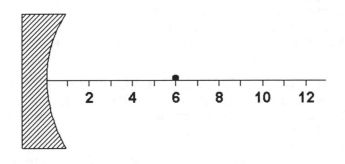

2   4   6   8   10   12

*A) 6   B) 12   C) 3   D) 4   E) 9

52. A concave spherical mirror has a focal length of 12 cm. If an object is placed 6 cm in front of it the image position is:

A) 4 cm behind the mirror   D) 12 cm in front of the mirror
B) 4 cm in front of the mirror   E) at infinity
*C) 12 cm behind the mirror

53. A concave spherical mirror has a focal length of 12 cm. If an object is placed 18 cm in front of it the image position is:

A) 7.2 cm behind the mirror   *D) 36 cm in front of the mirror
B) 7.2 cm in front of the mirror   E) at infinity
C) 36 cm behind the mirror

54. A convex spherical mirror has a focal length of 12 cm. If an object is placed 6 cm in front of it the image position is:

A) 4 cm behind the mirror   *D) 12 cm in front of the mirror
B) 4 cm in front of the mirror   E) at infinity
C) 12 cm behind the mirror

55. A concave spherical mirror has a focal length of 12 cm. If an erect object is placed 6 cm in front of it:

*A) the magnification is 2 and the image is erect
B) the magnification is 2 and the image is inverted
C) the magnification is 0.67 and the image is erect
D) the magnification is 0.67 and the image is inverted
E) the magnification is 0.5 and the image is erect

56. A concave refracting surface is one with a center of curvature:

   A) to the left of the surface
   B) to the right of the surface
 *C) on the side of the incident light
   D) on the side of the refracted light
   E) on the side with the higher index of refraction

57. A convex refracting surface has a radius of 12 cm. Light is incident in air (n = 1) and refracted into a medium with an index of refraction of 2. Light incident parallel to the central axis is focused at a point:

   A) 3 cm from the surface   D) 18 cm from the surface
   B) 6 cm from the surface   *E) 24 cm from the surface
   C) 12 cm from the surface

58. A convex refracting surface has a radius of 12 cm. Light is incident in air (n = 1) and refracted into a medium with an index of refraction of 2. To obtain light with rays parallel to the central axis after refraction a point source should be placed on the axis:

   A) 3 cm from the surface   D) 18 cm from the surface
   B) 6 cm from the surface   E) 24 cm from the surface
 *C) 12 cm from the surface

59. A concave refracting surface of a medium with index of refraction n produces a real image no matter where an object is placed outside:

   A) always
   B) only if the index of refraction of the surrounding medium is less than n
   C) only if the index of refraction of the surrounding medium is greater than n
   D) never
 *E) none of the above

60. A convex spherical refracting surface separates a medium with index of refraction 2 from air. The image of an object outside the surface is real:

   A) always
   B) never
   C) only if it is close to the surface
 *D) only if it is far from the surface
   E) only if the radius of curvature is small

61. A convex spherical surface with radius r separates a medium with index of refraction 2 from air. As an object is moved toward the surface from far away along the central axis its image:

A) changes from virtual to real when it is r/2 from the surface
B) changes from virtual to real when it is 2r from the surface
*C) changes from real to virtual when it is r/2 from the surface
D) changes from real to virtual when it is 2r from the surface
E) remains real

62. A concave spherical surface with radius r separates a medium with index of refraction 2 from air. As an object is moved toward the surface from far away along the central axis its image:

A) changes from virtual to real when it is r/2 from the surface
B) changes from virtual to real when it is 2r from the surface
C) changes from real to virtual when it is r/2 from the surface
D) changes from real to virtual when it is 2r from the surface
*E) remains virtual

63. Where must an object be placed in front of a converging lens in order to obtain a virtual image?

A) at the focal point
B) at twice the focal length
C) greater than the focal length
*D) between the focal point and the lens
E) between the focal length and twice the focal length

64. An erect object placed outside the focal point of a converging lens will produce an image that is:

A) erect and virtual   *D) inverted and real
B) inverted and virtual   E) impossible to locate
C) erect and real

65. An object is 30 cm in front of a converging lens of focal length 10 cm. The image is:

A) real and larger than the object
B) real and the same size than the object
*C) real and smaller than the object
D) virtual and the same size than the object
E) virtual and smaller than the object

66. Let p denote the object-lens distance and i the image-lens distance. The image produced by a lens of focal length f has a height that can be obtained from the object height by multiplying it by:

A) p/i   *B) i/p   C) f/p   D) f/i   E) i/f

67. A camera with a lens of focal length 3 inches takes a picture of a 6 foot man standing 90 feet away. The height of the image is about:

   A) 0.10 in   *B) 0.20 in   C) 0.30 in   D) 0.60 in   E) 0.50 in

68. A hollow lens is made of thin glass as shown. It can be filled with air, water (n = 1.3) or CS_2 (n = 1.6). The lens will diverge a beam of parallel light if it is filled with:

   A) air and immersed in air   *D) CS_2 and immersed in water
   B) air and immersed in water   E) CS_2 and immersed in CS_2
   C) water and immersed in CS_2

69. The object-lens distance, for a converging lens, is 400 mm. The image is three times the size of the object. To make the image five times the size of the object-lens distance must be changed to:

  *A) 360 mm   B) 540 mm   C) 600 mm   D) 720 mm   E) 960 mm

70. An erect object is 2f in front of a convex lens of focal length f. The image is:

   A) real, inverted, magnified   D) virtual, inverted, reduced
   B) real, erect, same size   E) real, inverted, reduced
  *C) real, inverted, same size

71. An ordinary magnifying glass in front of an erect object produces an image which is:

   A) real and erect   *D) virtual and erect
   B) real and inverted   E) none of these
   C) virtual and inverted

72. The sun subtends 0.5° as seen from the earth. Its image, using a 1.0 m focal length lens, is about:

   A) 10 cm   B) 2 cm   *C) 1 cm   D) 5 mm   E) 1 mm

73. An object is in front of a convex lens, at a distance less than the
focal length from the lens. Its image is:

  A) virtual and larger than the object
 *B) real and smaller than the object
  C) virtual and smaller than the object
  D) real and larger than the object
  E) virtual and the same size as the object

74. A plano-convex glass (n = 1.5) lens has a curved side whose radius
is 50 cm. If the image size is to be the same as the object size,
the object should be placed at a distance from the lens of:

  A) 50 cm   B) 100 cm   *C) 200 cm   D) 400 cm   E) 340 cm

75. Which of the following five glass lenses is a diverging lens?

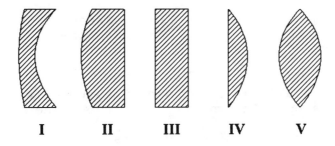

                I   II   III   IV   V

 *A) I.   B) II.   C) III.   D) IV.   E) V.

76. The bellows of an adjustable camera can be extended so that the
largest film to lens distance is one and one-half times the focal
length. If the focal length is 6 in, the nearest object which can be
sharply focused on the film must be what distance from the lens?

  A) 6 in   B) 12 in   *C) 18 in   D) 24 in   E) 36 in

77. A 3-cm high object is in front of a thin lens. The object distance
is 4 cm and the image distance is -8 cm. The image height is:

  A) 0.5 cm   B) 1 cm   C) 1.5 cm   *D) 6 cm   E) 24 cm

78. When a single-lens camera is focused on a distant object, the lens-
to-film distance is found to be 40.0 mm. To focus on an object 0.54
m in front of the lens, the film-to-lens distance must be:

  A) not changed   D) increased by 2.7 mm
  B) decreased by 2.7 mm   *E) increased by 3.2 mm
  C) decreased by 3.2 mm

79. In a cinema, a picture 1 inch wide on the film is projected to an image 10 feet wide on a screen which is 60 feet away. The focal length of the lens is about:

A) 4 in   B) 8 in   C) 3 in   D) 5 in   *E) 6 in

80. The term "virtual" as applied to an image made by a mirror means that the image:

A) is on the mirror surface
B) cannot be photographed by a camera
C) is in front of the mirror
D) is the same size as the object
*E) cannot be shown directly on a screen

81. Which instrument uses a single converging lens with the object placed just inside the focal point?

A) camera   D) overhead projector
B) compound microscope   E) telescope
*C) magnifying glass

82. Let f_o and f_e be the focal lengths of the objective and eyepiece of a compound microscope. In ordinary use, the object:

A) is less than f_o from the objective lens
*B) is more that f_o from the objective
C) produces an intermediate image which is slightly more than f_e from the eyepiece
D) produces an intermediate image which is $2f_e$ away from the eyepiece
E) produces an intermediate image which is less than f_o from the objective

83. Consider the following four statements concerning a compound microscope:
    I.   Each lens produces an image that is virtual and inverted.
    II.   The objective lens has a very short focal length.
    III. The eyepiece is used as a simple magnifying glass.
    IV.   The objective lens is convex and the eyepiece is concave.
Which two of the four statements are correct?

A) I, II   B) I, III   C) I, IV   *D) II, III   E) II, IV

84. What type of eyeglasses should a nearsighted person wear?

*A) diverging lenses   D) plano-convex lenses
B) bifocal lenses   E) double convex lenses
C) converging lenses

85. Which of the following is NOT correct for a simple magnifying glass?

   A) the image is virtual
   B) the image is erect
   C) the image is larger than the object
   D) the object is inside the focal point
  *E) the lens is diverging

86. A nearsighted person can see clearly only objects within 6 feet of her eye. To see distant objects, she should wear eyeglasses of what type and focal length?

   A) diverging, 12 ft   D) converging, 6 ft
  *B) diverging, 6 ft   E) diverging, 3 ft
   C) converging, 12 ft

87. A magnifying glass has a focal length of 15 cm. If the image is 15 cm from the eye (and the eye is adjacent to the lens), the angular magnification is:

   A) 0.5   *B) 1.0   C) 1.5   D) 2.0   E) 4.0

88. An object is 20 cm to the left of a lens of focal length +10 cm. A second lens, of focal length +12.5 cm, is 30 cm to the right of the first lens. The distance between the original object and the final image is:

   A) 28 cm   B) 50 cm   C) 100 cm   *D) zero   E) infinity

89. A converging lens of focal length 20 cm is placed in contact with a diverging lens of focal length 30 cm. The focal length of this combination is:

  *A) +60 cm   B) +25 cm   C) +12 cm   D) -10 cm   E) +10 cm

90. A student sets the cross-hairs of an eyepiece in line with an image which he is measuring. He then notes that when he moves his head slightly to the right, the image moves slightly to the left (with respect to the cross-hairs). Therefore the image is:

   A) infinitely far away
   B) farther away from him that the cross-hairs
  *C) nearer to him than the cross-hairs
   D) in the focal plane of the eyepiece
   E) in the plane of the cross-hairs

91. In a two lens microscope, the intermediate image is:

A) virtual, erect and magnified
B) real, erect and magnified
*C) real, inverted and magnified
D) virtual, inverted and reduced
E) virtual, inverted and magnified

92. Two thin lenses (focal lengths f_1 and f_2) are in contact. Their equivalent focal length is:

A) $f_1 + f_2$
*B) $f_1 f_2/(f_1 + f_2)$
C) $1/f_1 + 1/f_2$

D) $f_1 - f_2$
E) $f_1(f_1 - f_2)/f_2$

93. The two lenses shown are illuminated by a beam of parallel light from the left. Lens B is then moved slowly toward lens A. The beam emerging from lens B is:

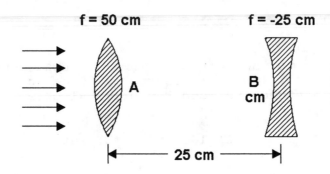

*A) initially parallel and then diverging
B) always diverging
C) initially converging and finally parallel
D) always parallel
E) initially converging and finally diverging

1. A "wave front" is a surface of constant:

*A) phase
 B) frequency
 C) wavelength

D) amplitude
E) speed

2. Huygens' construction can be used only:

 A) for light
 B) for an electromagnetic wave
 C) if one of the media is vacuum (or air)
 D) for transverse waves
*E) for all of these and other situations

3. Consider (I) the law of reflection and (II) the law of refraction.
   Huygens' principle can be used to derive:

 A) only I
 B) only II
*C) both I and II
 D) neither I nor II
 E) the question is meaningless because Huygen's principle is for wave
    fronts whereas both I and II concern rays

4. Units of "optical path length" are:

 A) 1/m   *B) m   C) m/s   D) Hz/m   E) m/Hz

5. Interference of light is evidence that:

 A) the speed of light is very large
 B) light is a transverse wave
 C) light is electromagnetic in character
*D) light is a wave phenomenon
 E) light does not obey conservation of energy

6. The reason there are two slits, rather than one, in a Young's
   experiment is:

 A) to increase the intensity
 B) one slit is for frequency, the other for wavelength
*C) to create a path length difference
 D) one slit is for E fields, the other is for B fields
 E) two slits in parallel offer less resistance

7. In a Young's double-slit experiment the center of a bright fringe occurs wherever waves from the slits differ in the distance they travel by a multiple of:

A) a fourth of a wavelength   D) three-fourths of a wavelength
B) a half a wavelength   E) none of the above
*C) a wavelength

8. In a Young's double-slit experiment the center of a bright fringe occurs wherever waves from the slits differ in phase by a multiple of:

A) $\pi/4$ D) $3\pi/4$
B) $\pi/2$ *E) none of the above
C) π

9. A monochromatic light source illuminates a double slit and the resulting interference pattern is observed on a distant screen. Let d = center-to-center slit spacing, a = individual slit width, D = screen-to-slit distance, ℓ = adjacent dark line spacing in the interference pattern. The wavelength of the light is then:

*A) $d\ell/D$ B) Ld/a C) da/D D) $\ell D/a$ E) Dd/ℓ

10. Light from a small region of an ordinary incandescent bulb is passed through a yellow filter and then serves as the source for a Young's double-slit experiment. Which of the following changes would cause the interference pattern to be more closely spaced?

A) use slits that are closer together
B) use a light source of lower intensity
C) use a light source of higher intensity
*D) use a blue filter instead of a yellow filter
E) move the light source further away from the slits

11. In a Young's double-slit experiment, the slit separation is doubled. To maintain the same fringe spacing on the screen, the screen-to-slit distance D must be changed to:

A) D/2   B) $D/\sqrt{2}$ C) $D\sqrt{2}$ *D) 2D   E) 4D

12. In a Young's double-slit experiment, light of wavelength 500 nm illuminates two slits which are separated by 1 mm. The separation between adjacent bright fringes on a screen 5 m from the slits is:

A) 0.10 cm   D) 1.0 cm
*B) 0.25 cm   E) none of the above
C) 0.50 cm

13. In a Young's double-slit experiment, the separation between slits is d and the screen is a distance D from the slits. The number of bright fringes per unit length on the screen is:

A) Dd/λ B) $D\lambda/d$ C) $D/d\lambda$ D) λ/Dd *E) $d/D\lambda$

14. In a Young's double-slit experiment, the slit separation is doubled. This results in:

  A) an increase in fringe intensity
  B) a decrease in fringe intensity
  C) a halving of the wavelength
 *D) a halving of the fringe spacing
  E) a doubling of the fringe spacing

15. In an experiment to measure the wavelength of light using a double slit, it is found that the fringes are too close together to easily count them. To spread out the fringe pattern, one could:

 *A) halve the slit separation   D) halve the width of each slit
  B) double the slit separation   E) none of these
  C) double the width of each slit

16. The phase difference between the two waves which give rise to a dark spot in a Young's double-slit experiment is (where m = integer):

  A) zero   D) $2\pi m + \pi/2$
  B) $2\pi m + \pi/8$ *E) $2\pi m + \pi$
  C) $2\pi m + \pi/4$

17. In a Young's experiment, it is essential that the two beams:

  A) have exactly equal intensity
  B) be exactly parallel
  C) travel equal distances
 *D) come originally from the same source
  E) be composed of a broad band of frequencies

18. One of the two slits in a Young's experiment is painted over so that it transmits only one-half the intensity of the other slit. As a result:

  A) the fringe system disappears
  B) the bright fringes get brighter and the dark ones get darker
  C) the fringes just get dimmer
  D) the dark fringes just get brighter
 *E) the dark fringes get brighter and the bright ones get darker

19. In a Young's double-slit experiment, a thin sheet of mica is placed over one of the two slits. As a result, the center of the fringe pattern (on the screen) shifts by an amount corresponding to 30 dark bands. The wavelength of the light in this experiment is 480 mm and the index of the mica is 1.60. The mica thickness is:

A) 0.090 mm   B) 0.012 mm   C) 0.014 mm   *D) 0.024 mm   E) 0.062 mm

20. Light from a point source X contains only blue and red components. After passing through a mysterious box, the light falls on a screen. Red and blue hands are observed as shown. The box must contain:

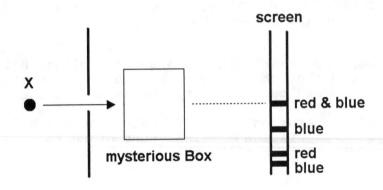

A) a lens
B) a mirror
C) a prism

*D) a double slit
E) a blue and red filter

436

21. Binoculars and microscopes are frequently made with "coated optics" by adding a thin layer of transparent material to the lens surface as shown. One wants:

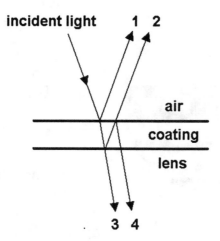

incident light   1   2

air

coating

lens

3   4

   A) constructive interference between 1 and 2
   B) the coating to be more transparent than the lens
   C) destructive interference between 3 and 4
   D) the speed of light in the coating to be less than that in the lens
*E) destructive interference between 1 and 2

22. Monochromatic light, at normal incidence, strikes a thin film in air. If λ denotes the wavelength in the film, what is the thinnest film in which the reflected light will be a maximum?

   A) much less than λ D) $3\lambda/4$
*B) $\lambda/4$ E) λ
   C) $\lambda/2$

23. A soap film, 4×10^{-5} cm thick, is illuminated by white light normal to its surface. The index of refraction of the film is 1.50. Which wavelengths will be intensified in the reflected beam?

   A) 400 nm and 600 nm   D) 400 nm and 800 nm
*B) 480 nm and 800 nm   E) 510 nm and 720 nm
   C) 360 nm and 533 nm

24. Red light is viewed through a thin vertical soap film. At the second dark area shown, the thickness of the film, in terms of the wavelength within the film, is:

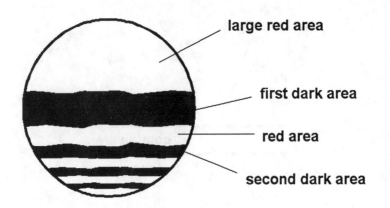

large red area

first dark area

red area

second dark area

A) λ
*B) 3λ/4
C) λ/2

D) λ/4
E) much less than λ

25. Yellow light is viewed by reflection from a thin vertical soap film. Let λ be the wavelength of the light within the film. Why is there a large dark space at the top of the film?

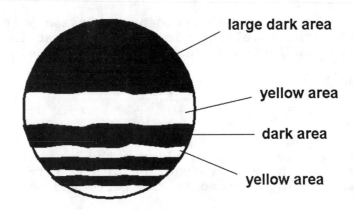

large dark area

yellow area

dark area

yellow area

A) no light is transmitted through this part of the film
B) the film thickness there is λ/4
*C) the light reflected from exactly one of the two surfaces undergoes a 180° phase change
D) the film is too thick in this region for thin film formulas to apply
E) the reflected light is in the infra-red

26. Three experiments involving a thin film (in air) are shown. If t denotes the film thickness and λ denotes the wavelength of the light in the film, which experiments will produce constructive interference as seen by the observer?

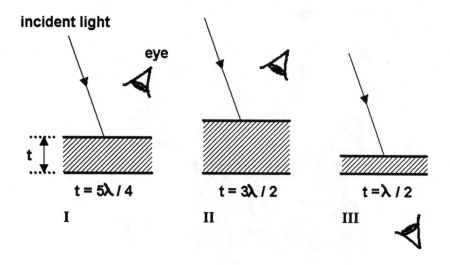

incident light

eye

$t = 5\lambda / 4$ $t = 3\lambda / 2$ $t = \lambda / 2$

I   II   III

A) I only
B) II only
C) III only

*D) I and III only
E) II and III only

27. A liquid of refractive index n = 4/3 replaces the air between a fixed wedge formed from two glass plates as shown. As a result, the spacing between adjacent dark bands in the interference pattern:

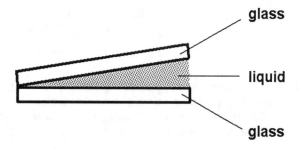

glass

liquid

glass

A) increases by a factor of 4/3
B) increases by a factor of 3
C) remains the same
*D) decreases to 3/4 of its original value
E) decreases to 1/3 of its original value

28. A lens is coated with a material of index 1.2 in order to minimize reflection. If λ denotes the wavelength of the incident light in air, what is the thinnest possible such coating?

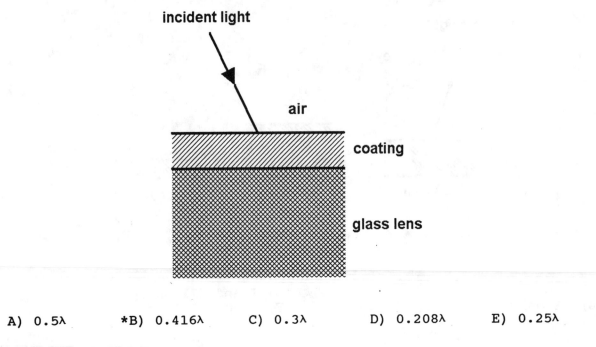

A) 0.5λ   *B) 0.416λ   C) 0.3λ   D) 0.208λ   E) 0.25λ

29. In a thin film experiment, a wedge of air is used between two glass plates. If the wavelength of the incident light in air is 480 nm, how much thicker is the air wedge at the 16th dark fringe than it is at the 6th?

*A) 2400 nm   D) 480 nm
 B) 4800 nm   E) none of these
 C) 240 nm

30. An air wedge is formed from two glass plates which are in contact at their left edges. There are ten dark bands when viewed by reflection using monochromatic light. The left edge of the top plate is now slowly lifted until the plates are parallel. During this process:

A) the dark bands crowd toward the right edge
B) the dark bands remain stationary
C) the dark bands crowd toward the left edge
D) the dark bands spread out, disappearing off the right edge
*E) the dark bands spread out, disappearing off the left edge

31. An air wedge is formed using two glass plates which are in contact along their left edge. When viewed by highly monochromatic light, there are exactly 4001 dark bands in the reflected light. The air is now evacuated (with the glass plates remaining rigidly fixed) and the number of dark bands decreases to 4000. The index of refraction of the air is:

A) 0.00025
B) 0.00050
*C) 1.00025

D) 1.00050
E) 1.00000 by definition

32. A glass (n = 1.6) lens is coated with a thin film (n = 1.3) to reduce reflection of certain incident light. If λ is the wavelength of the light in the film, the least film thickness is:

A) less than $\lambda/4$
*B) $\lambda/4$
C) $\lambda/2$

D) λ
E) more than λ

33. Two point sources, vibrating in phase, produce an interference pattern in a ripple tank. If the frequency is increased by 20%, the number of nodal lines:

*A) is increased by 20%
B) is increased by 40%
C) remains the same

D) is decreased by 20%
E) is decreased by 40%

34. In a Newton's ring pattern, as one approaches the pattern's edge, the dark rings:

*A) get closer and thinner
B) get closer but remain of equal thickness
C) are equally spaced but get thinner
D) get further apart but remain of equal thickness
E) get further apart and thinner

35. If two light waves are coherent:

A) their amplitudes are the same
B) their frequencies are the same
C) their wavelengths are the same
*D) their phase difference is constant
E) the difference in their frequencies is constant

36. To obtain an observable double-slit fringe pattern:

A) the light must be incident normally on the slits
B) the light must be monochromatic
C) the light must consist of plane waves
*D) the light must be coherent
E) the screen must be far away from the slits

1. Sound differs from light in that sound:

   A) is not subject to diffraction
   B) is a torsional wave rather than a longitudinal wave
   C) does not require energy for its origin
   *D) is a longitudinal wave rather than a transverse wave
   E) is always monochromatic

2. Radio waves are readily diffracted around buildings whereas light
   waves are negligibly diffracted around buildings. This is because
   radio waves:

   A) are plane polarized
   *B) have much longer wavelengths than light waves
   C) have much shorter wavelengths than light waves
   D) are nearly monochromatic (single frequency)
   E) are amplitude modulated (AM).

3. Diffraction plays an important role in which of the following
   phenomena?

   A) the sun appears as a disk rather than a point to the naked eye
   B) light is bent as it passes through a glass prism
   *C) a cheerleader yells through a megaphone
   D) a farsighted person uses eyeglasses of positive focal length
   E) a thin soap film exhibits colors when illuminated with white light

4. The rainbow seen after a rain shower is caused by:

   A) diffraction   D) polarization
   B) interference   E) absorption
   *C) refraction

5. When a highly coherent beam of light is directed against a very fine
   wire, the shadow formed behind it is not just that of a single wire
   but rather looks like the shadow of several parallel wires. The
   explanation of this involves:

   A) refraction   D) Doppler effect
   *B) diffraction   E) an optical illusion
   C) reflection

6. When the atmosphere is not quite clear, one may sometimes see colored circles concentric with the sun or the moon. These are generally not more than a few diameters of the sun or moon and invariably the innermost ring is blue. The explanation for this phenomena involves:

A) reflection
B) refraction
C) interference

*D) diffraction
E) Doppler effect

7. The shimmering or wavy lines that can often be seen near the ground on a hot day are due to:

A) Brownian movement
B) reflection
*C) refraction

D) diffraction
E) dispersion

8. A point source of monochromatic light is placed in front of a bowling ball and a screen is placed behind the ball. The light intensity pattern on the screen is best described as:

A) a dark disk
B) a dark disk with bright rings outside
C) a dark disk with a bright spot at its center
*D) a dark disk with a bright spot at its center and bright rings outside
E) a bright disk with bright rings outside

9. In the equation $\sin\theta = \lambda/a$ for single-slit diffraction, "θ" is:

*A) the angle to the first minimum
B) the angle to the second maximum
C) the phase angle between the extreme rays
D) $N\pi$ where N is an integer
E) $(N + 1/2)\pi$ where N is an integer

10. In the equation $\Phi = (2\pi a/\lambda)\sin\theta$ for single-slit diffraction, "Φ" is:

A) the angle to the first minimum
B) the angle to the second maximum
*C) the phase angle between the extreme rays
D) $N\pi$ where N is an integer
E) $(N + 1/2)\pi$ where N is an integer

11. No fringes are seen in a single-slit diffraction pattern if:

A) the screen is far away
B) the slit width is greater than a wavelength
*C) the slit width is less than a wavelength
D) the wavelength is less than the distance to the screen
E) none of the above (fringes are always seen)

12. A student wishes to produce a single-slit diffraction pattern in a ripple tank experiment. He considers the following parameters:
    I.   frequency
    II. wavelength
    III. water depth
    IV. slit width
    Which two of the above should be decreased to produce more bending?

A) I, III   *B) I, IV   C) II, III   D) II, IV   E) III, IV

13. A parallel beam of monochromatic light is incident on a slit of width 2 cm. The light passing through the slit falls on a screen 2 m away. As the slit width is decreased:

A) the width of the pattern on the screen continuously decreases
*B) the width of the pattern on the screen at first decreases but then increases
C) the width of the pattern on the screen increases and then decreases
D) the width of the pattern on the screen remains the same
E) the pattern on the screen changes color going from red to blue

14. Monochromatic plane waves of light are incident normally on a single slit. Which one of the five figures below correctly shows the diffraction pattern observed on a distant screen?

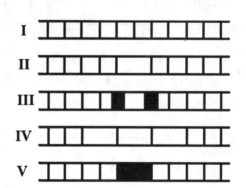

A) I.   *B) II.   C) III.   D) IV.   E) V.

15. The diagram shows a single slit with the direction to a point P on a distant screen shown. At P, the pattern has its second minimum (from its central maximum). If X and Y are the edges of the slit, what is the path length difference (PX) - (PY)?

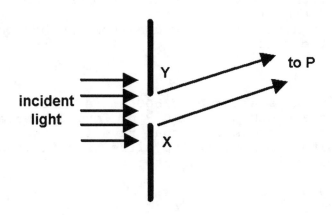

A) $\lambda/2$ B) λ C) $3\lambda/2$ *D) 2λ E) $5\lambda/2$

16. The diagram shows a single slit with the direction to a point P on a distant screen shown. At P, the pattern has its maximum nearest the central maximum. If X and Y are the edges of the slit, what is the path length difference (PX) - (PY)?

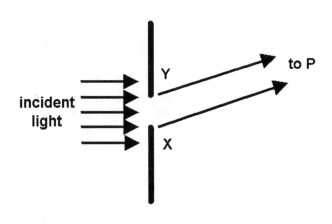

A) $\lambda/2$ B) λ *C) $3\lambda/2$ D) 2λ E) $5\lambda/2$

17. At the first minimum adjacent to the central maximum of a single-slit diffraction pattern the Huygens wavelet from the top of the slit is 180° out of phase with the wavelet from:

A) a point one-fourth of the slit width from the top
*B) the midpoint of the slit
C) a point one-fourth of the slit width from the bottom of the slit
D) the bottom of the slit
E) none of these

445

18. At the second minimum adjacent to the central maximum of a single-slit diffraction pattern the Huygens wavelet from the top of the slit is 180° out of phase with the wavelet from:

    A) a point one-fourth of the slit width from the top
    B) the midpoint of the slit
   *C) a point one-fourth of the slit width from the bottom of the slit
    D) the bottom of the slit
    E) none of these

19. A plane wave with a wavelength of 500 nm is incident normally on a single slit with a width of 5.0×10^{-6} m. Consider waves that reach a point on a far-away screen such that rays from the slit make an angle of 1.0° with the normal. The difference in phase for waves from the top and bottom of the slit is:

    A) 0   B) 0.55 rad   *C) 1.1 rad   D) 1.6 rad   E) 2.2 rad

20. In order to obtain a good single-slit diffraction pattern, the slit width could be:

    A) λ B) $\lambda/10$ *C) 10λ D) $10^4\lambda$ E) $\lambda/10^4$

21. Consider a single-slit diffraction pattern caused by a slit of width a. There is a maximum at $\sin\theta$ equal to:

    A) slightly more than $3\lambda/2a$ D) exactly $\lambda/2a$
   *B) slightly less than $3\lambda/2a$ E) very nearly $\lambda/2a$
    C) exactly $3\lambda/2a$

22. Consider a single-slit diffraction pattern caused by a slit of width a. There is a minimum at $\sin\theta$ equal to:

   *A) exactly λ/a D) exactly $\lambda/2a$
    B) slightly more than λ/a E) very nearly $\lambda/2a$
    C) slightly less than λ/a

23. In a single-slit diffraction pattern, the central maximum is about twice as wide as the other maxima. This is because:

    A) half the light is diffracted up and half is diffracted down
    B) the central maximum has both **E** and **B** fields present
    C) the small angle approximation applies only near the central maximum
    D) the screen is flat instead of spherical
   *E) none of the above

24. The intensity at a secondary maximum of a single-slit diffraction pattern is less than the intensity at the central maximum chiefly because:

*A) some Huygens wavelets sum to zero at the secondary maximum but not at the central maximum
 B) the secondary maximum is further from the slits than the central maximum and intensity decreases as the square of the distance
 C) the Huygens construction is not valid for a secondary maximum
 D) the amplitude of every Huygens wavelet is smaller when it travels to a secondary maximum than when it travels to the central maximum
 E) none of the above

25. Figure (i) shows a double-slit pattern obtained using monochromatic light. Consider the following five possible changes in conditions:
    1. decrease the frequency
    2. increase the frequency
    3. increase the width of each slit
    4. increase the separation between the slits
    5. decrease the separation between the slits
Which of the above would change Figure (i) into Figure (ii)?

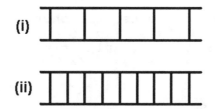

A) 3 only   D) 1 and 5 only
B) 5 only   *E) 2 and 4 only
C) 1 and 3 only

26. Two slits of width a and separation d are illuminated by a beam of light of wavelength λ. The separation of the interference fringes on a screen a distance D away is:

A) λa/D   B) λd/D   *C) λD/d   D) dD/λ   E) λD/a

27. Two slits in an opaque barrier each have a width of 0.020 mm and are separated by 0.050 mm. When coherent monochromatic light passes through the slits the number of interference maxima within the central diffraction maximum is:

A) 1   B) 2   *C) 3   D) 4   E) 5

28. When 450-nm light is incident normally on a certain double-slit system the number of interference maxima within the central diffraction maximum is 5. When 900-nm light is incident on the same slit system the number is:

A) 2   B) 3   *C) 5   D) 9   E) 10

29. In a double-slit diffraction experiment the number of interference fringes within the central diffraction maximum can be increased by:

A) increasing the wavelength   D) decreasing the slit separation
B) decreasing the wavelength   E) increasing the slit width
*C) increasing the slit separation

30. A diffraction-limited laser of length ℓ and aperture diameter d generates light of wavelength λ. If the beam is directed at the surface of the moon a distance D away, the radius of the illuminated area on the moon is approximately:

A) dD/ℓ B) dD/λ C) $D\lambda/\ell$ *D) $D\lambda/d$ E) $\ell\lambda/d$

31. Two stars that are close together are photographed through a telescope. The black and white film is equally sensitive to all colors. Which situation would result in the most clearly separated images of the stars?

A) small lens, red stars
B) small lens, blue stars
C) large lens, red stars
*D) large lens, blue stars
E) large lens, one star red and the other blue

32. The resolving power of a telescope can be increased by:

A) increasing the objective focal length and decreasing the eyepiece focal length
*B) increasing the lens diameters
C) decreasing the lens diameters
D) inserting a correction lens between objective and eyepiece
E) none of the above

33. In the equation d sinθ = mλ for the lines of a multiple-slit system m is:

A) the number of slits   *D) the order of the line
B) the slit width   E) the index of refraction
C) the slit separation

34. In the equation d sinθ = mλ for the lines of a multiple-slit system
    d is:

    A) the number of slits   D) the order of the line
    B) the slit width   E) the index of refraction
   *C) the slit separation

35. As more slits with the same spacing are added to a multiple-slit
    system the lines:

    A) spread further apart
    B) move closer together
    C) become wider
   *D) becomes narrower
    E) do not change in position or width

36. An N-slit system has slit separation d and slit width a. Plane waves
    with intensity I and wavelength λ are incident normally on it. The
    angular separation of the lines depends only on:

    A) a and N   B) a and λ   C) N and λ   *D) d and λ   E) I and N

37. 600-nm light is incident on a grating with a ruling separation of
    1.7×10^{-6} m. The first order line occurs at a diffraction angle of:

    A) 0   B) 10°   *C) 21°   D) 42°   E) 45°

38. Monochromatic light is normally incident on a grating that is 1 cm
    wide and has 10,000 slits. The first order line is deviated at a 30°
    angle. What is the wavelength, in nm, of the incident light?

    A) 300   B) 400   *C) 500   D) 600   E) 1000

39. A light spectrum is formed on a screen using a diffraction grating.
    The entire apparatus (source, grating and screen) is now immersed in
    a liquid of index 1.33. As a result, the pattern on the screen:

    A) remains the same
    B) spreads out
   *C) crowds together
    D) becomes reversed, with the previously blue end becoming red
    E) disappears because the index isn't an integer

40. The spacing between adjacent slits on a diffraction grating is 3λ.
    The deviation θ of the first order diffracted beam is given by:

    A) $\sin(θ/2) = 1/3$ D) $\tan(θ/2) = 1/3$
    B) $\sin(θ/3) = 2/3$ E) $\tan(θ) = 2/3$
   *C) $\sin(θ) = 1/3$

41. When light of a certain wavelength is incident normally on a certain diffraction grating the line of order 1 is at a diffraction angle of 25°. The diffraction angle for the second order line is:

A) 25°   B) 42°   C) 50°   *D) 58°   E) 75°

42. A diffraction grating of width W produces a deviation θ in second order for light of wavelength λ. The total number N of slits in the grating is given by:

A) 2Wλ/sinθ   *D) (W/2λ)sinθ
B) (W/λ)sinθ   E) 2λ/sinθ
C) λW/2sinθ

43. Light of wavelength λ is normally incident on a diffraction grating G. On the screen S, the central line is at P and the first order line is at Q as shown. The distance between adjacent slits in the grating is:

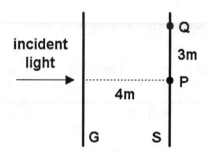

A) 3λ/5   B) 3λ/4   C) 4λ/5   D) 5λ/4   *E) 5λ/3

44. If 550-nm light is incident normally on a grating with a ruling separation of 1.75×10^{-6} m the number of lines produced is:

A) 1   B) 3   C) 4   D) 6   *E) 7

45. A mixture of 450-nm and 900-nm light is incident on a multiple-slit system. Which of the following is true?

*A) Even order lines of the 450-nm light coincide with lines of the 900-nm light
B) Even order lines of the 900-nm light coincide with lines of the 450-nm light
C) Odd order lines of the 450-nm light coincide with lines of the 900-nm light
D) None of the lines of the 450-nm light coincide with lines of the 900-nm light
E) All of the lines of the 450-nm light coincide with lines of the 900-nm light

450

46. A beam of white light (from 400 nm for violet to 700 nm for red) is normally incident on a diffraction grating. It produces two orders on a distant screen. Which diagram below (R = red, V = violet) correctly shows the pattern on the screen?

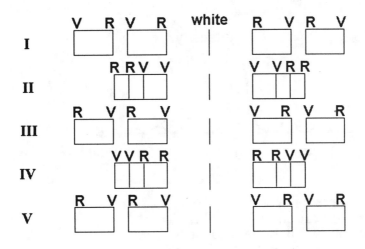

A) I.   B) II.   *C) III.   D) IV.   E) V.

47. If white light is incident on a multiple-slit system:

*A) the first order lines for all visible wavelengths occur at smaller diffraction angles than any of the second order lines
B) some first order line overlap the second order lines if the ruling separation is small but do not if it is large
C) some first order lines overlap second order lines if the ruling separation is large but do not if it is small
D) some first order lines overlap second order lines no matter what the ruling separation
E) first and second order lines have the same range of diffraction angles

48. Light of wavelength is normally incident on some plane optical
    device. The intensity pattern shown is observed on a distant screen
    (θ is the angle measured to the normal of the device). The device
    could be:

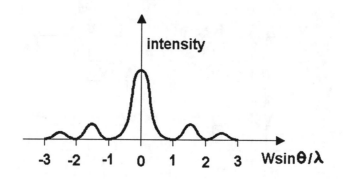

*A) a single slit of width W
 B) a single slit of width 2W
 C) two narrow slits with separation W
 D) two narrow slits with separation 2W
 E) a diffraction grating with slit separation W

49. A person with her eye relaxed looks through a diffraction grating at
    a distant monochromatic point source of light. The slits of the
    grating are vertical. She sees:

 A) one point of light
 B) a hazy horizontal strip of light of the same color as the source
 C) a hazy strip of light varying from violet to red
*D) a sequence of horizontal points of light
 E) a sequence of closely spaced vertical lines

50. Monochromatic light is normally incident on a diffraction grating.
    The m th order line is at an angle of diffraction θ and has width w.
    A wide single slit is now placed in front of the grating and its
    width is then slowly reduced. As a result:

 A) both θ and w increase
 B) both θ and w decrease
*C) θ remains the same and w increases
 D) θ remains the same and w decreases
 E) θ decreases and w increases

452

51. At a diffraction line phasors associated with waves from the slits of a multiple-slit barrier:

*A) are aligned
B) form a closed polygon
C) form a polygon with several sides missing
D) are parallel but adjacent phasors point in opposite directions
E) form the arc of a circle

52. At a minimum adjacent to the central line waves from adjacent slits in an 8-slit barrier differ in phase by:

A) 0   B) $\pi/8$ *C) $\pi/4$ D) π E) 2π

53. For a certain multiple-slit barrier the slit separation is 4 times the slit width. For this system:

A) the orders of the lines that appear are all multiples of 4
B) the orders of lines that appear are all multiples of 2
*C) the orders of the missing lines are all multiples of 4
D) the orders of the missing lines are all multiples of 2
E) none of the above are true

54. The dispersion D of a grating can have units:

A) cm
*B) degree/nm
C) nm/cm

D) radian
E) none of these

55. The resolving power R of a grating can have units:

A) cm
B) degree/nm
C) watt

*D) nm/cm
E) watt/nm

56. The dispersion of a diffraction grating indicates:

A) the resolution of the grating
*B) the separation of lines of the same order
C) the number of rulings in the grating
D) the width of the lines
E) the separation of lines of different order for the same wavelength

57. The resolving power of a diffraction grating is defined by $R = \lambda/\Delta\lambda$. Here λ and $\lambda+\Delta\lambda$ are:

  A) any two wavelengths
  B) any two wavelengths that are nearly the same
  C) two wavelengths for which lines of the same order are separated by π radians
  D) two wavelengths for which lines of the same order are separated by 2π radians
  *E) two wavelengths for which lines of the same order are separated by half the width of a maximum

58. A light beam incident on a diffraction grating consists of waves with two different wavelengths. The separation of the two first order lines is great if:

  *A) the dispersion is great
  B) the resolution is great
  C) the dispersion is small
  D) the resolution is small
  E) none of the above (line separation does not depend on either dispersion or resolution)

59. To obtain greater dispersion by a multiple-slit system:

  A) the slit width should be increased
  B) the slit width should be decreased
  C) the slit separation should be increased
  *D) the slit separation should be decreased
  E) more slits with the same width and separation should be added to the system

60. Two nearly equal wavelengths of light are incident on an N slit grating. The two wavelengths are not resolvable. When N is increased they become resolvable. This is because:

  A) more light gets through the grating
  B) the lines get more intense
  C) the entire pattern spreads out
  D) there are more orders present
  *E) the lines narrow

61. A diffraction grating just resolves the wavelengths 400.0 nm and 400.1 nm in first order. The number of slits in the grating is:

  A) 400
  B) 1000
  C) 2500
  *D) 4000
  E) not enough information is given

62. The "D line" in the spectrum of sodium is a "doublet" with wavelengths 589.0 nm and 589.6 nm. What is the minimum number of slits in a grating to just resolve this doublet in second order?

A) 982   *B) 491   C) 245   D) 123   E) 61

63. X rays are:

*A) electromagnetic waves
 B) negatively charged ions
 C) rapidly moving electrons

D) rapidly moving protons
E) rapidly moving neutrons

64. In Bragg's law for x-ray diffraction, $2d \sin\theta = m\lambda$, where θ is the angle between the incident beam and:

*A) a reflecting plane of atoms
 B) the normal to a reflecting plane of atoms
 C) the scattered beam
 D) the normal to the scattered beam
 E) the refracted beam

65. In Bragg's law for x-ray diffraction, $2d \sin\theta = m\lambda$, the quantity "d" is:

 A) the height of a unit cell
 B) the smallest interatomic distance
 C) the distance from detector to sample
*D) the distance between planes of atoms
 E) the usual calculus symbol for a differential

66. Which of the following is true for Bragg diffraction but not for diffraction from a grating?

 A) two different wavelengths may be used
 B) for a given wavelength, a maximum may exist in several directions
 C) long waves are deviated more than short ones
 D) there is only one grating spacing
*E) maxima occur only for particular angles of incidence

67. The largest x-ray wavelength that could be diffracted by rock salt crystal planes with a separation of 0.282 nm is:

*A) 0.564 nm
 B) 0.282 nm
 C) 0.0282 nm

D) 0.141 nm
E) 0.831 nm

68. A beam of x-rays of wavelength 0.2 Å is diffracted by a set of
    planes in a crystal whose separation is 3.1×10^{-8} cm. The smallest
    angle between the beam and the crystal planes for which a reflection
    occurs is:

    A) 0.56 rad
    B) 0.32 rad
    *C) 0.032 rad

    D) 0.064 rad
    E) no such angle exists

69. An x-ray beam of wavelength 3×10^{-11} m is incident on a calcite
    crystal of lattice spacing 0.3 nm. The smallest angle between
    crystal planes and the x-ray beam which will result in constructive
    interference is:

    *A) 2°52'
    B) 5°44'
    C) 11°38'

    D) 23°16'
    E) none of these

70. A beam of x rays of wavelength 1 Å is found to diffract in second
    order from the face of a LiF crystal at a Bragg angle of 30°. The
    distance between adjacent crystal planes, in nm, is about:

    A) 0.15   *B) 0.20   C) 0.25   D) 0.30   E) 0.40

1. A basic postulate of Einstein's theory of relativity is:

A) moving clocks run more slowly than when they are at rest
B) moving rods are shorter than when they are at rest
C) light has both wave and particle properties
*D) the laws of physics must be the same for observers moving with
   uniform velocity relative to each other
E) everything is relative

2. A consequence of Einstein's theory of relativity is:

*A) moving clocks run more slowly than when they are at rest
B) moving rods are longer than when they are at rest
C) light has both wave and particle properties
D) the laws of physics must appear the same to all observers moving
   with uniform velocity relative to each other
E) everything is relative

3. A consequence of Einstein's theory of relativity is:

A) moving clocks run faster than when they are at rest
*B) moving rods are shorter than when they are at rest
C) light has both wave and particle properties
D) the laws of physics must appear the same to all observers moving
   with uniform velocity relative to each other
E) everything is relative

4. According to the theory of relativity:

A) moving clocks run fast
B) energy is not conserved in high speed collisions
C) the speed of light must be measured relative to the ether
D) momentum is not conserved in high speed collisions
*E) none of the above

5. Two events occur simultaneously at separated points on the x axis of
   reference frame S. According to an observer moving in the positive x
   direction:

A) the event with the greater x coordinate occurs first
B) the event with the greater x coordinate occurs last
*C) either event might occur first, depending on spatial separation of
   the events and the observer's speed
D) the events are simultaneous
E) none of the above

6. Two events occur simultaneously at separated points on the y axis of reference frame S. According to an observer moving in the positive x direction:

A) the event with the greater y coordinate occurs first
B) the event with the greater y coordinate occurs last
C) either event might occur first, depending on the observer's speed
*D) the events are simultaneous
E) none of the above

7. A train traveling very fast (v = 0.6c) has an engineer (E) at the front, a guard (G) at the rear and an observer (S') exactly half way between them. Both E and G are equipped with yellow signaling lamps. The train passes a station, closely observed by the station master (S). Both E and G use their lamps to send signals. According to both S and S' these signals arrive simultaneously at the instant S' is passing S. According to S':

A) E and G sent their signals simultaneously from different distances
B) G sent his signal before E and from further away
C) G sent his signal before E but was the same distance away
D) E sent his signal before G and from further away
*E) none of the above

8. The proper time between two events is measured by clocks at rest in a reference frame in which the two events:

A) occur at the same time
*B) occur at the same coordinates
C) are separated by the distance a light signal can travel during the time interval
D) occur in Boston
E) satisfy none of the above

9. The spaceship U.S.S. Enterprise, traveling through the galaxy, sends out a smaller explorer craft that travels to a nearby planet and signals its findings back. The proper time for the trip to the planet is measured by clocks:

A) on board the Enterprise
*B) on board the explorer craft
C) on earth
D) at the center of the galaxy
E) none of the above

10. Two events occur on the x axis separated in time by Δt and in space by Δx. A reference frame, traveling at less than the speed of light, in which the two events occur at the same time:

A) exists no matter what the values of Δx and Δt
B) exists only if $\Delta x/\Delta t < c$
*C) exists only if $\Delta x/\Delta t > c$
D) exists only if $\Delta x/\Delta t = c$
E) does not exist under any condition

11. Two events occur on the x axis separated in time by Δt and in space by Δx. A reference frame, traveling at less than the speed of light, in which the two events occur at the same coordinate:

 A) exists no matter what the values of Δx and Δt
 *B) exists only if Δx/Δt < c
 C) exists only if Δx/Δt > c
 D) exists only if Δx/Δt = c
 E) does not exist under any condition

12. A millionairess was told in 1992 that she had exactly 15 years to live. However, if she travels away from the earth at 0.8 c and then returns at the same speed, the last New Year the doctors expect her to celebrate is:

 A) 2001   B) 2003   C) 2007   D) 2010   *E) 2017

13. Two events occur 100 m apart with an intervening time interval of 0.60 μs. The speed of a reference frame in which they occur at the same coordinate is:

 A) 0   B) 0.25c   *C) 0.56c   D) 1.1c   E) 1.8c

14. Two independent events occur 100 m apart with an intervening time interval of 0.42 μs. The proper time in μs between the events is:

 A) 0   B) 0.16   *C) 0.26   D) 0.42   E) 0.69

15. Two events occur 100 m apart with an intervening time interval of 0.30 μs. The speed of a clock that measures the proper time between the events is:

 A) 0   B) 0.45c   C) 0.56c   *D) 0.90c   E) 1.8c

16. A rocket traveling with constant velocity makes a 3.5×10^{14} m trip in 1 year. The proper time in years between events which mark the beginning and end of the trip is:

 A) 0.21   *B) 0.46   C) 1.0   D) 2.2   E) 4.7

17. An observer notices that a moving clock runs slow by a factor of exactly 10. The speed of the clock is:

 A) 0.100c   B) 0.0100c   C) 0.990c   D) 0.900c   *E) 0.995 c

18. A meson when at rest decays 2 μs after it is created. If moving in the laboratory at 0.99c, its lifetime according to laboratory clocks would be:

A) the same
B) 0.28 s
*C) 14 μs

D) 4.6 s
E) none of these

19. Pi mesons at rest have a half-life of T. If a beam of pi mesons is traveling at a speed of $v = \beta c$, the distance in which the intensity of the beam is halved is:

*A) $c\beta T(1 - \beta^2)^{-(1/2)}$
B) $c\beta T[(1 + \beta)/(1 - \beta)]^{(1/2)}$
C) $\beta v T$

D) $(1 - \beta^2)^{(1/2)}$
E) none of the above

20. A meson moving through a laboratory of length x at a speed v decays after a lifetime T as measured by an observer at rest in the laboratory. If the meson were at rest in the laboratory its lifetime would be:

A) $T(1 - v/c)$
B) $T(1 - v/c)^{-1}$
C) $T(1 - v^2/c^2)^{-(1/2)}$

*D) $T(1 - v^2/c^2)^{(1/2)}$
E) $(T - vx/c^2)(1 - v^2/c^2)^{-(1/2)}$

21. A measurement of the length of an object that is moving relative to the laboratory consists of noting the coordinates of the front and back:

A) at different times according to clocks at rest in the laboratory
B) at the same time according to clocks that move with the object
*C) at the same time according to clocks at rest in the laboratory
D) at the same time according to clocks at rest with respect to the fixed stars
E) none of the above

22. A meter stick moves at 0.95c in the direction of its length through a laboratory. According to measurements taken in the laboratory, its length is:

A) 0   B) 0.098 m   *C) 0.31 m   D) 3.2 m   E) 1.0 m

23. A meter stick moves sideways at 0.95c. According to measurements taken in the laboratory, its length is:

A) 0   B) 0.098 m   C) 0.31 m   D) 3.2 m   *E) 1.0 m

24. A rocket ship of rest length 100 m is moving at speed 0.8c past a timing device which records the time interval between the passage of the front and back ends of the ship. This time interval is:

A) 0.20 μs   *B) 0.25 μs   C) 0.33 μs   D) 0.52 μs   E) 0.69 μs

25. The length of a meter stick moving at 0.95c in the direction of its length is measured by simultaneously marking its ends on a stationary axis. As measured by clocks moving with the stick, the time interval between the making of the back mark and the making of the front mark is:

A) 0
B) 3.1×10^{-10} s
C) 1.0×10^{-9} s

*D) 3.2×10^{-9} s
E) 1.0×10^{-8} s

26. A certain automobile is 18 ft long if at rest. If it is measured to be 4/5 as long, its speed is:

A) 0.1c   B) 0.3c   *C) 0.6c   D) 0.8c   E) > 0.95c

27. As a rocket ship moves by at 0.95c a mark is made on a stationary axis at the front end of the rocket and 9×10^{-8} s later a mark is made on the axis at the back end. The marks are found to be 100 m apart. The rest length of the rocket is:

A) 31 m   B) 78 m   C) 100 m   *D) 240 m   E) 320 m

28. A clock is moving along the x axis at 0.6c. It reads zero as it passes the origin (x = 0). When it passes the x = 180 m mark on the x axis the clock reads:

A) 0.60 μs   *B) 0.80 μs   C) 1.00 μs   D) 1.25 μs   E) 1.67 μs

29. An event occurs at x = 500 m, t = 0.90 μs in one frame of reference. Another frame is moving at 0.90c in the positive x direction. The origins coincide at t = 0 and clocks in the second frame are zeroed when the origins coincide. The coordinate and time of the event in the second frame is:

A) 500 m, 0.90 μs
B) 1700 m, 5.5 μs
C) 740 m, 2.4 μs

D) 260 m, −0.60 μs
*E) 590 m, −1.4 μs

30. An event occurs at x = 500 m, t = 0.90 µs in one frame of reference.
    Another frame is moving at 0.90c in the negative x direction. The
    origins coincide at t = 0 and clocks in the second frame are zeroed
    when the origins coincide. The coordinate and time of the event in
    the second frame is:

   A) 500 m, 0.90 µs   D) 260 m, −0.60 µs
*B) 1700 m, 5.5 µs   E) 590 m, −1.4 µs
   C) 740 m, 2.4 µs

31. Two flashes of light occur simultaneously at t = 0 in reference
    frame S, one at x = 0 and the other at x = 600 m. They are observed
    in reference frame S′, which is moving at 0.95c in the positive x
    direction. The origins of the two frames coincide at t = 0 and the
    clocks of S′ are zeroed when the origins coincide. In S′ the
    coordinate where the leading edges of the two light flashes meet and
    the time when they meet are:

   A) 300 m, 1.0 µs   *D) 48 m, 0.16 µs
   B) 15 m, 0.050 µs   E) 1900 m, 0.16 µs
   C) 585 m, 1.95 µs

32. Frame S′ moves in the positive x direction at 0.6c with respect to
    frame S. A particle moves in the positive x direction at 0.4c as
    measured by an observer in S′. The speed of the particle as measured
    by an observer in S is:

   A) c/5   B) 5c/19   C) 8c/25   *D) 25c/31   E) c

33. Quasar Q1 is moving away from us at a speed of 0.8c. Quasar Q2 is
    moving away from us in the opposite direction at a speed of 0.5c.
    The speed of Q1 as measured by an observer on Q2 is:

   A) 0.21c   B) 0.5c   *C) 0.93c   D) 1.3c   E) 2.17c

34. Observer A measures the velocity of a rocket as **v** and a comet as **u**.
    Here **u** and **v** are parallel and in the direction of the observer's
    positive x axis. The speed of the comet as measured by an observer
    on the rocket is:

*A) $(u-v)/(1-uv/c^2)$ D) $(u-v)/(1+uv/c^2)$
   B) $(u-v)/(1-v^2/c^2)$ E) $(u+v)/(1-uv/c^2)$
   C) $(u-v)/(1-v^2/c^2)(1/2)$

35. Two electrons move in opposite directions at 0.70c as measured in
    the laboratory. The speed of one electron as measured from the other
    is:

   A) 0.35c   B) 0.70c   *C) 0.94c   D) 1.00c   E) 1.40c

36. Light from some stars shows an apparent change in frequency because of:

A) interference
B) refraction by layers of air
C) diffraction
D) reflection
*E) relative motion

37. Light from a stationary spaceship is observed, then the spaceship moves directly away from the observer at high speed. As a result, the light seen by the observer:

A) has a higher frequency and a longer wavelength
B) has lower frequency and a shorter wavelength
C) has a higher frequency and a shorter wavelength
*D) has a lower frequency and a longer wavelength
E) has the same frequency and wavelength

38. A train traveling very fast (v = 0.6c) has an engineer (E) at the front, a guard (G) at the rear and an passenger (S') exactly half way between them. Both E and G are equipped with yellow signaling lamps. The train passes a station, closely observed by the station master (S). Both E an G use their lamps to send signals. According to both S and S' these signals arrive simultaneously at the instant S' is passing S. According to S, the signal from E will look _____ and that from G will look _____ :

*A) red, blue
B) yellow, yellow
C) blue, red
D) blue, blue
E) red, red

39. A console lamp in the cabin of a spaceship appears green when the ship and observer are both at rest. When the ship is moving at 0.90c away from the earth, passengers on board see:

A) a dark lamp (the frequency is too high to be seen)
B) a dark lamp (the frequency is too low to be seen)
C) a red lamp
D) a violet lamp
*E) a green lamp

40. A spectral line of a certain quasar is observed to be "red shifted" from a wavelength of 500 nm to a wavelength of 1500 nm. Interpreting this as a Doppler effect, the speed of recession of this quasar is:

A) c/3   B) c/2   C) $c/\sqrt{2}$ *D) 0.8c   E) c

463

41. A source at rest emits light of wavelength 500 nm. When it is moving at 0.90c toward an observer, the observer detects light of wavelength:

    A) 26 nm   *B) 115 nm   C) 500 nm   D) 2200 nm   E) 9500 nm

42. A source at rest emits light of wavelength 500 nm. When it is moving at 0.90c away from an observer, the observer detects light of wavelength:

    A) 26 nm   B) 115 nm   C) 500 nm   *D) 2200 nm   E) 9500 nm

43. Visible light, with a frequency of 6.0×10^{14} Hz, is reflected from a spaceship moving directly away at a speed of 0.90c. The frequency of the reflected waves observed at the source is:

    *A) 3.0×10^{13} Hz   D) 2.6×10^{15} Hz
    B) 1.4×10^{14} Hz   E) 1.1×10^{16} Hz
    C) 6.0×10^{14} Hz

44. How fast should you move away from a 6.0×10^{14} Hz light source to observe waves with a frequency of 4.0×10^{14} Hz?

    A) 0.20c   *B) 0.39c   C) 0.45c   D) 0.51c   E) 0.76c

45. A particle with rest mass m moves with speed 0.6c. Its kinetic energy is:

    A) $0.18mc^2$ B) $0.22mc^2$ *C) $0.25mc^2$ D) mc^2 E) $1.25mc^2$

46. An electron is moving at 0.6c. If we calculate its kinetic energy using $(1/2)mv^2$, we get a result which is:

    A) just right   D) about 1% too low
    B) just half enough   *E) about 25% too low
    C) twice the correct value

47. The velocity of an electron is changed from c/2 in the -x direction to c/2 in the +x direction. As a result, its kinetic energy changes by:

    A) mc^2 B) $0.5mc^2$ C) $\sqrt{2}mc^2$ D) $2mc^2$ *E) zero

464

48. The work that must be done to increase the speed of an electron ($m = 9.11 \times 10^{-31}$ kg) from 0.90c to 0.95c is:

A) 2.6×10^{-13} J
B) 8.2×10^{-13} J
C) 3.2×10^{-13} J

*D) 7.4×10^{-14} J
E) 3.8×10^{-15} J

49. An electron ($m = 9.11 \times 10^{-31}$ kg) has a speed of 0.95c. Its kinetic energy is:

A) 8.2×10^{-14} J
*B) 1.8×10^{-13} J
C) 2.0×10^{-13} J

D) 2.2×10^{-13} J
E) 2.6×10^{-13} J

50. An electron ($m = 9.11 \times 10^{-31}$ kg) has a speed of 0.95c. Its momentum is:

A) 2.6×10^{-22} kg $\cdot$m/s
B) 2.9×10^{-22} kg $\cdot$m/s
C) 6.0×10^{-22} kg $\cdot$m/s

*D) 8.3×10^{-22} kg $\cdot$m/s
E) 8.8×10^{-22} kg $\cdot$m/s

51. According to the theory of relativity:

*A) all forms of energy have mass-like properties
B) moving particles lose mass
C) momentum is not conserved in high speed collisions
D) a rod moving rapidly sideways is shorter along its length
E) a rod moving rapidly sideways is longer along its length

52. The mass of a particle is m. In order for its total energy to be twice its rest energy, its momentum must be:

A) mc/2   B) $mc/\sqrt{2}$ C) mc   *D) $\sqrt{3}mc$ E) 2mc

53. If the kinetic energy of a particle is equal to its rest energy then its speed must be:

A) 0.25c
B) 0.50c
*C) 0.87c
D) c
E) unknown unless its mass is given

54. If the mass of a particle is zero its speed must be:

*A) c
B) infinite
C) 0

D) any speed less than c
E) any speed greater than c

55. A particle with zero mass and energy E carries momentum:

$$A) Ec \quad B) Ec^2 \quad C) \sqrt{Ec} \quad D) E/c \quad E) E/c^2$$

Ans. d

56. According to relativity theory a particle of mass m with a momentum of 2mc has a speed of:

A) 2c   B) 4c   C) c   D) c/2   *E) 0.89c

57. If the kinetic energy of a free particle is much greater than its rest energy then its kinetic energy is proportional to:

*A) the magnitude of its momentum
 B) the square of the magnitude of its momentum
 C) the square root of the magnitude of its momentum
 D) the reciprocal of the magnitude of its momentum
 E) none of the above

58. If the kinetic energy of a free particle is much less than its rest energy then its kinetic energy is proportional to:

 A) the magnitude of its momentum
*B) the square of the magnitude of its momentum
 C) the square root of the magnitude of its momentum
 D) the reciprocal of the magnitude of its momentum
 E) none of the above

59. The magnitude of the momentum of a particle can never exceed:

 A) mc, where m is its mass
 B) E/c, where E is its energy
 C) K/c, where K is its kinetic energy
 D) none of the above, but there is an upper limit
*E) none of the above; there is no upper limit

60. An electron (m = 9.11×10^{-31} kg) has a momentum of 4.0×10^{-13} kg ·m/s. Its kinetic energy is:

*A) 6.3×10^{-14} J   D) 1.5×10^{-13} J
 B) 8.2×10^{-14} J   E) 2.7×10^{-13} J
 C) 1.2×10^{-13} J

61. A certain particle has a kinetic energy of 3.2×10^{-10} J and a momentum of 1.7×10^{-18} kg ·m/s. Its mass is:

   A) 9.11×10^{-31} kg
   *B) 2.7×10^{-27} kg
   C) 4.5×10^{-27} kg

   D) 6.3×10^{-27} kg
   E) 8.6×10^{-27} kg

62. An electron ($m = 9.11 \times 10^{-31}$ kg, $q = 1.60 \times 10^{-19}$ C) travels at 0.95c around a circular orbit perpendicular to a uniform 1.8-T magnetic field. The radius of its orbit is:

   A) 0.28 mm   B) 0.90 mm   C) 1.1 mm   *D) 2.9 mm   E) 4.7 mm

63. An electron ($m = 9.11 \times 10^{-31}$ kg, $q = 1.60 \times 10^{-19}$ C) travels around a 1.7-mm radius circular orbit perpendicular to a 2.8-T magnetic field. Its speed is:

   A) 0.16 c   B) 0.36 c   *C) 0.94c   D) c   E) 2.8c

1. The units of the Planck constant h are those of:

A) energy

B) power

C) momentum

*D) angular momentum

E) frequency

2. Typical units for the spectral radiancy R(λ) are:

*A) $W/m^2 \cdot nm$ B) J/K C) $W/cm \cdot K$ D) W/K^4 E) $W/cm^3 \cdot K$

3. The area under the spectral radiancy curve has the significance of:

A) power

B) energy

*C) power/area

D) temperature

E) energy/temperature

4. The intensity of radiation in a cavity is given by the integral of the spectral radiancy over:

A) temperature

*B) wavelength

C) the cavity volume

D) frequency

E) time

5. The Wien displacement law relates:

A) the momentum of a photon and its position

B) the momentum of a photon and its energy

C) the wavelength of an electromagnetic wave and the momentum of a photon

*D) the temperature and the wavelength at the peak of a spectral radiancy function for a cavity

E) the temperature and the size of a cavity

6. When the temperature increases the wavelength corresponding to the maximum spectral radiancy:

A) increases at all temperatures

*B) decreases at all temperatures

C) increases at high temperature and decreases at low temperatures

D) increases at low temperatures and decreases at high temperatures

E) remains the same

7. At 500 K the peak in the spectral radiancy is at a wavelength of 5.8 μm. At 1000 K it is at a wavelength of:

A) 23 μm   B) 12 μm   C) 8.2 μm   D) 5.8 μm   *E) 2.9 μm

8. A feature of the spectral radiancy of a cavity that is NOT predicted by the Rayleigh-Jeans classical expression is:

A) its shape at long wavelengths
B) its slope at long wavelengths
C) the temperature dependence of the long wavelength limit
D) the dependence of the long wavelength limit on the cavity size
*E) the wavelength corresponding to the greatest radiancy

9. The basic quantization postulated by Planck in his theory of cavity radiation concerns:

A) the possible vibration frequencies of an oscillating particle
B) the possible mass of an oscillating particle
*C) the possible energies of a particle oscillating with a given frequency
D) the spatial distribution of energy radiated by an oscillating charged particle
E) the wavelength of the radiation produced by an oscillating charged particle

10. The quantization of energy, $E = nh\nu$, for mechanical oscillators was first proposed by:

A) Einstein   B) Newton   C) Bohr   *D) Planck   E) Maxwell

11. The quantization of energy for mechanical oscillators was first used to explain:

*A) spectral radiancy curves
B) frequencies of atomic oscillators
C) the photoelectric effect
D) line spectra
E) the Compton effect

12. The quantization of energy, $E = nh\nu$, is not important for an ordinary pendulum because:

A) the formula applies only to mass-spring oscillators
*B) the allowed energy levels are too closely spaced
C) the allowed energy levels are too widely spaced
D) the formula applies only to atoms
E) the value of h for a pendulum is too large

13. The frequency of light beam A is twice that of light beam B. The ratio E_A/E_B of photon energies is:

A) 1/2   B) 1/4   C) 1   *D) 2   E) 4

14. A photon in light beam A has twice the energy of one in light beam B. The ratio λ_A/λ_B of the wavelengths is:

*A) 1/2   B) 1/4   C) 1   D) 2   E) 4

15. A photon in light beam A has twice the energy of a photon in light beam B. The ratio p_A/p_B of their momenta is:

A) 1/2   B) 1/4   C) 1   *D) 2   E) 4

16. The intensity of a light beam with a wavelength of 500 nm is 2000 W/m^2. The photon flux (in number/m2 ·s) is about:

A) 5×10^{17} B) 5×10^{19} *C) 5×10^{21} D) 5×10^{23} E) 5×10^{25}

17. The intensity of a light beam with a wavelength of 500 nm is 2000 W/m^2. The concentration of photons in the beam is:

*A) 1.7×10^{13} photons/m^3
B) 5.0×10^{15} photons/m^3
C) 5.0×10^{21} photons/m^3
D) 1.7×10^{22} photons/m^3
E) not determined by the given data

18. Light beams A and B have the same intensity but the wavelength associated with beam A is longer than that associated with beam B. The photon flux (number crossing a unit area per unit time) is:

*A) greater for A than for B
B) greater for B than for A
C) the same for A and B
D) greater for A than for B only if both have short wavelengths
E) greater for B than for A only if both have short wavelengths

19. In a photoelectric effect experiment the stopping potential is:

A) the energy required to remove an electron from the sample
B) the kinetic energy of the most energetic electron ejected
C) the potential energy of the most energetic electron ejected
D) the photon energy
*E) the electric potential that causes the electron current to vanish

20. In a photoelectric effect experiment at a frequency above cut off, the stopping potential is proportional to:

  A) the energy of the least energetic electron before it is ejected
  B) the energy of the least energetic electron after it is ejected
  C) the energy of the most energetic electron before it is ejected
 *D) the energy of the most energetic electron after it is ejected
  E) the electron potential energy at the surface of the sample

21. In a photoelectric effect experiment at a frequency above cut off, the number of electrons ejected is proportional to:

  A) their kinetic energy
  B) their potential energy
  C) the work function
  D) the frequency of the incident light
 *E) the number of photons that hit the sample

22. In a photoelectric effect experiment no electrons are ejected if the frequency of the incident light is less than A/h, where h is the Planck constant and A is:

  A) the maximum energy needed to eject the least energetic electron
  B) the minimum energy needed to eject the least energetic electron
  C) the maximum energy needed to eject the most energetic electron
 *D) the minimum energy needed to eject the most energetic electron
  E) the intensity of the incident light

23. The work function for a certain sample is 2.3 eV. The stopping potential for electrons ejected from the sample by 7.0×10^{14}-Hz electromagnetic radiation is:

  A) 0   *B) 0.6 V   C) 2.3 V   D) 2.9 V   E) 5.2 V

24. The stopping potential for electrons ejected by 6.8×10^{14}-Hz electromagnetic radiation incident on a certain sample is 1.8 V. The kinetic energy of the most energetic electrons ejected and the work function of the sample, respectively, are:

  A) 1.8 eV, 2.8 eV   D) 2.8 eV, 1.0 eV
 *B) 1.8 eV, 1.0 eV   E) 1.0 eV, 4.6 eV
  C) 1.8 eV, 4.6 eV

25. In Compton scattering from stationary particles the maximum change in wavelength can be made smaller by using:

  A) higher frequency radiation   D) less massive particles
  B) lower frequency radiation   E) particles with greater charge
 *C) more massive particles

471

26. Of the following, Compton scattering from electrons is most easily observed for:

A) microwaves
B) infrared light
C) visible light
D) ultraviolet light
*E) x rays

27. In Compton scattering from stationary electrons the largest change in wavelength occurs when the photon is scattered through:

A) 0°   B) 45°   C) 90°   *D) 180°   E) 270°

28. In Compton scattering from stationary electrons the frequency of the emitted light is independent of:

A) the frequency of the incident light
B) the speed of the electron
C) the scattering angle
D) the electron recoil energy
*E) none of the above

29. In Compton scattering from stationary electrons the largest change in wavelength that can occur is:

A) 2.43×10^{-15} m
*B) 2.43×10^{-12} m
C) 2.43×10^{-9} m
D) dependent on the frequency of the incident light
E) dependent on the work function

30. Electromagnetic radiation with a wavelength of 5.7×10^{-12} m is incident on stationary electrons. The radiation that has been scattered through 50° has a wavelength of:

A) 2.43×10^{-12} m
B) 4.83×10^{-12} m
C) 5.13×10^{-12} m
D) 6.27×10^{-12} m
*E) 6.57×10^{-12} m

31. Electromagnetic radiation with a wavelength of 3.5×10^{-12} m is scattered from stationary electrons and photons that have been scattered through 50° are detected. An electron from which one of these photons was scattered receives an energy of:

A) 0
*B) 1.1×10^{-14} J
C) 1.9×10^{-14} J
D) 2.3×10^{-14} J
E) 1.3×10^{-13} J

472

32. Electromagnetic radiation with a wavelength of 3.5×10^{-12} m is scattered from stationary electrons and photons that have been scattered through 50° are detected. After a scattering event the magnitude of the electron's momentum is:

A) 0
*B) 1.5×10^{-22} kg ·m/s
C) 2.0×10^{-22} kg ·m/s
D) 2.2×10^{-22} kg ·m/s
E) 8.7×10^{-23} kg ·m/s

33. Consider the following:
   I.   A photoelectric process in which some emitted electrons have kinetic energy greater than $h\nu$, where ν is the frequency of the incident light.
   II. A photoelectric process in which all emitted electrons have energy less than $h\nu$.
   III. Compton scattering from stationary electrons for which the emitted light has a frequency that is greater than that of the incident light.
   IV. Compton scattering from stationary electrons for which the emitted light has a frequency that is less than that of the incident light.

   The only possible processes are:

A) I
B) III
C) I and III
D) I and IV
*E) II and IV

34. The diagram shows the energy levels for an electron in a certain atom. Which transition shown represents the emission of a photon with the most energy?

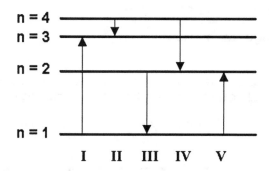

A) I.   B) II.   *C) III.   D) IV.   E) V.

473

35. An electron in an atom initially has an energy 5.5 eV above the ground state energy. It drops to a state with energy 3.2 eV above the ground state energy and emits a photon in the process. The wave associated with the photon has a frequency of:

A) 7.7×10^{14} Hz
*B) 1.0×10^{15} Hz
C) 1.8×10^{15} Hz

D) 2.6×10^{15} Hz
E) 2.9×10^{15} Hz

36. An electron in an atom drops from an energy level at -1.1×10^{-18} J to an energy level at -2.4×10^{-18} J. The wave associated with the emitted photon has a frequency of:

A) 2.0×10^{17} Hz
*B) 2.0×10^{15} Hz
C) 2.0×10^{13} Hz

D) 2.0×10^{11} Hz
E) 2.0×10^{9} Hz

37. An electron in an atom initially has an energy 7.5 eV above the ground state energy. It drops to a state with an energy of 3.2 eV above the ground state energy and emits a photon in the process. The momentum of the photon is:

A) 1.7×10^{-27} kg $\cdot$m/s
*B) 2.3×10^{-27} kg $\cdot$m/s
C) 4.0×10^{-27} kg $\cdot$m/s

D) 5.7×10^{-27} kg $\cdot$m/s
E) 8.0×10^{-27} kg $\cdot$m/s

38. The quantum number n is most closely associated with what property of the electron in a hydrogen atom?

*A) energy
B) orbital angular momentum
C) spin angular momentum
D) magnetic moment
E) z component of angular momentum

39. According to the Bohr theory of the hydrogen atom the energy E_n of a state with principal quantum number n is proportional to:

A) n   B) n^2 C) $1/n$ *D) $1/n^2$ E) e^{-n}

40. The binding energy of an electron in the ground state in a hydrogen atom is about:

*A) 13.6 eV   B) 3.4 eV   C) 10.2 eV   D) 1.0 eV   E) 27.2 eV

41. The ground state energy of a hydrogen atom is -13.6 eV. The energy of the first excited state is:

A) 0   *B) -3.4 eV   C) -6.8 eV   D) -9.6 eV   E) -27 eV

42. The ground state energy of a hydrogen atom is -13.6 eV. The minus sign indicates:

   A) the kinetic energy is negative
   B) the potential energy is positive
   C) the electron might escape from the atom
   *D) the electron and proton are bound together
   E) none of the above

43. The ground state energy of a hydrogen atom is -13.6 eV. When the electron is in the first excited state its excitation energy is:

   A) 0   B) 3.4 eV   C) 6.8 eV   *D) 10.2 eV   E) 13.6 eV

44. The ground state energy of a hydrogen atom is -13.6 eV. When the electron is in the first excited state the ionization energy is:

   A) 0   *B) 3.4 eV   C) 6.8 eV   D) 10.2 eV   E) 13.6 eV

45. When a hydrogen atom makes the transition from the second excited state to the ground state (at -13.6 eV) the energy of the photon emitted is:

   A) 0   B) 1.5 eV   C) 9.1 eV   *D) 12.1 eV   E) 13.6 eV

46. The series limit for the Balmer series represents a transition m → n, where (m,n) is

   A) (2,1)   B) (3,2)   C) (∞,0)   D) (∞,1)   *E) (∞,2)

47. The Balmer series of hydrogen is important because:

   A) it is the only one for which the Bohr theory can be used
   B) it is the only series which occurs for hydrogen
   *C) it is in the visible region
   D) it involves the lowest possible quantum number n
   E) it involves the highest possible quantum number n

48. The Bohr model of the hydrogen atom correctly predicts:

   A) the radius of the electron orbit
   B) the angular momentum of the electron
   C) the speed of the electron
   D) the value of the permittivity ϵ_0
   *E) the value of the Rydberg constant

49. Bohr theory does NOT correctly predict:

 *A) the angular momentum of the ground state
  B) quantization of energy
  C) wavelengths of emitted photons
  D) the Lyman series
  E) the value of the Rydberg constant

50. In the Bohr model of the hydrogen atom which of the following pairs
    of quantities are NOT related to each other in the same way as they
    are classically?

  A) kinetic energy and orbit radius
  B) potential energy and orbit radius
  C) kinetic energy and angular momentum
  D) angular momentum and orbit radius
 *E) none of the above

51. The radius r_n of the orbit of an electron in a hydrogen atom,
    according to Bohr theory, depends on n as follows:

  A) n   *B) n^2 C) $1/n$ D) $1/n^2$ E) $n^{1/2}$

52. The principle of complementarity is due to:

  A) Einstein   *D) Bohr
  B) Maxwell   E) Schrodinger
  C) Newton

1. J. J. Thompson's measurement of e/m for electrons provides evidence
   of the:

 A) wave nature of matter
*B) particle nature of matter
 C) wave nature of radiation
 D) particle nature of radiation
 E) transverse wave nature of light

2. Evidence for the wave nature of matter is:

*A) electron diffraction experiments of Davisson and Germer
 B) Thompson's measurement of e/m
 C) Young's double slit experiment
 D) the Compton effect
 E) Lenz's law

3. Which of the following is NOT evidence for the wave nature of
   matter?

*A) the photoelectric effect
 B) the diffraction pattern obtained when electrons pass through a slit
 C) electron tunneling
 D) the validity of the Heisenberg uncertainty principle
 E) the interference pattern obtained when electrons pass through a two-
    slit system

4. Of the following which is the best evidence for the wave nature of
   matter?

 A) the photoelectric effect
 B) the Compton effect
 C) the spectral radiancy of cavity radiation
 D) the relationship between momentum and energy for an electron
*E) the reflection of electrons by crystals

5. Monoenergetic electrons are incident on a single slit barrier. If
   the energy of each incident electron is increased the central
   maximum of the diffraction pattern:

 A) widens
*B) narrows
 C) stays the same width
 D) widens for slow electrons and narrows for fast electrons
 E) narrows for slow electrons and widens for fast electrons

6. A free electron has a momentum of 5.0×10^{-24} kg ·m/s. The wavelength (in m) of its wave function is:

A) 1.5×10^{-8}
*B) 1.5×10^{-10}
C) 1.5×10^{-12}

D) 1.5×10^{-14}
E) none of these

7. The frequency and wavelength of the matter wave associated with a 10-eV free electron are:

A) 1.5×10^{34} Hz, 3.9×10^{-10} m
B) 1.5×10^{34} Hz, 1.3×10^{-34} m
C) 2.4×10^{15} Hz, 1.2×10^{-9} m

*D) 2.4×10^{15} Hz, 3.9×10^{-10} m
E) 4.8×10^{15} Hz, 1.9×10^{-10} m

8. If the kinetic energy of a free electron doubles, the frequency of its wave function changes by the factor:

A) $1/\sqrt{2}$ B) 1/2   C) 1/4   D) $\sqrt{2}$ *E) 2

9. If the kinetic energy of a non-relativistic electron doubles, the wavelength of its wave function changes by the factor:

*A) $1/\sqrt{2}$ B) 1/2   C) 1/4   D) $\sqrt{2}$ E) 2

10. The probability that a particle is in a given small region of space is proportional to:

A) its energy
B) its momentum
C) the frequency of its wave function
D) the wavelength of its wave function
*E) the square of the magnitude of its wave function

11. $\Psi(x)$ is the wave function for a particle moving along the x axis. The probability that the particle is in the interval from x=a to x=b is given by:

A) $\Psi(b) - \Psi(a)$
B) $|\Psi(b)|^2 - |\Psi(a)|^2$
C) $|\Psi(b) - \Psi(a)|^2$
D) $\int_a^b \Psi(x)\, dx$

*E) $\int_a^b |\Psi(x)|^2\, dx$

12. If a wave function ψ for a particle moving along the x axis is "normalized" then:

A) $\int |\psi|^2 dt = 1$
*B) $\int |\psi|^2 dx = 1$
C) $\partial \psi / \partial x = 1$

D) $\partial \psi / \partial t = 1$
E) $|\psi|^2 = 1$

13. The significance of $|\psi|^2$ is:

A) probability
B) energy
*C) probability density

D) energy density
E) wavelength

14. Maxwell's equations are to **E** and **B** as _____'s equation is to ψ.

A) Einstein
B) Fermi
C) Newton

*D) Schrodinger
E) Bohr

15. The energy of a particle in a one-dimensional trap with zero potential energy in the interior and infinite potential energy at the walls is proportional to (n = quantum number):

A) n   B) 1/n   C) $1/n^2$ D) $\sqrt{n}$ *E) n^2

16. The ground state energy of an electron in a one-dimensional trap with zero potential energy in the interior and infinite potential energy at the walls is 2.0 eV. If the width of the well is doubled, the ground state energy will be:

*A) 0.5 eV   B) 1.0 eV   C) 2.0 eV   D) 4.0 eV   E) 8.0 eV

17. An electron is in a one-dimensional trap with zero potential energy in the interior and infinite potential energy at the walls. The ratio E_3/E_1 of the energy for n = 3 to that for n = 1 is:

A) 1/3   B) 1/9   C) 3/1   *D) 9/1   E) 1/1

18. The ground state energy of an electron in a one-dimensional trap with zero potential energy in the interior and infinite potential energy at the walls:

A) is zero
B) decreases with temperature
C) increases with temperature

*D) is independent of temperature
E) oscillates with time

19. An electron is in a one-dimensional trap with zero potential energy in the interior and infinite potential energy at the walls. A graph of its wave function $\Psi(x)$ versus x is shown. The value of quantum number n is:

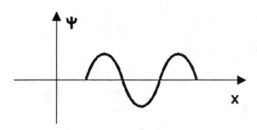

A) 0   B) 1   C) 2   *D) 3   E) 4

20. An electron is in a one-dimensional trap with zero potential energy in the interior and infinite potential energy at the walls. A graph of its probability density P(x) versus x is shown. The value of the quantum number n is:

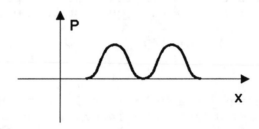

A) 0   B) 1   *C) 2   D) 3   E) 4

21. An electron is trapped in a deep well with a width of 0.3 nm. If it is in the state with quantum number n = 3 its kinetic energy is:

A) 6.0×10^{-28} J
B) 1.8×10^{-27} J
C) 6.7×10^{-19} J

D) 2.0×10^{-18} J
*E) 6.0×10^{-18} J

22. An electron is trapped in a deep well with a width of 0.3 nm. If it is in the state with quantum number n = 3 the magnitude of its momentum is:

A) 3.3×10^{-29} kg $\cdot$m/s
B) 5.7×10^{-29} kg $\cdot$m/s
C) 1.1×10^{-24} kg $\cdot$m/s

D) 1.9×10^{-24} kg $\cdot$m/s
*E) 3.3×10^{-24} kg $\cdot$m/s

23. An electron is trapped in a deep well with a width of 0.3 nm. If it is in the state with quantum number n = 3 the possible values of its momentum are:

   *A) -3.3×10^{-24} kg $\cdot$m/s and $+3.3 \times 10^{-24}$ kg $\cdot$m/s
   B) 0 and $+3.3 \times 10^{-24}$ kg $\cdot$m/s
   C) any value from -3.3×10^{-24} kg $\cdot$m/s to $+3.3 \times 10^{-24}$ kg $\cdot$m/s
   D) any value from 0 to $+3.3 \times 10^{-24}$ kg $\cdot$m/s
   E) only $+3.3 \times 10^{-24}$ kg $\cdot$m/s

24. An electron is trapped in a deep well with a width of 0.3 nm. If it is in the state with quantum number n = 3 the uncertainty in its momentum is about:

   A) 0
   B) 10^{-27} kg $\cdot$m/s
   *C) 10^{-24} kg $\cdot$m/s
   D) 10^{-21} kg $\cdot$m/s
   E) 10^{-18} kg $\cdot$m/s

25. An electron is trapped in a deep potential well. As the well width is decreased the energy of the ground state increases. This is a direct result of:

   *A) the uncertainty principle
   B) the complementarity principle
   C) conservation of energy
   D) conservation of angular momentum
   E) electron spin

26. An electron passes through a single slit of width 5×10^{-10} m. The uncertainty in the component of its momentum parallel to the slit width is about:

   A) 0
   B) 10^{-27} kg $\cdot$m/s
   *C) 10^{-24} kg $\cdot$m/s
   D) 10^{-21} kg $\cdot$m/s
   E) 10^{-18} kg $\cdot$m/s

27. An electron passes through a single slit and as a result the component of its momentum parallel to the slit is uncertain by $\Delta p_{\shortparallel}$. $\Delta p_{\shortparallel}$ is reduced if:

   A) the energy of the electron is increased
   B) the energy of the electron is decreased
   *C) the slit width is increased
   D) the slit width is decreased
   E) the momentum of the electron is increased

28. A free electron in motion along the x axis has a localized wave
    function. The uncertainty in its momentum is decreased if:

  A) the wave function is made more narrow
 *B) the wave function is made less narrow
  C) the wave function remains the same but the energy of the electron is
     increased
  D) the wave function remains the same but the energy of the electron is
     decreased
  E) none of the above

29. The uncertainty in position of an electron in a certain state is
    5×10^{-10} m. The uncertainty in its momentum (in kg ·m/s) must be

  A) less than 10^{-26} D) greater than 10^{-22}
  B) less than 10^{-22} E) greater than 10^{-20}
 *C) greater than 10^{-24}

30. The reflection coefficient R for a certain barrier tunneling problem
    is 0.80. The corresponding transmission coefficient T is:

  A) 0.80   B) 0.60   C) 0.50   *D) 0.20   E) zero

31. An electron with energy E is incident upon a potential energy
    barrier of height Uo > E and thickness L. The transmission
    coefficient T:

  A) is zero
 *B) decreases exponentially with L
  C) is proportional to 1/L
  D) is proportional to $1/L^2$
  E) is non-zero and independent of L

32. In order to tunnel through a potential barrier a particle must:

  A) have energy greater than the barrier height
  B) have spin
  C) be massive
  D) have a wavelength longer than the barrier width
 *E) none of the above

33. An electron with energy E is incident on a potential energy barrier
    of height U_0 and thickness L. The probability of tunneling increases
    if:

  A) E decreases without any other changes
  B) U_0 increases without any other changes
 *C) L decreases without any other changes
  D) E and U_0 increase by the same amount
  E) E and U_0 decrease by the same amount

1. A Bohr radius is a useful unit of distance because:

 A) it is the radius of the ground state electron orbit for hydrogen
 B) the radii of all electron orbits are small multiples of a Bohr
    radius
*C) in a low-lying shell of hydrogen the electron is nearly always
    within a few Bohr radii of the proton
 D) the electron in a hydrogen atom is never closer to the proton than a
    Bohr radius
 E) the electron in the ground state of hydrogen has a 50-50 chance of
    being closer to the proton than a Bohr radius

2. For an electron in the ground state of a hydrogen atom the Bohr
   radius is:

 A) the radius of its orbit
*B) the most probable radial coordinate
 C) the least probably radial coordinate
 D) the maximum radial coordinate
 E) the minimum radial coordinate

3. The diameter of a hydrogen atom in its ground state is about:

 A) 10^{-23} m   B) 10^{-19} m   C) 10^{-15} m   *D) 10^{-10} m   E) 10^{-7} m

4. The quantum number n is most closely associated with what property
   of the electron in a hydrogen atom?

*A) energy
 B) orbital angular momentum
 C) spin angular momentum
 D) magnetic moment
 E) z component of angular momentum

5. Let the central charge of a Bohr model atom be Ze. The energy of a
   state with principal quantum number n is proportional to:

 A) Z   *B) Z^2 C) $1/Z$ D) $1/Z^2$ E) Z^4

6. The magnitude of the orbital angular momentum of an electron is what multiple of $\hbar$? (ℓ is a positive integer.)

$$A)1 \quad B)1/2 \quad C) \sqrt{\ell(\ell+1)} \quad D)2\ell+1 \quad E)\ell^2$$

Ans. c

7. The magnetic quantum number m_ℓ is most closely associated with what property of the electron in a hydrogen atom?

A) magnitude of the orbital angular momentum
B) energy
C) z component of the spin angular momentum
*D) z component of the orbital angular momentum
E) radius of the orbit

8. The quantum number m_s is most closely associated with what property of the electron in a hydrogen atom?

A) magnitude of the orbital angular momentum
B) energy
*C) z component of the spin angular momentum
D) z component of the orbital angular momentum
E) radius of the orbit

9. Possible values of the principal quantum number n for an electron in an atom are:

A) only 0 and 1
B) only 0,1,2,..., ∞
C) only 0,1,..., $\ell-1$
D) only 1/2 and -1/2
*E) only 1,2,3,..., ∞

10. The number of values of the orbital quantum number ℓ associated with the principal quantum number n = 3 is:

A) 1   B) 2   *C) 3   D) 4   E) 7

11. The number of possible values of the magnetic quantum number m_ℓ associated with a given value of the orbital quantum number ℓ is:

A) 1   B) 2   C) ℓ D) 2ℓ *E) $2\ell + 1$

12. The number of states in an orbital with orbital quantum number ℓ = 3 is:

A) 2   B) 3   C) 7   D) 9   *E) 14

13. The number of states in a shell with principal quantum number n = 3 is:

A) 3   B) 9   C) 15   *D) 18   E) 25

14. A hydrogen atom is in a state with principal quantum number n = 3. The possible values of the orbital quantum number ℓ are:

A) 1, 2   D) 0, 1, 2, 3
B) 1, 2, 3   *E) 0, 1, 2
C) -3, -2, -1, 0, 1, 2, 3

15. "Space quantization" means that:

A) space is quantized
*B) L_z can have only certain discrete values
C) **L** and μ are in the same direction
D) **L** and μ are in opposite directions
E) an electron has a magnetic dipole moment

16. A hydrogen atom is in a state with orbital quantum number ℓ = 2. Possible values of the magnetic quantum number m_ℓ are:

A) 1, 2   D) -1, 0, 1
B) 0, 1, 2   *E) -2, -1, 0, 1, 2
C) 0, 1

17. An electron in a hydrogen atom is in a state with ℓ = 3 and m = 2. The angle between **L** and the z axis is:

A) 48.2°   B) 60°   C) 30°   D) 35.3°   *E) 54.7°

18. An electron in a hydrogen atom is in a state with ℓ = 5. The minimum angle between **L** and the z axis is:

A) 0°   B) 18.0°   *C) 24.1°   D) 36.7°   E) 33.6°

19. In the relation $\mu_z = -m_\ell \mu_B$, the quantity μ_B is:

*A) the Bohr magneton
B) the component of the dipole moment along the magnetic field
C) the permeability of the material
D) a friction coefficient
E) none of the above

485

20. The electron states in a hydrogen atom which constitute a single shell all have:

*A) the same value of n
 B) the same value of ℓ
 C) the same value of n and the same value of ℓ
 D) the same value of ℓ and the same value of m_ℓ
 E) the same set of all four quantum numbers

21. The electron states in a hydrogen atom which constitute a single orbital all have:

 A) only the same value of n
 B) only the same value of ℓ
*C) only the same value of n and the same value of ℓ
 D) only the same value of ℓ and the same value of m_ℓ
 E) the same set of all four quantum numbers

22. The total number of electron states with n < 3 for a hydrogen atom is:

 A) two   B) four   C) six   D) eight   *E) ten

23. The total number of electron states with n = 2 and ℓ = 1 for a hydrogen atom is:

 A) two   B) four   *C) six   D) eight   E) ten

24. The possible values for the magnetic quantum number m_s of an electron in a hydrogen atom:

 A) depend on n
 B) depend on ℓ
 C) depend on both n and ℓ
 D) depend on whether or not there is an external magnetic field present
*E) are $\pm 1/2$

25. The Stern-Gerlach experiment makes use of:

 A) a strong uniform **B** field
*B) a strong non-uniform **B** field
 C) a strong uniform **E** field
 D) a strong non-uniform **E** field
 E) strong perpendicular **E** and **B** fields

26. The magnetic field **B** is along the z axis in a Stern-Gerlach experiment. The force it exerts on a magnetic dipole is proportional to:

 A) B   B) B^2 *C) dB/dz   D) d^2B/dz^2 E) $\int B\, dz$

486

27. A magnetic dipole μ is placed in a strong uniform magnetic field **B**. The associated force exerted on the dipole is:

A) along μ
B) along -μ
C) along **B**

D) along μx**B**
*E) zero

28. The force exerted on a magnetic dipole as it moves with velocity **v** through a Stern-Gerlach apparatus is:

A) proportional to v
B) proportional to 1/v
C) zero

D) proportional to v^2
*E) independent of v

29. A magnetic dipole is placed between the poles of a magnet as shown. The direction of the associated force exerted on the dipole is:

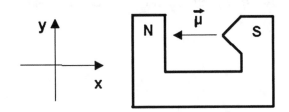

*A) positive x
B) positive y
C) negative x

D) negative y
E) into or out of the page

30. To observe the Zeeman effect one uses:

A) a strong uniform magnetic field
*B) a strong non-uniform magnetic field
C) a strong uniform electric field
D) a strong non-uniform electric field
E) mutually perpendicular electric and magnetic fields

31. The wave function for an electron in a state with 0 angular momentum:

A) is 0 everywhere
*B) is spherically symmetric
C) depends on the angle from the z axis
D) depends on the angle from the x axis
E) is spherically symmetric for some shells and depends on the angle from the z axis for others

32. Consider the following:
    I.   the probability density for an $\ell = 0$ state
    II. the probability density for a state with $\ell \neq 0$
    III. the average of the probability densities for all states in
         an $\ell \neq 0$ subshell
  Of these which are spherically symmetric?

A) only I   *D) only I and III
B) only II   E) I, II, and III
C) only I and II

33. If the wave function ψ is spherically symmetric then the radial
probability density is given by:

A) $4\pi r^2 \psi$ B) $|\psi|^2$ *C) $4\pi r^2|\psi|^2$ D) $4\pi|\psi|^2$ E) $4\pi r|\psi|^2$

34. If P(r) is the radial probability density then the probability that
the separation of the electron and proton is between r and r + dr
is:

*A) P dr   D) $4\pi r^2|P|$ dr
B) $|P|^2$ dr   E) $4\pi P$ dr
C) $4\pi r^2 P$ dr

35. The radial probability density for the electron in the ground state
of a hydrogen atom has a peak at about:

A) 0.5 pm   B) 5 pm   *C) 50 pm   D) 500 pm   E) 5000 pm

36. An electron in a K shell of an atom has the principal quantum
number:

A) n = 0   *B) n = 1   C) n = 2   D) n = 3   E) n = ∞

37. An electron in an L shell of an atom has the principal quantum
number:

A) n = 0   B) n = 1   *C) n = 2   D) n = 3   E) n = ∞

38. The most energetic photon in a continuous x-ray spectrum has an
energy approximately equal to:

A) the energy of all the electrons in a target atom
*B) the kinetic energy of an incident-beam electron
C) the rest energy, mc^2, of an electron
D) the kinetic plus potential energy of a K-electron in the target atom
E) the kinetic energy of a K-electron in the target atom

39. A photon with the smallest wavelength in the continuous z-ray spectrum is emitted when:

A) an electron is knocked from a K shell
B) a valence electron is knocked from the atom
C) the incident electron becomes bound to the atom
D) the atom has the greatest recoil energy
*E) the incident electron loses all its energy in a single decelerating event

40. Radiation with the minimum wavelength as well as the K x-ray lines are detected for a certain target. The energy of the incident electrons is then doubled, with the result that:

A) the minimum wavelength increases and the wavelengths of the K lines remain the same
*B) the minimum wavelength decreases and the wavelengths of the K lines remain the same
C) the minimum wavelength and the wavelengths of the K lines all increase
D) the minimum wavelength and the wavelengths of the K lines all decrease
E) the minimum wavelength increases and the wavelengths of the K lines all decrease

41. Characteristic K x-radiation of an element is caused by:

A) stoppage of electrons by the nucleus
B) scattering of the incident radiation with a change of wavelength
C) ejection of an electron from an outer shell
*D) transition of an electron to the innermost orbit
E) none of the above

42. The ratio of the wavelength of the K_α x-ray line for Nb (Z = 41) to that of Ga (Z = 31) is:

*A) 9/16   B) 16/9   C) 3/4   D) 4/3   E) 1.15

43. In connection with x-ray emission the symbol K_α refers to:

A) an alpha particle radiation
B) an effect of the dielectric constant on energy levels
C) x-ray radiation from potassium
D) x-ray radiation associated with an electron going from n = ∞ to n = 1
*E) x-ray radiation associated with an electron going from n = 2 to n = 1

44. In connection with x-ray emission the symbol L_β refers to:

  A) a beta particle radiation
  B) an atomic state of angular momentum $h/2\pi$
  C) the inductance associated with an orbiting electron
 *D) x-radiation associated with an electron going from n = 4 to n = 2
  E) none of the above

45. The transition shown gives rise to an x-ray. The correct label for this is:

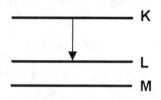

 *A) K_α B) K_β C) L_α D) L_β E) KL

46. In a Moseley graph:

  A) the x-ray frequency is plotted as a function of atomic number
  B) the square of the x-ray frequency is plotted as a function of atomic number
 *C) the square root of the x-ray frequency is plotted as a function of atomic number
  D) the x-ray frequency is plotted as a function of the square root of atomic number
  E) the square root of the x-ray frequency is plotted as a function of atomic mass

47. In calculating the x-ray energy levels the effective charge of the nucleus is taken to be Z-b, where Z is the atomic number. The parameter b enters because:

  A) an electron is removed from the inner shell
  B) a proton is removed from the nucleus
  C) the quantum mechanical force between two charges is less than the classical force
 *D) the nucleus is screened by electrons
  E) the Pauli exclusion principle must be obeyed

48. The Pauli exclusion principle is obeyed by:

  A) all particles
  B) all charged particles
 *C) all particles with spin quantum numbers of 1/2
  D) all particles with spin quantum numbers of 1
  E) all particles with mass

49. No state in an atom can be occupied by more than one electron. This is most closely related to the:

   A) wave nature of matter
   B) finite value for the speed of light
   C) Bohr magneton
  *D) Pauli exclusion principle
   E) Zeeman effect

50. When a lithium atom is made from a helium atom by adding a proton (and neutron) to the nucleus and an electron outside, the electron goes into an n = 2, ℓ = 0 state rather than an n = 1, ℓ = 0 state. This is an indication that electrons:

  *A) obey the Pauli exclusion principle
   B) obey the minimum energy principle
   C) undergo the Zeeman effect
   D) are diffracted
   E) and protons are interchangeable

51. When a lithium atom in its ground state is made from a helium atom by adding a proton (and neutron) to the nucleus and an electron outside, the electron goes into an n = 2, ℓ = 0 state rather than an n = 3, ℓ = state. This is an indication that electrons:

   A) obey the Pauli exclusion principle
  *B) obey the minimum energy principle
   C) undergo the Zeeman effect
   D) are diffracted
   E) and protons are interchangeable

52. If electrons did not have intrinsic angular momentum (spin) but still obeyed the Pauli exclusion principle the states occupied by electrons in the ground state of helium would be:

   A) (n = 1, ℓ = 0); (n = 1, ℓ = 0)   D) (n = 2, ℓ = 0); (n = 2, ℓ = 1)
   B) (n = 1, ℓ = 0); (n = 1, ℓ = 1)   E) (n = 2, ℓ = 1); (n = 2, ℓ = 1)
  *C) (n = 1, ℓ = 0); (n = 2, ℓ = 0)

53. The minimum energy principle tells us that:

   A) the energy of an atom with a high atomic number is less than the energy of an atom with a low atomic number
   B) the energy of an atom with a low atomic number is less than the energy of an atom with high atomic number
   C) when an atom makes an upward transition the energy of the absorbed photon is the least possible
  *D) the ground state configuration of any atom is the one with the least energy
   E) the ground state configuration of any atom is the one with the least ionization energy

54. Which of the following (n, ℓ, m_ℓ, m_s) combinations is impossible for an electron in an atom?

A) 3, 1, 1, -1/2
B) 6, 2, 0, 1/2
C) 3, 2, -2, -1/2

*D) 3, 1, -2, 1/2
E) 1, 0, 0, -1/2

55. The energy of states with the same principal quantum number n:

*A) increases with orbital quantum number ℓ
B) increases with magnetic quantum number m_ℓ
C) does not depend on either the orbital quantum number ℓ or the magnetic quantum number m_ℓ
D) decreases with orbital quantum number ℓ for low ℓ and increases for high ℓ
E) increases with orbital quantum number ℓ for low ℓ and decreased for high ℓ

56. For any atom other that hydrogen and helium all electrons in the same shell have:

A) the same energy
B) the same magnitude of angular momentum
C) the same magnetic quantum number
D) the same spin quantum number
*E) none of the above

57. The states being filled from the beginning to end of the lanthanide series of atoms are:

A) $n = 3$, $\ell = 2$ states
B) $n = 4$, $\ell = 1$ states
C) $n = 4$, $\ell = 2$ states

*D) $n = 4$, $\ell = 3$ states
E) $n = 5$, $\ell = 2$ states

58. The most energetic electron in any atom at the beginning of a period of the periodic table is in:

*A) an $\ell = 0$ state
B) an $\ell = 1$ state
C) an $\ell = 2$ state
D) an $n = 0$ state with unspecified angular momentum
E) an $n = 1$ state with unspecified angular momentum

59. The most energetic electron in any atom at the end of a period of the periodic table is in:

A) an $\ell = 0$ state
*B) an $\ell = 1$ state
C) an $\ell = 2$ state
D) an $n = 0$ state with unspecified angular momentum
E) an $n = 1$ state with unspecified angular momentum

60. The group of atoms at the ends of periods of the periodic table are called:

A) alkali metals
B) rare earths
C) transition metal atoms
D) alkaline atoms
*E) inert gas atoms

61. The group of atoms at the beginning of periods of the periodic table are called:

*A) alkali metal atoms
B) rare earth atoms
C) transition metal atoms
D) alkaline atoms
E) inert gas atoms

62. Suppose the energy required to ionize an argon atom is i, the energy to excite it is e, and its thermal energy at room temperature is t. In increasing order, these three energies are:

A) i, e, t   B) t, i, e   *C) e, t, i   D) i, t, e   E) t, e, i

63. The ionization energy of an atom in its ground state is:

A) the energy required to remove the least energetic electron
*B) the energy required to remove the most energetic electron
C) the energy difference between the most energetic electron and the least energetic electron
D) the same as the energy of a K_α photon
E) the same as the excitation energy of the most energetic electron

64. The effective charge acting on a single valence electron outside a closed shell is about Ne, where N is:

A) the atomic number of the nucleus
B) the atomic mass of the atom
*C) usually between 1 and 3
D) half the atomic number
E) less than 1

65. In a laser:

A) excited atoms are stimulated to emit photons by radiation external to the laser
B) the transitions for laser emission are directly to the ground state
C) the states which give rise to laser emission are usually very unstable states which decay rapidly
*D) the transition in which an atom is initially excited is never between two states which are involved in the stimulated emission
E) a minimum of two energy levels are required.

66. Photons in a laser beam have the same energy, wavelength, polarization direction, and phase because:

 *A) each is produced in an emission that is stimulated by another
  B) all come from the same atom
  C) the lasing material has only two quantum states
  D) all photons are alike, no matter what their source
  E) none of the above

67. A laser must be pumped to achieve:

  A) a metastable state
  B) fast response
  C) stimulated emission
 *D) population inversion
  E) the same wavelength for all photons

68. Photons in a laser beam are produced by:

 *A) transitions from a metastable state
  B) transitions from a state that decays rapidly
  C) splitting of other photons
  D) pumping
  E) reflection from mirrors

69. Population inversion is important for the generation of a laser beam because it assures that:

  A) spontaneous emission does not occur more often than stimulated emission
  B) photons do not split too rapidly
 *C) more photons are emitted than are absorbed
  D) photons do not collide with each other
  E) photons do not make upward transitions

70. A metastable state is important for the generation of a laser beam because it assures that:

 *A) spontaneous emission does not occur more often than stimulated emission
  B) photons do not split too rapidly
  C) more photons are emitted than are absorbed
  D) photons do not collide with each other
  E) photons do not make upward transitions

71. Electrons in a certain laser make transitions from a metastable state to the ground state. Initially there are 6×10^{20} atoms in the metastable state and 2×10^{20} atoms in the ground state. The number of photons that can be produced in a single burst is about:

  A) 2×10^{20} B) 3×10^{20} *C) 4×10^{20} D) 6×10^{20} E) 8×10^{20}

72. In a helium-neon laser, the laser light arises from a transition from a _____ state to a _____ state:

A) He, He   *B) Ne, Ne   C) He, Ne   D) Ne, He   E) N, He

73. The purpose of the mirrors at the ends of a helium-neon laser is:

A) to assure that no laser light leaks out
*B) to increase the number of stimulated emissions
C) to absorb some of the photons
D) to keep the light used for pumping inside the laser
E) to double the effective length of the laser

74. A group of electromagnetic waves might
    I.   be monochromatic
    II. be coherent
    III. have the same polarization direction
   Which of these describe the waves from a laser?

A) I only   D) I and II only
B) II only   *E) I, II, and III
C) III only

75. A laser beam can be sharply focused because it is:

A) highly coherent   D) circularly polarized
B) plane polarized   *E) highly directional
C) intense

76. The "e" in "laser" stands for:

A) electric   B) emf   C) energy   *D) emission   E) entropy

1. In a pure metal the collisions that are characterized by the mean free time τ in the expression for the resistivity are chiefly between:

A) electrons and other electrons
*B) electrons with energy about equal to the Fermi energy and atoms
C) all electrons and atoms
D) electrons with energy much less than the Fermi energy and atoms
E) atoms and other atoms

2. A certain metal has 5.3×10^{29} conduction electrons/m^3, with a mean time between collisions of 3.6×10^{-14} s. Its resistivity is about:

A) $3.4 \times 10^{-25} \ \Omega \cdot m$
B) $6.8 \times 10^{-12} \ \Omega \cdot m$
*C) $1.9 \times 10^{-9} \ \Omega \cdot m$
D) $3.6 \times 10^{-6} \ \Omega \cdot m$
E) $5.4 \times 10^{8} \ \Omega \cdot m$

3. Which one of the following statements concerning electron energy bands in solids is true?

A) the bands occur as a direct consequence of the Fermi-Dirac distribution function
B) electrical conduction arises from the motion of electrons in completely filled bands
C) within a given band, all electron energy levels are equal to each other
*D) an insulator has a large energy separation between the highest filled band and the lowest empty band
E) only insulators have energy bands

4. If E_O and E_T are the average energies of the "free" electrons in a metal at 0 K and room temperature respectively, then the ratio E_T/E_O is approximately:

A) 0   *B) 1   C) 100   D) 10^6 E) infinity

5. In a metal at 0 K, the Fermi energy is:

*A) the highest energy of any electron
B) the lowest energy of any electron
C) the mean thermal energy of the electrons
D) the energy of the top of the valence band
E) the energy at the bottom of the conduction band

6. The energy level diagram shown applies to:

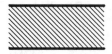

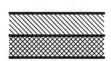

unfilled:

filled:

*A) a conductor
 B) an insulator
 C) a semiconductor

D) an isolated atom
E) a free electron gas

7. The energy level diagram shown applies to:

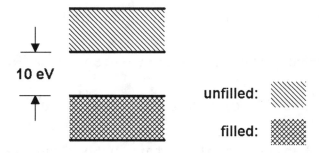

10 eV

unfilled:

filled:

 A) a conductor
*B) an insulator
 C) a semiconductor

D) an isolated atom
E) a free electron gas

8. The energy level diagram shown applies to:

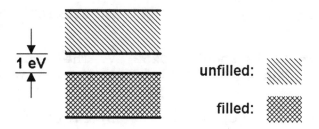

1 eV

unfilled:

filled:

 A) a conductor
 B) an insulator
*C) a semiconductor

D) an isolated atom
E) a free electron gas

9. Possible units for the density of states function n(E) are:

A) J/m^3 B) $1/J$ C) m^{-3} *D) $J^{-1} \cdot m^{-3}$ E) kg/m^3

10. The energy gap (in eV) between the valence and conduction bands of an insulator is of the order:

A) 10^{-19} B) 0.001   C) 0.1   *D) 10   E) 1000

11. The Fermi-Dirac probability function p(E) varies between:

*A) 0 and 1   D) -1 and 1
B) 0 and infinity   E) 0 and E_F
C) 1 and infinity

12. The ratio v_F/v_d of the Fermi speed to the drift speed of an electron involved with the conduction of electricity in copper is of the order:

*A) 10^7 B) 10^{-7} C) 1   D) 10^{20} E) 10^{-20}

13. At T = 0 K the probability that a state 0.50 eV below the Fermi level is occupied is:

A) 0   B) 5.0×10^{-9} C) 5.0×10^{-6} D) 5.0×10^{-3} *E) 1

14. At T = 0 K the probability that a state 0.50 eV above the Fermi level is occupied is:

*A) 0   B) 5.0×10^{-9} C) 5.0×10^{-6} D) 5.0×10^{-3} E) 1

15. At room temperature kT is about 0.0259 eV. The probability that a state 0.50 eV above the Fermi level is occupied at room temperature is:

A) 1   B) 0.05   C) 0.025   D) 5.0×10^{-6} *E) 4.1×10^{-9}

16. At room temperature kT is about 0.0259 eV. The probability that a state 0.50 eV below the Fermi level is unoccupied at room temperature is:

A) 1   B) 0.05   C) 0.025   D) 5.0×10^{-6} *E) 4.1×10^{-9}

17. A hole refers to:

   A) a proton
   B) a positively charged electron
   C) an electron which has somehow lost its charge
   D) a microscopic defect in a solid
   *E) the absence of an electron in an otherwise filled band

18. Electrons in a full band do not contribute to the current when an
    electric field exists in a solid because:

   A) the field cannot exert a force on them
   *B) the individual contributions cancel
   C) they are not moving
   D) they make transitions to other bands
   E) they leave the solid

19. For a pure semiconductor the Fermi level is:

   A) in the conduction band
   B) well above the conduction band
   C) in the valence band
   D) well below the valence band
   *E) near the center of the gap between the valence and conduction bands

20. A pure semiconductor at room temperature has:

   A) more electrons/m^3 in its conduction band than holes/m^3 in its
      valence band
   B) more electrons/m^3 in its conduction band than a typical metal
   C) more electrons/m^3 in its valence band than at T = 0 K
   D) more holes/m^3 in its valence band than electrons/m^3 in its valence
      band
   *E) none of the above

21. For a metal at room temperature the temperature coefficient of
    resistivity is determined primarily by:

   A) the number of electrons in the conduction band
   B) the number of impurity atoms
   C) the binding energy of outer shell electrons
   *D) collisions between conduction electrons and atoms
   E) none of the above

22. For a pure semiconductor at room temperature the temperature
    coefficient of resistivity is determined primarily by:

    *A) the number of electrons in the conduction band
    B) the number of replacement atoms
    C) the binding energy of outer shell electrons
    D) collisions between conduction electrons and atoms
    E) none of the above

23. A certain material has a resistivity of 7.8 $\Omega \cdot$m at room temperature
    and it increases as the temperature is raised by 100°C. The material
    is most likely:

    A) a metal   D) an insulator
    B) a pure semiconductor   E) none of the above
    *C) a heavily doped semiconductor

24. A certain material has a resistivity of 7.8 $\Omega \cdot$m at room temperature
    and it decreases as the temperature is raised by 100°C. The material
    is most likely:

    A) a metal   D) an insulator
    *B) a pure semiconductor   E) none of the above
    C) a heavily doped semiconductor

25. A certain material has a resistivity of 7.8×10^{-8} $\Omega \cdot$m at room
    temperature and it increases as the temperature is raised by 100°C.
    The material is most likely:

    *A) a metal   D) an insulator
    B) a pure semiconductor   E) none of the above
    C) a heavily doped semiconductor

26. Donor atoms introduced into a pure semiconductor at room
    temperature:

    *A) increase the number of electrons in the conduction band
    B) increase the number of holes in the valence band
    C) lower the Fermi level
    D) increase the electrical resistivity
    E) none of the above

27. Acceptor atoms introduced into a pure semiconductor at room
    temperature:

    A) increase the number of electrons in the conduction band
    *B) increase the number of holes in the valence band
    C) lower the Fermi level
    D) increase the electrical resistivity
    E) none of the above

28. An acceptor replacement atom in silicon might have _____ electrons in its outer shell.

   *A) 3   B) 4   C) 5   D) 6   E) 7

29. A donor replacement atom in silicon might have _____ electrons in its outer shell.

   A) 1   B) 2   C) 3   D) 4   *E) 5

30. A given semiconductor can be identified as p or n type by:

   A) measuring its electrical conductivity
   B) measuring its magnetic susceptibility
   C) measuring its coefficient of resistivity
   D) measuring its heat capacity
  *E) performing a Hall effect experiment

31. The contact electric field in the depletion region of a p-n junction is produced by:

   A) electrons in the conduction band alone
   B) holes in the valence band alone
   C) electrons and holes together
  *D) charged impurity atoms
   E) an external source

32. For an unbiased p-n junction, the bottom of the conduction band on the n side is:

   A) higher than the bottom of the conduction band on the p side
  *B) lower than the bottom of the conduction band on the p side
   C) lower than the top of the valence band on the n side
   D) lower than the top of the valence band on the p side
   E) none of the above

33. In an unbiased p-n junction:

   A) the electric potential vanishes everywhere
   B) the electric field vanishes everywhere
   C) the drift current vanishes everywhere
   D) the diffusion current vanishes everywhere
  *E) the diffusion and drift currents cancel

34. Application of a forward bias to a p-n junction:

  *A) widens the depletion zone
   B) increases the electric field in the depletion zone
   C) increases the potential difference across the depletion zone
   D) increases the number of donors on the n side
   E) decreases the number of donors on the n side

35. Application of a forward bias to a p-n junction:

   A) increases the drift current in the depletion zone
  *B) increases the diffusion current in the depletion zone
   C) decreases the drift current on the p side outside the depletion zone
   D) decreases the drift current on the n side outside the depletion zone
   E) does not change the current anywhere

36. When a forward bias is applied to a p-n junction the concentration
    of electrons on the p side:

   A) increases slightly   D) decreases dramatically
  *B) increases dramatically   E) does not change
   C) decreases slightly

37. Which of the following is NOT true when a back bias is applied to a
    p-n junction?

   A) electrons flow from the p to the n side
  *B) holes flow from the p to the n side
   C) the electric field in the depletion zone increases
   D) the potential difference across the depletion zone increases
   E) the depletion zone narrows

38. Switch S is closed to apply a potential difference V across a p-n
    junction as shown. Relative to the energy levels of the n-type
    material, with the switch open, the electron levels of the p-type
    material are:

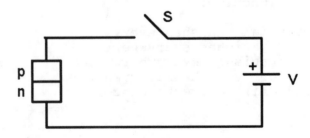

   A) unchanged   D) raised by Ve
   B) raised by $e^{-Ve/kT}$ E) lowered by Ve
  *C) lowered by $e^{-Ve/kT}$

39. A sinusoidal potential difference $V_{in} = V_o\sin(\omega t)$ is applied to the p-n junction as shown. Which graph correctly shows V_{out} as a function of time?

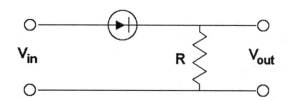

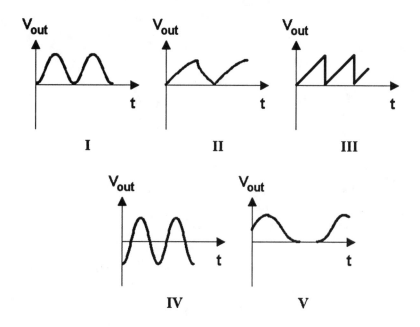

I

II

III

IV

V

A) I.   B) II.   C) III.   D) IV.   *E) V.

40. In normal operation the current in a MOSFIT device is controlled by changing:

   A) the number of donors and acceptors
  *B) the width of the depletion zone
   C) the resistivity of the n type material outside the depletion zone
   D) the resistivity of the p type material outside the depletion zone
   E) the temperature

41. "LED" stands for:

   A) Less Energy Donated   D) Laser Energy Detonator
   B) Light Energy Degrader   *E) none of the above
   C) Luminescent Energy Developer

42. A light emitting diode emits light when:

  A) electrons are excited from the valence to the conduction band
 *B) electrons from the conduction band recombine with holes from the
     valence band
  C) electrons collide with atoms
  D) electrons are accelerated by the electric field in the depletion
     region
  E) the junction gets hot

1. The smallest particle of any chemical element that can exist by itself and yet retain the qualities that distinguish it as that element is:

A) an electron
B) a proton
C) a neutron

*D) an atom
E) a molecule

2. Which of the following has the smallest rest energy?

A) neutron   *B) electron   C) ion   D) proton   E) atom

3. The mass of an electron:

A) is almost that of a neutron
B) is negative
C) equals that of a proton
D) is zero if the electron is at rest
*E) is much less than that of a proton

4. The mass of a neutron:

A) equals that of an electron
B) equals that of a proton
*C) is a little more than that of a proton
D) is exactly that of a proton plus an electron
E) is as yet unmeasured

5. The mass of a hydrogen atom, in kilograms, is approximately:

*A) 10^{-27} B) 10^{-31} C) 10^{-24} D) 10^{-13} E) 10^{-8}

6. 1 atomic mass unit is about:

A) 1.66×10^{-31} kg
B) 9.11×10^{-31} kg
*C) 1.66×10^{-27} kg

D) 9.11×10^{-27} kg
E) 1.66×10^{-25} kg

7. The atomic number of an element is:

A) the whole number nearest to its mass
*B) the number of protons in its nucleus
C) the nearest whole number of hydrogen atoms having the same mass as a single atom of the given element
D) the number of neutrons in its nucleus
E) its order of discovery

8. Iron has atomic number 26. Naturally mined iron contains isotopes of mass numbers 54, 56, 57, and 58. Which of the following statements is FALSE?

A) every atom of iron has 26 protons
B) some iron atoms have 30 neutrons
*C) some iron atoms have 54 neutrons
D) the isotopes may be separated in a mass spectrometer
E) there are four kinds of naturally occurring iron atoms with the same chemical properties

9. Let Z denote the atomic number and A denote the mass number of a nucleus. The number of neutrons in this nucleus is:

A) Z *B) $A - Z$ C) $A - 2Z$ D) A E) $2A - Z$

10. The isotopes of an element:

A) cannot be separated at all
B) occur well separated in nature
*C) have similar chemical behavior
D) cannot be separated by physical methods
E) have equal masses

11. Bromine, with atomic mass 79.942 u, is composed of nearly equal amounts of two isotopes, one of which contains 79 nucleons per atom. The mass number of the other isotope is:

A) 78   B) 79   C) 80   *D) 81   E) 82

12. The mass density of an atomic nucleus is:

A) about 10^{15} kg/m^3
B) about 10^{12} kg/m^3
C) increases with increasing nuclear mass
D) increases with decreasing nuclear radius
*E) about the same as that of all other nuclei

13. Volumes of atomic nuclei are proportional to:

   *A) the mass number
    B) the atomic number
    C) the total nuclear spin
    D) the number of neutrons
    E) none of these

14. A fermi is:

    A) larger than 10^{-9} m
    B) 10^{-9} m
    C) 10^{-12} m
   *D) 10^{-15} m
    E) 10^{-18} m

15. A nucleus with an atomic number of 64 has a mean radius of about:

   *A) 4.8 fm
    B) 19 fm
    C) 77 fm
    D) 260 fm
    E) 2.6×10^5 fm

16. A proton in a large nucleus:

    A) attracts all other protons
    B) repels all other protons
    C) repels all neutrons
   *D) attracts some protons and repels others
    E) attracts some neutrons and repels others

17. Two protons are separated by 10^{-16} m. The nuclear (N), electrostatic
    (E), and gravitational (G) forces between these protons when written
    in order of increasing strength are:

    A) E, N, G   B) N, G, E   *C) G, E, N   D) G, N, E   E) E, G, N

18. An electron and a proton are about 10^{-10} m apart. Their relative
    motion is chiefly determined by:

    A) gravitational forces
   *B) electrical forces
    C) nuclear forces
    D) magnetic forces
    E) torque due to electric dipole moments

19. The binding energy of a nucleus is the energy that must be supplied
    to:

    A) remove a nucleon
    B) remove an alpha particle
    C) remove a beta particle
   *D) separate the nucleus into its constituent nucleons
    E) separate the nucleus into a collection of alpha particles

20. If a nucleus has mass M, Z protons (mass m_p) and N neutrons (mass m_n) its binding energy is equal to:

A) Mc^2

B) $(M - Zm_p - Nm_n)c^2$

*C) $(Zm_p + Nm_n - M)c^2$

D) $(Zm_p + Nm_n)c^2$

E) $(Zm_p - M)c^2$

21. Stable nuclei generally:

A) have a greater number of protons than neutrons
B) have low mass numbers
C) have high mass numbers
D) are beta emitters
*E) none of the above

22. Nuclei have mass number A and atomic number Z. Which of the following is approximately correct for light nuclei?

A) $A = Z/2$ B) $Z = A$ *C) $Z = A/2$ D) $Z = \sqrt{A}$ E) $A = z^3$

23. The greatest binding energy per nucleon occurs for nuclides with masses near that of:

A) helium   B) sodium   *C) iron   D) mercury   E) uranium

24. The half-life of a radioactive substance is:

A) half the time it takes for the entire substance to decay
B) usually about 50 years
C) the time for radium to change into lead
D) calculated from $E = mc^2$
*E) the time for half the substance to decay

25. Which expression correctly describes the radioactive decay of a substance whose half-life is T?

*A) $N = N_o e^{-(t\ell n2)/T}$

B) $N = N_o e^{-t/T}$

C) $N = N_o e^{-tT}$

D) $N = N_o e^{-tT\ell n2}$

E) $N = N_o e^{-t/(T\ell n2)}$

26. Radioactive element A decays to the stable element B with a half-life T. Starting with a sample of pure A and no B, which graph below correctly shows the number of A atoms, N_A, as a function of time t?

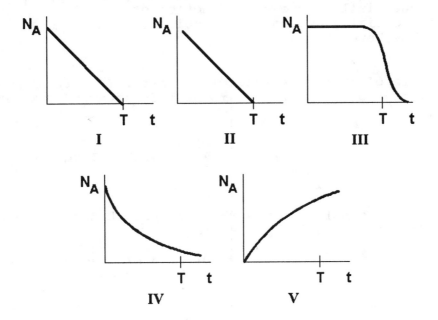

A) I.   B) II.   C) III.   *D) IV.   E) V.

27. A large collection of nuclei are undergoing alpha decay. The rate of decay at any instant is:

*A) proportional to the number of undecayed nuclei present at that instant
B) proportional to the time since the decays started
C) proportional to the time remaining before all have decayed
D) proportional to the half-life of the decay
E) a universal constant

28. The relation between the disintegration constant λ and the half-life T of a radioactive substance is:

A) $\lambda = 2T$
B) $\lambda = 1/T$
C) $\lambda = 2/T$

*D) $\lambda T = \ln 2$
E) $\lambda T = \ln(1/2)$

29. Possible units for the disintegration constant λ are:

A) kg/s   B) s/kg   C) hour   *D) 1/day   E) 1/cm

30. The half-life of a given nuclear disintegration A → B:

   A) depends on the initial number of A atoms
   B) depends on the initial number of B atoms
   C) is an exponentially increasing function of time
   D) is an exponentially decreasing function of time
  *E) none of the above

31. The half-life of radium is about 1600 years. If a rock initially contains 1 gram of radium, the amount left after 8000 years will be about:

   A) 200 mg   D) 16 mg
   B) 63 mg   E) less than 1 mg
  *C) 31 mg

32. Starting with a sample of pure ^{66}Cu, 7/8 of it decays into Zn in 15 minutes. The corresponding half-life is:

   A) 15 minutes   D) 3.75 minutes
  *B) 5 minutes   E) 10 minutes
   C) 7 minutes

33. ^{210}Bi (an isotope of bismuth) has a half-life of 5.0 days. The time for three-quarters of a sample of ^{210}Bi to decay is:

   A) 2.5 days   D) 20 days
  *B) 10 days   E) 3.75 days
   C) 15 days

34. Radioactive ^{90}Sr has a half-life of 30 years. What percent of a sample of ^{90}Sr will remain after 60 years?

   A) 0%   *B) 25%   C) 50%   D) 75%   E) 14%

35. The half-life of a radioactive isotope is 6.5 h. If there are initially 48×10^{32} atoms of this isotope, the number of atoms of this isotope remaining after 26 h is:

   A) 12×10^{32} B) 6×10^{32} *C) 3×10^{32} D) 6×10^4 E) 3×10^2

36. At the end of 14 min, 1/16 of a sample of radioactive polonium remains. The corresponding half-life is:

   A) 7/8 min   B) 8/7 min   C) 7/4 min   *D) 7/2 min   E) 14/3 min

37. The half-life of a radioactive isotope is 140 days. How many days would it take for a sample of this isotope to lose 3/4 of its initial decay rate R_0?

A) 35   B) 105   C) 187   D) 210   *E) 280

38. Of the three common types of radiation (alpha, beta, gamma) from radioactive sources, electric charge is carried by:

A) only beta and gamma   D) only alpha
B) only beta   *E) only alpha and beta
C) only alpha and gamma

39. An alpha particle is:

*A) a helium nucleus   D) a negative particle
B) an electron   E) a hydrogen atom
C) a radioactive element

40. An alpha particle is:

*A) a helium atom with two electrons removed
B) an aggregate of two or more electrons
C) a hydrogen atom
D) the ultimate unit of positive charge
E) sometimes negatively charged

41. A nucleus with mass number A and atomic number Z emits an alpha particle. The mass number and atomic number, respectively, of the daughter nucleus are:

A) A+2, Z+2   B) A-2, Z-2   C) A-2, Z   D) A-4, Z   *E) A-4, Z-2

42. Radioactive polonium, ^{214}Po, decays by alpha emission to:

A) ^{214}Po (Z = 83)   D) ^{218}Po (Z = 84)
*B) ^{210}Pb (Z = 82)   E) ^{210}Bi (Z = 83)
C) ^{214}At (Z = 85)

43. A radium atom, ^{226}Ra (Z = 86), emits an alpha particle. The number of protons in the resulting atom is:

*A) 84   D) 88
B) 85   E) some other number
C) 86

44. Some alpha emitters have longer half-lives than others because:

   A) their alpha particles have greater mass
   B) their alpha particles have less mass
 *C) their barriers to decay are higher and wider
   D) their barriers to decay are lower and narrower
   E) their decays include the emission of a photon

45. In an alpha decay the disintegration energy appears as:

   A) photon energies
 *B) the kinetic energies of the alpha and the daughter nucleus
   C) the excitation energy of the daughter nucleus
   D) the excitation energy of the alpha particle
   E) heat

46. A beta particle is:

   A) a helium nucleus   D) any negative particle
 *B) an electron or a positron   E) a hydrogen atom
   C) a radioactive element

47. Beta particles from various radioactive sources all have:

 *A) the same mass
   B) the same speed
   C) the same charge
   D) the same deflection
   E) the same energy in a magnetic field

48. A radioactive atom X emits a β^- particle. The resulting atom:

   A) must be very reactive chemically
 *B) has a Z one more than that of X
   C) has an A one less than that of X
   D) must be radioactive
   E) is the same chemical element as X

49. A nucleus with mass number A and atomic number Z undergoes β^- decay.
    The mass number and atomic number, respectively, of the daughter
    nucleus are:

   A) A-1, Z-1   B) A-1, Z+1   C) A+1, Z-1   *D) A, Z+1   E) A, Z-1

50. A nucleus with mass number A and atomic number Z undergoes β^+ decay.
    The mass number and atomic number, respectively, of the daughter
    nucleus are:

   A) A-1, Z-1   B) A-1, Z+1   C) A+1, Z-1   D) A, Z+1   *E) A, Z-1

512

51. In addition to the daughter nucleus and an electron or positron, the products of a beta decay include:

A) a neutron
*B) a neutrino
C) a proton

D) an alpha particle
E) no other particle

52. The energies of electrons emitted in β^- decays have a continuous spectrum because:

A) the original neutron has a continuous spectrum
*B) the neutrino can carry off any energy up to a certain maximum
C) free electrons always have a continuous spectrum
D) more than one electron is emitted in each decay
E) the daughter nucleus may have any energy

53. If ^{204}Tl (Z = 81) emits a β^- particle from its nucleus:

A) stable Tl is formed
B) ^{202}Hg (Z = 80) is formed
*C) ^{204}Pb (Z = 82) is formed

D) radioactive Tl is formed
E) ^{197}Au (Z = 79) is formed

54. An atom of ^{235}U (Z = 92) disintegrates to ^{207}Pb (Z = 82) with a half-life of about a billion years by emitting seven alpha particles and _____ β^- particles:

A) 3   *B) 4   C) 5   D) 6   E) 7

55. When ordinary sodium (^{23}Na) is bombarded with deuterons, the products are a neutron and:

A) ^{27}Al B) ^{24}Na *C) ^{24}Mg D) ^{25}Mg E) ^{20}Ne

56. ^{65}Cu will be turned into ^{66}Cu, with no accompanying product except a gamma ray, if bombarded with:

A) protons
*B) neutrons
C) deuterons

D) electrons
E) alpha particles

57. Magnesium has atomic number 12, hydrogen has atomic number 1, and helium has atomic number 2. In the nuclear reaction $^{24}Mg + {}^2H \rightarrow ( )$ + ^4He the missing quantity is:

A) ^{23}Na (Z = 11)
B) ^{22}Ne (Z = 10)
C) ^{21}Na (Z = 11)

D) ^{21}Ne (Z = 10)
*E) ^{22}Na (Z = 11)

58. Aluminum has atomic number 13, helium has atomic number 2, and silicon has atomic number 14. In the nuclear reaction $^{27}Al + {}^{4}He \rightarrow {}^{30}Si + (\ )$ the missing particle is:

A) α B) β^{+} C) β^{-} *D) proton   E) neutron

59. The ^{66}Cu (Z = 29) produced in a nuclear bombardment is unstable, changing to ^{66}Zn (Z = 30) by the emission of:

A) a proton   *D) an electron
B) a gamma ray photon   E) an alpha particle
C) a positron

60. When ordinary sulfur, ^{32}S (Z = 16), is bombarded with neutrons, the products are ^{32}P (Z = 15) and:

A) an alpha particle   D) a gamma ray
*B) a proton   E) an electron
C) a deuteron

61. A certain nucleus, after absorbing a neutron, emits a β^{-} and then splits into two alpha particles. The (A,Z) of the original nucleus must have been:

A) 6, 2   B) 6, 3   C) 7, 2   *D) 7, 3   E) 8, 4

62. When ^{23}Na (Z = 11) is bombarded with protons, the products are ^{20}Ne (Z = 10) and:

A) a neutron   D) a gamma ray
*B) an alpha particle   E) two beta particles
C) a deuteron

63. Bombardment of ^{28}Si (Z = 14) with alpha particles may produce:

*A) a proton and ^{31}P (Z = 15)   D) helium and ^{31}P (Z = 15)
B) hydrogen and ^{32}S (Z = 16)   E) ^{35}Cl (Z = 17)
C) a deuteron and ^{27}Al (Z = 13)

64. The curie is the correct unit to use in reporting the measurement of:

*A) the rate of decay of a radioactive source
B) the ability of a beam of gamma ray photons to produce ions in a target
C) the energy delivered by radiation to a target
D) the biological effect of radiation
E) none of the above

514

65. The roentgen is the correct unit to use in reporting the measurement of:

    A) the rate of decay of a radioactive source
   *B) the ability of a beam of gamma ray photons to produce ions in a
       target
    C) the energy delivered by radiation to a target
    D) the biological effect of radiation
    E) none of the above

66. The rad is the correct unit to use in reporting the measurement of:

    A) the rate of decay of a radioactive source
    B) the ability of a beam of gamma ray photons to produce ions in a
       target
   *C) the energy delivered by radiation to a target
    D) the biological effect of radiation
    E) none of the above

67. The rem is the correct unit to use in reporting the measurement of:

    A) the rate of decay of a radioactive source
    B) the ability of a beam of gamma ray photons to produce ions in a
       target
    C) the energy delivered by radiation to a target
   *D) the biological effect of radiation
    E) none of the above

1. If the nucleus of a lead atom were broken into two identical nuclei, the total mass of the result would be:

A) the same as before
B) greater than before
*C) less than before

D) converted into radiation
E) converted into kinetic energy

2. Consider the following energies:
   I.   minimum energy needed to excite a hydrogen atom
   II. energy needed to ionize a hydrogen atom
   III. energy released in ^{235}U fission
   IV. energy needed to remove a neutron from a ^{12}C nucleus
   In order of increasing value they are:

A) I, II, III, IV
B) I, III, II, IV
*C) I, II, IV, III

D) II, I, IV, III
E) II. IV, I, III

3. Fission is possible because the binding energy per nucleon:

A) increases with mass number at low mass numbers
B) decreases with mass number at low mass numbers
C) increases with mass number at high mass numbers
*D) decreases with mass number at high mass numbers
E) none of the above

4. When uranium undergoes fission as a result of neutron bombardment, the energy released is due to:

A) oxidation of the uranium
B) kinetic energy of the bombarding neutrons
C) radioactivity of the uranium nucleus
D) radioactivity of the fission products
*E) a reduction in binding energy

5. The energy supplied by a thermal neutron in a fission event is essentially its:

A) excitation energy
*B) binding energy
C) kinetic energy

D) rest energy
E) electric potential energy

6. The barrier to fission comes about because the fragments:

*A) attract each other via the strong nuclear force
 B) repel each other electrically
 C) produce magnetic fields
 D) have large masses
 E) attract electrons electrically

7. ^{235}U is readily made fissionable by a thermal neutron but ^{238}U is not because:

 A) the neutron has a smaller binding energy in ^{236}U
 B) the neutron has a smaller excitation energy in ^{236}U
 C) the potential barrier for the fragments is less in ^{239}U
*D) the neutron binding energy is greater than the barrier height for ^{236}U and less than the barrier height for ^{239}U
 E) the neutron binding energy is less than the barrier height for ^{236}U and greater than the barrier height for ^{239}U

8. An explosion does not result from a small piece of ^{235}U because:

 A) it does not fission
 B) the neutrons released move too fast
 C) ^{238}U is required
*D) too many neutrons escape, preventing a chain reaction from starting
 E) a few neutrons must be injected to start the chain reaction

9. When ^{236}U fissions the fragments are:

 A) always Xe and Sr   D) never identical
 B) always identical   *E) none of the above
 C) never Xe and Sr

10. Fission fragments usually decay by emitting:

 A) alpha particles   D) only neutrons
*B) electrons and neutrinos   E) only electrons
 C) positrons and neutrinos

11. When ^{236}U fissions, the products may be:

 A) Ba, Kr, and a proton   D) I, Sr, and an alpha particle
*B) Ba, Kr, and a neutron   E) two uranium nuclei
 C) Cs and Br

517

12. Which one of the following represents a fission reaction that can be activated by slow neutrons?

A) $^{238}U_{92} + ^1n_0 \rightarrow ^{90}Kr_{36} + ^{146}Cs_{55} + ^2H_1 + ^1n_0$ B) $^{239}Pu_{94} + ^1n_0 \rightarrow ^{96}Sr_{38} + ^{141}Ba_{56} + 3^1n_0$

C) $^{238}U_{92} \rightarrow ^{234}Th_{90} + ^4He_2$

D) $^3H_1 + ^2H_1 \rightarrow ^4He_2 + ^1n_0$

E) $^{107}Ag_{47} + ^1n_0 \rightarrow ^{108}Ag_{47} \rightarrow ^{108}Cd_{48} + ^0e_{-1}$

Ans. b

13. In the uranium disintegration series:

A) the loss of a β^- particle increases the mass number A by one and decreases the atomic number Z by one
B) the disintegrating element merely ejects atomic electrons
*C) the loss of an α particle decreases the mass number A by four and decreases the atomic number Z by two
D) the nucleus always remains unaffected
E) the series of disintegrations continues until an element having eight outermost orbital electrons is obtained

14. Separation of the isotopes of uranium requires a physical, rather than chemical, method because:

A) mixing other chemicals with uranium is too dangerous
*B) the isotopes are chemically the same
C) the isotopes have exactly the same number of neutrons per nucleus
D) natural uranium contains only 0.7% ^{235}U
E) uranium is the heaviest element in nature

15. Which one of the following is NOT needed in a nuclear fission reactor?

A) moderator
B) fuel
C) coolant

D) control device
*E) accelerator

16. The function of the control rods in a nuclear reactor is to:

A) increase fission by slowing down the neutrons
B) decrease the energy of the neutrons without absorbing them
C) increase the ability of the neutrons to cause fission
*D) decrease fission by absorbing neutrons
E) provide the critical mass for the fission reaction

17. The purpose of a moderator in a nuclear reactor is to:

 A) provide neutrons for the fission process
 B) react with the uranium to release energy
*C) slow down fast neutrons to increase the probability of fission
 D) absorb dangerous gamma radiation
 E) shield the reactor operator from dangerous radiation

18. In a neutron-induced fission process, delayed neutrons come from:

*A) the fission products
 B) the original nucleus just before it absorbs the neutron
 C) the original nucleus just after it absorbs the neutron
 D) the moderator material
 E) the control rods

19. In a nuclear reactor the fissionable fuel is formed into pellets rather than finely ground and mixed with the moderator. This reduces the probability of:

*A) non-fissioning absorption of neutrons
 B) loss of neutrons through the reactor container
 C) absorption of two neutrons by single fissionable nucleus
 D) loss of neutrons in the control rods
 E) none of the above

20. In a subcritical nuclear reactor:

*A) the number of fission events per unit time decreases with time
 B) the number of fission events per unit time increases with time
 C) each fission event produces fewer neutrons than when the reactor is critical
 D) each fission event produces more neutrons than when the reactor is critical
 E) none of the above

21. In the normal operation of a nuclear reactor:

 A) control rods are adjusted so the reactor is subcritical
*B) control rods are adjusted so the reactor is critical
 C) the moderating fluid is drained
 D) the moderating fluid is continually recycled
 E) none of the above

22. Fusion is possible because the binding energy per nucleon:

*A) increases with mass number at low mass numbers
 B) decreases with mass number at low mass numbers
 C) increases with mass number at high mass numbers
 D) decreases with mass number at high mass numbers
 E) none of the above

23. To produce energy by fusion of two nuclei, the nuclei:

  *A) must have at least several thousand electron volts of kinetic energy
   B) must both be above iron in mass number
   C) must have more neutrons than protons
   D) must be unstable
   E) must be magic number nuclei

24. Which one of the following represents a fusion reaction that would yield large amounts of energy?

   A) $^{238}U_{92} + {}^1n_0 \, 2 \rightarrow {}^{90}Kr_{36} + {}^{146}Cs_{55} + {}^2H_1 + {}^1n_0$ B) $^{239}Pu_{92} + {}^1n_0 \rightarrow {}^{96}Sr_{38} + {}^{141}Ba_{56} + 3{}^1n_0$

   C) $^{238}U_{92} \rightarrow {}^{234}Th_{90} + {}^4He_2$ D) $^3H_1 + {}^2H_1 \rightarrow {}^4He_2 + {}^1n_0$

                 E) $^{107}Ag_{47} + {}^1n_0 \rightarrow {}^{108}Ag_{47} \rightarrow {}^{108}Cd_{48} + {}^0e_{-1}$

Ans. d

25. The barrier to fusion comes about because protons:

   A) attract each other via the strong nuclear force
  *B) repel each other electrically
   C) produce magnetic fields
   D) attract neutrons via the strong nuclear force
   E) attract electrons electrically

26. High temperatures are required in thermonuclear fusion so that

  *A) some nuclei are moving fast enough to overcome the barrier to fusion
   B) there is a high probability some nuclei will strike each other head on
   C) electrons will boil off from the atoms
   D) fused nuclei are in high energy states
   E) the Pauli exclusion principle does not prohibit fusion

27. For a controlled nuclear fusion reaction, one needs:

 *A) high density n and high temperature T
  B) high n and low T
  C) low n and high T
  D) low n and low T
  E) high n and T = 0 K

28. Most of the energy produced by the sun is due to:

  A) nuclear fission
 *B) nuclear fusion
  C) chemical reaction
  D) gravitational collapse
  E) induced emf's associated with the sun's magnetic field

29. Nuclear fusion in stars produce all the chemical elements with mass numbers less than:

 *A) 56   B) 66   C) 70   D) 82   E) 92

30. Nuclear fusion in the sun is increasing its supply of:

  A) hydrogen   D) positrons
 *B) helium   E) neutrons
  C) nucleons

31. The first step of the proton-proton cycle is:

  A) $^1H + {}^1H \to {}^2H$ D) $^1H + {}^1H \to {}^2H + \gamma$
 *B) $^1H + {}^1H \to {}^2H + e^+ + \nu$ E) $^1H + {}^1H \to {}^3H + e^- + \nu$
  C) $^1H + {}^1H \to {}^2H + e^- + \nu$

32. The overall proton-proton cycle is equivalent to:

  A) $2\,{}^1H \to {}^2H$ *D) $4\,{}^1H + 2e^- \to {}^4He + 2\nu + 6\gamma$
  B) $4\,{}^1H \to {}^4H$ E) $4\,{}^1H + 2e^+ \to {}^4He + 2\nu$
  C) $4\,{}^1H \to {}^4H + 4n$

33. The energy released in a complete proton-proton cycle is about:

  A) 30 keV   B) 300 keV   C) 3 MeV   *D) 30 MeV   E) 300 MeV

34. For purposes of a practical (energy producing) reaction one wants a disintegration energy Q which is:

A) positive for fusion and negative for fission
B) negative for fusion and positive for fission
C) negative for both fusion and fission
*D) positive for both fusion and fission
E) as close to zero as possible for both fusion and fission

35. Lawson's number is 10^{20} s $\cdot m^{-3}$. If the density of deuteron nuclei is 2×10^{21} m^{-3} what should the confinement time be to achieve sustained fusion?

A) 16 ms   *B) 50 ms   C) 160 ms   D) 250 ms   E) 500 ms

36. Tokamaks confine deuteron plasmas using:

A) thick steel walls
*B) magnetic fields
C) laser beams
D) vacuum tubes
E) electric fields

37. Most magnetic confinement projects attempt:

A) proton-proton fusion
B) proton-deuteron fusion
*C) deuteron-deuteron fusion
D) deuteron-triton fusion
E) triton-triton fusion

38. Compared to fusion in a tokamak, laser fusion makes use of:

A) smaller particle densities
*B) greater particle densities
C) longer confinement times
D) higher temperatures
E) lower temperatures

39. Most laser fusion projects attempt:

A) proton-proton fusion
B) proton-deuteron fusion
C) deuteron-deuteron fusion
*D) deuteron-triton fusion
E) triton-triton fusion

40. In laser fusion, the laser light:

A) is emitted by the reacting nuclei
B) is used to cause transitions between nuclear energy levels
C) is used to cause transitions between atomic energy levels
D) is used to replace the emitted gamma rays
*E) is used to heat the fuel pellet

1. Which of the following particles is stable?

A) neutron   *B) proton   C) pion   D) muon   E) kaon

2. The stability of the proton is predicted by the laws of conservation of energy and conservation of:

A) momentum   D) lepton number
B) angular momentum   E) strangeness
*C) baryon number

3. When a kaon decays via the strong interaction the products must include a:

A) baryon   D) electron
B) lepton   E) neutrino
*C) strange particle

4. A particle with spin angular momentum $\hbar/2$ is called a:

A) lepton   B) hadron   *C) fermion   D) boson   E) electron

5. A particle with spin angular momentum $\hbar$ is called a:

A) lepton   B) hadron   C) fermion   *D) boson   E) electron

6. An example of a fermion is a:

A) photon   D) kaon
B) pion   E) none of these
*C) neutrino

7. An example of a boson is a:

*A) photon   B) electron   C) neutrino   D) proton   E) neutron

8. All particles with spin angular momentum $\hbar/2$:

A) interact via the strong force
B) travel at the speed of light
*C) obey the Pauli exclusion principle
D) have non-zero rest mass
E) are charged

9. All leptons interact with each other via the:

A) strong force   D) strange force
*B) weak force   E) none of these
C) electromagnetic force

10. An electron participates in:

A) the strong force only
B) the strong and weak forces only
C) the electromagnetic and gravitational forces only
*D) the electromagnetic, gravitational, and weak forces only
E) the electromagnetic, gravitational, and strong forces only

11. A particle can decay to particles with greater rest mass:

A) only if antiparticles are produced
B) only if photons are also produced
C) only if neutrinos are also produced
D) only if the original particle has kinetic energy
*E) never

12. The interaction $\pi^- + p \rightarrow \pi^- + \Sigma^+$ violates the principle of
    conservation of:

A) baryon number   D) angular momentum
B) lepton number   E) none of these
*C) strangeness

13. The interaction $\pi^- + p \rightarrow K^- + \Sigma^+$ violates the principle of
    conservation of:

A) baryon number   D) angular momentum
B) lepton number   *E) none of these
C) strangeness

14. Two particles interact to produce only photons, with the original
    particles disappearing. The particles must have been:

A) mesons   D) leptons
B) strange particles   *E) a particle, antiparticle pair
C) strongly interacting

15. Two baryons interact to produce pions only, the original baryons
    disappearing. One of the baryons must have been:

A) a proton   *D) an antiparticle
B) an omega minus   E) none of these
C) a sigma

16. A baryon with strangeness +1 decays via the strong interaction into two particles, one of which is a baryon with strangeness 0. The other might be:

    A) a baryon with strangeness 0   *D) a meson with strangeness +1
    B) a baryon with strangeness +1   E) a meson with strangeness 0
    C) a baryon with strangeness -1

17. A baryon with strangeness 0 decays via the strong interaction into two particles, one of which is a baryon with strangeness +1. The other might be:

    A) a baryon with strangeness 0   D) a meson with strangeness +1
    B) a baryon with strangeness +1   *E) a meson with strangeness -1
    C) a baryon with strangeness -1

18. In order of increasing strength the four basic interactions are:

    *A) gravitational, weak, electromagnetic, and strong
     B) gravitational, electromagnetic, weak, and strong
     C) weak, gravitational, electromagnetic, and strong
     D) weak, electromagnetic, gravitational, and strong
     E) weak, electromagnetic, strong, and gravitational

19. The two basic interactions that have finite ranges are:

    A) electromagnetic and gravitational
    B) electromagnetic and strong
    C) electromagnetic and weak
    D) gravitational and weak
   *E) weak and strong

20. A certain process produces baryons that decay with a lifetime of 4×10^{-24} s. The decay is a result of:

    A) the gravitational interaction
    B) the weak interaction
    C) the electromagnetic interaction
   *D) the strong interaction
    E) some combination of the above

21. A certain process produces mesons that decay with a lifetime of 6×10^{-10} s. The decay is a result of:

    A) the gravitational interaction
   *B) the weak interaction
    C) the electromagnetic interaction
    D) the strong interaction
    E) some combination of the above

22. Compared to the lifetimes of particles that decay via the weak interaction, the lifetimes of particles that decay via the strong interaction are:

*A) 10^{-12} times as long   D) 10^{12} times as long
 B) 10^{-23} times as long   E) about the same
 C) 10^{24} times as long

23. Strangeness is conserved in:

 A) all particle decays   *D) all strong particle decays
 B) no particle decays   E) some strong particle decays
 C) all weak particle decays

24. Different types of neutrinos can be distinguished from each other by:

 A) the directions of their spins
*B) the leptons with which they interact
 C) the baryons with which they interact
 D) the number of photons that accompany them
 E) their baryon numbers

25. All known quarks have:

 A) charges that are multiples of e and integer baryon numbers
 B) charges that are multiples of e and baryon numbers that are either +1/3 or -1/3
 C) charges that are multiples of e/3 and integer baryon numbers
*D) charges that are multiples of e/3 and baryon numbers that are either +1/3 or -1/3
 E) none of the above

26. The baryon number of a quark is:

 A) 0   B) 1/2   *C) 1/3   D) 2/3   E) 1

27. Quarks are the constituents of:

 A) all particles
 B) all leptons
*C) all strongly interacting particles
 D) only strange particles
 E) only mesons

28. Any meson is a combination of:

 A) three quarks   *D) one quark and one antiquark
 B) two quarks and an antiquark   E) two quarks
 C) one quark and two antiquarks

29. Any baryon is a combination of:

*A) three quarks
 B) two quarks and an antiquark
 C) one quark and two antiquarks

D) one quark and one antiquark
E) two quarks

30. In terms of quark content a beta decay can be written:

*A) udd → uud + e⁻ + ν̄
 B) udd → udd + dd + ν̄
 C) udd → udd + dd + e⁻

D) udd → uud + ud + ν̄
E) udd → uud + ud + e⁻ + ν̄

31. Messenger particles of the electromagnetic interaction are called:

 A) gluons
*B) photons
 C) W and Z

D) gravitons
E) pions

32. Messenger particles of the strong interaction are called:

*A) gluons
 B) photons
 C) W and Z

D) gravitons
E) pions

33. Messenger particles of the weak interaction are called:

 A) gluons
 B) photons
*C) W and Z

D) gravitons
E) pions

34. A u quark can be changed into a d quark by:

 A) the gravitational interaction
 B) the electromagnetic interaction
*C) the weak interaction
 D) the strong interaction
 E) none of these

35. The color theory explains why quarks:

*A) form particles in pairs and triplets
 B) have charge that is a multiple of e/3
 C) have spin
 D) have mass
 E) none of the above

36. Color is carried by:

    A) only quarks   *D) only quarks and gluons
    B) only leptons   E) only photons and gluons
    C) only quarks and leptons

37. Hubble's law is evidence that:

     A) the speed of light is increasing
    *B) the universe is expanding
     C) the earth is slowing down in its orbit
     D) galaxies have rotational motion
     E) none of the above

38. Objects in the universe are receding from us with a speed that is:

     A) inversely proportional to their distance
     B) the same as that of every other object
    *C) proportional to their distance
     D) proportional to the square of their distance
     E) none of the above

39. The velocities of distant objects in the universe indicate that the
    time elapsed since the big bang is about:

    A) 10^5 y   *B) 10^{10} y   C) 10^{15} y   D) 10^{20} y   E) 10^{25} y

40. A remnant of the big bang, the microwave background radiation:

     A) is strongest in directions away from the center of the galaxy
     B) is strongest in directions toward the center of the galaxy
     C) varies from place to place on the surface of the earth
    *D) is nearly the same intensity in all directions
     E) none of the above

41. As a result of the big bang there is in addition to the microwave
    background radiation, a uniform distribution of background:

    A) electrons   *D) neutrinos
    B) quarks   E) atoms
    C) gluons

42. Evidence for the existence of dark matter in the universe is:

   A) the night sky is dark between stars
   B) the orbital period of stars in the outer parts of a galaxy is
      greater than the orbital period of stars near the galactic center
   C) the orbital period of stars in the outer parts of a galaxy is less
      than the orbital period of stars near the galactic center
  *D) the orbital period of stars in the outer parts of a galaxy is about
      the same as the orbital period of stars near the galactic center
   E) all galaxies have about the same mass

43. If dark matter did not exist it is likely that:

  *A) the universe would expand forever
   B) the universe would begin contracting soon
   C) the night sky would be brighter
   D) the night sky would be darker
   E) we would be able to see the center of the universe

NOTES

NOTES

NOTES

NOTES

NOTES

NOTES

NOTES

NOTES